GOING DIGITAL

OTHER TITLES FROM
THE ECONOMIST BOOKS

The Economist Desk Companion
The Economist Guide to Economic Indicators
The Economist Guide to the European Union
The Economist Numbers Guide
The Economist Style Guide
The International Dictionary of Finance

Pocket Accounting
Pocket Director
Pocket Finance
Pocket Information Technology
Pocket Manager
Pocket Marketing
Pocket MBA
Pocket Negotiator
Pocket Strategy
Pocket Telecommunications

The Economist Pocket Africa
The Economist Pocket Asia
The Economist Pocket Britain in Figures
The Economist Pocket Europe
The Economist Pocket Latin America
The Economist Pocket Middle East
The Economist Pocket USA
The Economist Pocket World in Figures

GOING DIGITAL

How new technology is changing our lives

THE ECONOMIST IN ASSOCIATION WITH
PROFILE BOOKS LTD

Profile Books Ltd, Registered Office:
62 Queen Anne Street, London WIM 9LA

First published by Profile Books Ltd
in association with
The Economist Newspaper Ltd 1996

Printed in Great Britain by Clays Ltd, St Ives plc

A CIP catalogue record for this book is available
from the British Library

ISBN 1 86197 001 3

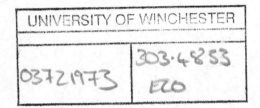

Contents

Introduction

WITH the exception of the first chapter entitled "Making a difference" this book comprises nine surveys and one article that were published in *The Economist* between March 1992 (Artificial intelligence) and September 1995 (Telecommunications); the date of publication is given at the end of each survey or article. In some instances the author has added a postscript but, by and large, the pieces remain as pertinent today as they were when originally published. Together they demonstrate how extensively the new technology revolution has changed, and continues to change, the world we live in and the lives we lead.

Bill Emmott

1

MAKING A DIFFERENCE

How bit by bit the world has been transformed.

OLIVER MORTON

Making a difference

IN 1947 Claude Shannon, an engineer at the Massachusetts Institute of Technology, cut up the world in a new way. Instead of dividing it into pieces of matter, as atomic physics had done so successfully, he cut it into pieces of information. These pieces of information are bits – binary digits. All messages, all information, can in principle be turned into a string of bits. Bits are the fundamental units of information.

Both the theoretical implications and practical effects were enormous. Shannon's work showed that every channel – no matter how narrow, no matter how long, from interplanetary radio links to the streaming light that pours down a fibre optic cable – could be treated in the same way: as a path for the bits into which all information can be cut. And he showed that that there is always a feasible way to send a signal along a channel, no matter what the background noise. It is possible to send back pictures from a spacecraft at the edge of the solar system with out only a few watts of power – as long as those messages are correctly encoded. Nothing need ever be lost.

While Mr Shannon was developing information theory, digital computing was being born in rooms full of vacuum tubes. The tubes were switches arranged in such a way that they could turn each other on or off; they represented and solved mathematical problems boiled down into pure logic. The switches could be open or closed, yes or no, 1s or 0s. That is to say, they worked in the world of bits – bits that could in principle be used to carry any information imaginable.

Because what matters about a computer is the bits, not the switches that represent them, the stage was set for an extraordinary technological leap, one unlike any seen before in history; that of exponential miniaturisation. In the industrial revolution and its aftermath, machines had to work in the world of men; they had to be of a size that men could relate to and control. The physical work that they did determined the size they should be. There was no point in building a printing press that produced newspapers too small to read.

In the information revolution, though, there is no real physical labour to do. The business of computing machines is to turn ones to zeros in orderly ways; the size of the things representing ones and zeros is entirely arbitrary. You can build the machines that embody them as big, or as small, as your ingenuity allows. This disconnection between the purpose of machinery and the world of physical objects allowed miniaturisation more profound than anyone would have believed possible – and, as a result, an extraordinary leap in performance.

Valves gave way to transistors. Transistors gave way to integrated circuits, made by printing presses that could put whole novels on to fingernails. The ones and zeros in computers now live in gates that are less than a millionth of a metre across, or are stored in grains of iron or flecks of glass. Smallness brings speed; the gates can open and close remarkably quickly, shuffling information hundreds of millions of times a second.

As a result the ability to treat information with mathematical precision, to transmit it with arbitrary accuracy and to manipulate it with unprecedented speed is bringing into being a whole new world within and around the physical world. The amount of calculational power now available to mankind is burgeoning astronomically. Computers and communications now account for most capital expenditure in American industry. The amount of communication that goes on today is, if anything, even more astonishing. And, strangest of all, the sorts of things that communicate are changing.

Communications used to be a strictly person to person matter. But now inanimate objects are getting in on the act: cans of baked beans tell cash machines what they cost; scalpels tell doctors how hard they are cutting; bombs tell bombardiers where they are; and, on the Internet, people prattle to each other and to computers in the largest, furthest reaching and fastest growing conversation the world has ever seen.

Speed and space

These changes in computation and communication add up to what is called the information revolution. This book brings together a range of explorations into its workings and implications at a stage when it is well under way, but far from over. It is hard to imagine that the next fifty years will not bring even greater changes in these areas than the half century since Shannon and the first computers.

These survey articles were written between 1992 and 1995. Some of them concentrate on the forces that are driving the revolution; computers, telecommunications systems, and their mutant hybrid first-born son, the Internet. Others look at the effects; the new approach to financial markets made possible by the acquisition and manipulation of huge amounts of data; the changes to retailing when stocks and consumers can be monitored in real time.

Some readers may find some of the surveys a little over enthusiastic.

It is true that almost the only thing that has grown as quickly as the computers and communications infrastructure is the hype about it. Predictions of robots replacing humans – whether as workers or as warriors – have not been fulfilled. The idea that telecommuting will dissolve cities into dust, and that distance will be made irrelevant to the affairs of mankind, now sounds unconvincing. Study after study points to the lack of measurable productivity growth attributable to computers in business – despite the money lavished on them. Education (of which, sadly, there is no survey included) has not been raised to a new plane by individualised teaching machines with the knowledge of every academician and the patience of every saint.

There are many reasons for these disappointments. Perhaps the most basic is that given by Arthur C. Clarke, the electronic engineer and science fiction writer who, while Shannon was thinking up the bit, came along with the idea of communication satellites. In "Profiles of the future", he writes that all technological predictions are too enthusiastic in the short term. Technologists see how their abilities could increase; consequently they think that this is how they should increase; to help make sure that this happens, they say that this is the rate at which they will increase. And then the lets and hindrances of the real world slow things down.

Mr Clarke is usually right, in this as in many other matters. But the information revolution is strange enough to undermine every rule. Thirty years ago Gordon Moore, one of the founders of the immensely successful chip making company Intel, predicted that the computing power available on a chip would double every 18 months. With few corrections, depending largely on what aspect of computing power is actually being measured, Moore's law has held.

Moore's law, though, is indeed an exception. It reflects the unique circumstances of computing; freed of the need to work in the physical world, information machines had no natural size, and could shrink as quickly as technology allowed. Other prophets, looking at the ways in which the technology will change the world, have been just as over optimistic as Mr Clarke would have expected.

The friction between technological advance and its application is not simply a waste. Its heat transforms both. The outside world takes technological potentials and changes them into things that their creators never dreamt of. And that underlies the second part of Mr Clarke's observation. The same people who overestimate change in the short term always underestimate it in the long term, largely because they think only of doing the same thing better, rather than of finding new things to do.

The information revolution is beginning to move into the realm of these long-term surprises, but the transformation is hard. To get the most out of the world of bits that now flows through and around the world of atoms you have to change the way things are done. The new world is not an addition, it is a transformation. Misapplied, it will do harm.

To add robots to a production line without rethinking the way it works; to give laser guidance to bombs without retraining the air crews; to put a PC on every executive's desk without deciding how those executives are meant to work together and share information; these are all ways to ask for trouble. This book contains stories of such failures, and of the ways in which some organisations have adapted to avoid them and get more out of the new technology.

A natural lag between potential and realisation is one reason why the information revolution, like all technological changes, is easy for some to dismiss. There seems to be a deeper reason, as well. At its heart, it is a revolution in communication, and communication is the oldest trick in the human book. Humans have always been communicators; the need to build trust and community through communication is, according to many schools of thought, the reason why mankind evolved its peculiar intelligence.

Humans, born to communication like fish to water, see it as the most natural thing, and can absorb all sorts changes in the ways in which it is done. That makes new ways to communicate easy to discount. People chat around the world by phone, videoconference from office to office, insult people by e-mail and feel that there is nothing new under the sun.

At the same time, though, this is the source of the revolution's remarkable potential. It provides new ways to converse, and new spaces to converse in – virtual realities. The notion of virtual reality is, at present, over exposed and misunderstood. The idea is not to make an individual feel as though he is in some alien place by fooling his senses. It is to provide a place where many individuals can do something together – such as design an aircraft, or play a symphony. The information revolution promises not just the sharing of information, but the sharing of the contexts that give it meaning; and not just the sharing of existing contexts, but the shared creation of new ones.

Nanotech now

To the extent that new forms of digital communication are old wine in new bottles, the age of the wine should not detract from the real novelty in the bottling. The world of digital information is in many practical ways entirely unlike the physical world that humans live in. To see the differences, indulge in a little speculation.

In the 1980s Eric Drexler, an American researcher inspired by the miniaturisation that was propelling the electronics industry, started to think about what it might mean if taken to its furthest possible extent. What would it be like to be able to manipulate matter atom by atom? The nanotechnological world that he imagined is an extraordinarily bizarre one. Tiny robots build other tiny robots; these nanomachines can make absolutely anything from a little bit of raw material, as long as it contains the right chemicals. They can make guns or butter, buildings or blue whales. Another of Arthur Clarke's reasonably wise dicta is that any sufficiently advanced technology is indistinguishable from magic. Mr Drexler's nanotechnology has the strangeness and potency of the most arcane grimoire; if it were to come into being, everything would be changed.

As a technological prophecy nanotechnology must be taken with all the usual caveats and more. As a metaphor, though, it is illuminating. Its strangeness all comes from positing the power to manipulate the most fundamental building blocks of the physical world: its atoms. In the digital world, the manipulation of the fundamental building blocks, the bits, is a given. That makes the world of information as unlike that of everyday life as a world of nanotechnology might be.

Take two examples: reproduction and encryption. Because computers do everything bit by bit, digital reproduction can be flawless, the copy and the original perfectly indistinguishable. A copy of the copy will be just as good. So while non-digital copies degrade with every generation, in the digital world everything can be always as good as new. The whole notion of "an original" is beginning to lose its meaning.

Since bits are almost costless to create – the cost is basically that of the storage medium on to which they are put – these perfect copies can also be extremely cheap. Mix this copyability with wide-spread access, as the linked computers of the internet do, and you have a system where any information can be copied by anyone. The implications of this state of affairs for all sorts of activities, most notably entertainment, are enormous. When it loses the degradability that the physical world enforces, information becomes hard to restrain; intellectual property becomes hard, even impossible, to hold on to.

In another way, though, information can be protected far better than any mere matter can. A piece of information is a string of bits. By putting these bits through a mathematical mangle, they can be turned into a different string of bits, unintelligible to anyone who does not know the details of the mangling. Because some mathematical processes are easily done in one direction and very hard to reverse, the computer age has brought with it the potential for codes which there is every reason to believe genuinely uncrackable. Clever codes of this sort mean that totally private communication seems feasible for almost anyone who desires it.

Many governments are alarmed; some seek to ban such "strong encryption". This is unlikely to work. The codes themselves are easily transmitted, and a a coded message is just another string of bits easy to hide in a longer string – a video clip, say – in such a way that it becomes unfindable. And encryption is not just about secrecy; it is also a technology of trust. The same techniques make it possible to ensure that messages really do come from the source that they claim. They make possible unforgeable signatures, perfect watermarks. You can know your letter comes from the lawyer named, or that your e-money was issued by the bank it says. Without encryption, business in the information world would be impossible.

When worlds collide

The details of duplication and encryption make the world of bits very unlike the world of atoms. This difference is probably clearer now than at any other time, past or future. The world of information is now visible enough for its strangeness to be discerned, but it does not yet permeate everything. When it does, the strangeness will cease to stand out. Everything will be strange, to today's eyes – nothing will be, to tomorrow's.

The distinctions between the worlds are already breaking down, and that breakdown will continue. The difference between physical keys and information codes will disappear, as even the most humble lock learns to read information, rather than merely respond to the grating of metal teeth. Precision instruments, too fine ever to have been developed when manual control was the only possibility, will make the copying of physical objects almost as good as the duplication of digital data. Today's two worlds will merge into one.

This is not just true in a technological sense. Philosophers and priests have divided their worlds into realms of mind and body, of spirit and flesh. This distinction will not break down – but it will change. Minds and spirits will not be given to inanimate objects like computers or cars, at least not for a long while. But the power of communication will be theirs. They will measure the world and respond to it. People who talk to inanimate objects will no longer be mad. And inanimate objects will talk to one another. They will not have viewpoints or feelings; but they will be able to inform, and to be informed.

Until technology set it free, information relied on people to carry it, to disperse it, to create it. Now information can be gathered by inanimate systems and filtered to human minds. And it can be sent off on its own into the world. If there is a key to the revolution described in this book, that is it.

2

TELECOMMUNICATIONS

Thanks to technology and competition in telecoms, distance will soon be no object. The effect on people's lives will be dramatic.

FRANCES CAIRNCROSS

The death of distance

ON MOTHERS' Day in 1995 MCI, America's second-largest long-distance telephone company, offered many of its domestic customers free calls. Struck by an annual outbreak of filial sentiment, Americans make more long-distance calls on Mothers' Day than on any other day of the year. Americans also have almost a quarter of the world's telephone lines, so Mothers' Day traffic in the United States is probably the heaviest anywhere in the world. Yet MCI felt it could offer a free service without overloading its network.

In time, every day may well be Mothers' Day, everywhere. Relentless technological change is driving down many of the elements in the cost of a telephone call. Already, the cost of carrying an additional call is often so tiny that it might as well be free. More significant, carrying a call from London to New York costs virtually the same as carrying it from one house to the next.

The death of distance as a determinant of the cost of communications will probably be the single most important economic force shaping society in the first half of the next century. It will alter, in ways that are only dimly imaginable, decisions about where people live and work; concepts of national borders; patterns of international trade. Its effects will be as pervasive as those of the discovery of electricity. Who could have foreseen, in Michael Faraday's time, that electricity would eventually release women to go out to work, transforming the shape of the family, or allow the development of cities such as Manhattan and Hong Kong, whose skyscrapers could never have been built without the lift?

The discovery of electricity created new industries, but it killed some too. The change in the cost structure of telecommunications will do the same. For the moment, telecoms is a business on the crest of a wave. Profitability has climbed almost without interruption for a decade, and is still accelerating. In 1994 the ten largest telecoms giants made bigger profits than the 25 largest commercial banks. Demand is soaring: over 38m new subscribers were connected to the fixed network in 1994, more than twice as many newcomers as in 1986. Another 19m joined a mobile network in 1994 alone. Yet costs have tended to fall faster than prices, which is why the industry has been so profitable. Now those fat profits are coming under attack from an ever-growing band of competitors.

There was a time when telecoms seemed to be a natural monopoly.

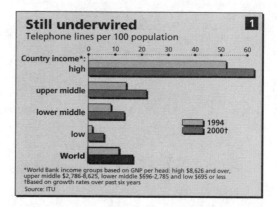

Still underwired
Telephone lines per 100 population

Country income*: high / upper middle / lower middle / low / World

1994
2000†

*World Bank income groups based on GNP per head: high $8,626 and over, upper middle $2,786-8,625, lower middle $696-2,785 and low $695 or less
†Based on growth rates over past six years
Source: ITU

Most governments liked it that way because they owned the monopoly and siphoned off some of the profits. Even now, most homes are served by only one wire, so customers cannot switch telephone services in the way they can change their hairdresser or their lawyer. But as new technologies reduce the costs of entry, competition is spreading. Enthusiastically in some countries and gingerly in most, governments have begun to accept that competition offers the best way to ensure that changing technology is fully translated into lower tariffs.

In each of the world's three big markets, reforms are in train to foster competition. In the United States, if the telecommunications proposals that passed Congress in August 1995 become law, the long-distance carriers, the regional Bell companies and the cable-television operators will be able to compete freely in each other's markets. In Japan, the government is wondering how to reduce NTT's iron grip on the local network. In Europe, the commission in Brussels is determined to create a single market in telecommunications services.

The benefits to an economy of even a little competition are tremendous. A recent study by the OECD ("Telecommunications Infrastructure: The Benefits of Competition") concluded that liberalisation not only reduced prices, but expanded the market and improved customer choice. This is true not just in developed countries but in developing ones too. In the Philippines, for example, the government's decision in 1993 to allow new entrants to provide local telephone services on a large scale persuaded PLDT, the country's main operator, to make a serious effort to cut waiting lists.

The case for competition is dawning even on China. A new telecoms operator, United Telecommunications Co (Unicom), was set up in 1994

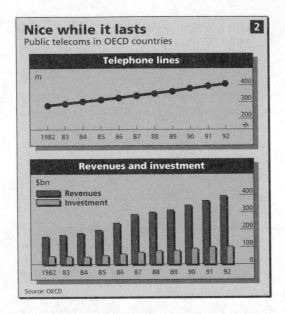

Nice while it lasts 2
Public telecoms in OECD countries

Telephone lines

m

400
300
200

1982 83 84 85 86 87 88 89 90 91 92

Revenues and investment

$bn

■ Revenues
□ Investment

400
300
200
100
0

1982 83 84 85 86 87 88 89 90 91 92

Source: OECD

by the ministries of electronics, railways and power, the industries from which many competitors have emerged in the rich world. Using the railway ministry's routes as a backbone, Unicom is constructing a fibre-optic network, starting with 15,000–20,000 subscribers in each of four large cities.

Changing shape

Competition has already begun to transform some of the companies that gathered in Geneva in October 1995 for Telecom 95, a giant jamboree for the industry. A dramatic instance came shortly before, when AT&T announced it was splitting into three. Where competition is toughest, telecoms giants are slimming their enormous workforces and trying to add value to their basic services. AT&T itself has built a popular credit card on its brand name and billing skills. Hongkong Telecom and Bell Atlantic, among others, are exploring ways to provide interactive entertainment. Several giants, including BT and MCI, are building alliances to provide sophisticated telephone packages for international business customers.

Their competitors are more diverse still. They now include not just other telecoms companies but also cable-television operators, software manufacturers, banks, water companies, railways and many more, all nibbling at the $500 billion market for global telecommunications. They are bringing new skills and new approaches, helping to transform telecommunications from an industry that builds and maintains networks into one that offers communications as an incidental part of a host of other services. In particular, telecommunications will vastly extend, and in its turn be extended by, the reach of the computer as the two technologies increasingly converge.

The direction of these changes is fairly clear, but their speed is uncertain. This survey will argue that the pace will be set not just by technology but by the interplay of regulation and competition. Governments can delay the revolution; they cannot prevent it. If they try, they will merely fail more spectacularly later.

All change

THE technological changes that have swept across the telecommunications industry have two distinct effects. One is to create glut instead of the capacity shortages of the past. The other is to reduce barriers to entry and make possible new sorts of competition. Together, they will transform the industry – although the pace at which they take effect will be partly set by regulation.

The increase in capacity is essentially due to two changes. The first is the increasing use of fibre-optic cables. These now cost much the same as copper wire to lay down and much less to maintain, but carry vastly more traffic. A single fibre thinner than a hair can carry 30,000 simultaneous telephone conversations. Second, switches – telephone exchanges – have moved on from eavesdropping operators and clunky electro-mechanical devices to become increasingly like computers, their costs falling and their capability expanding inexorably.

New cable has been laid most lavishly across the Atlantic and Pacific oceans and on routes between cities in the United States. Gluts are already appearing: more than one-third of the capacity under the Atlantic is unused (see chart 3). The growth in capacity will continue as competitors lay cables of their own. The most ambitious such project, the Fibre-optic Link Around the Globe (FLAG), is run by a consortium in which Nynex, one of America's regional Bell companies, has the largest stake at 40%; but most of its partners are from outside the industry.

Technological change will also allow huge reductions in the running costs of the network. "Maintenance accounts for a quarter of the costs of running a network, and the maintenance costs of a fibre-optic network are around one-fifth those of a wired network. Sending guys out in trucks is expensive," says Jeffrey Camp, a senior analyst at Morgan Stanley in Tokyo, explaining the pressure on NTT to replace copper with fibre. Clever switching installed in the basements of business premises allows telephone companies to press a button rather than send a workman.

The implications of these changes are enormous. Unlike the computer industry, which thanks to a similar increase in power and memory has been able to offer customers more sophisticated devices at the same price, the telecoms industry will have to offer the same product at a small fraction of its former price. Operators everywhere are struggling to find ways to add value to the basic

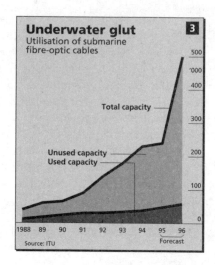

Underwater glut 3
Utilisation of submarine
fibre-optic cables

telephone call, but prices are likely to fall more quickly than premium products can be marketed.

Loopy

Up to now, the main impact of technological change has been on long-distance calls. In the United States, where four nationwide fibre networks have been built in a decade, long-distance revenue per minute has halved during that period. Now other technologies are cutting the cost of the "local loop" – the connection between the nearest exchange and the subscriber's home. This connection is usually made with a twisted pair of copper wires, a technology unchanged for almost 120 years. As a rule of thumb, local distribution accounts for 80% of a network's costs. Peter Huber, a telecoms specialist based in Washington, DC, reckons that it costs around $1,200–2,000 to connect a new customer with copper.

Two less expensive and more flexible alternatives to copper have now become available. One is to run telephone services over the same system as cable television. A breakthrough in laser design in the late 1980s made it possible to send analogue television pictures along optical fibres. Since then cable systems, like telephone systems, have increasingly acquired backbones of optical fibre. Adding telephony to an existing cable system usually costs much less than extending the copper-wire network.

The trouble is that a cable-television system, like a telephone network, involves high fixed costs and passes homes that do not want it, as well as homes that do; so building one from scratch (as in Britain) is expensive. These problems are avoided by the other technological breakthrough: the use of wireless transmission. Its extraordinary flexibility and low cost will allow the development of a new kind of network – or networks – competing directly with fixed wires. "Wireless is the answer to the local monopoly," says Robert Pepper, head of the office of plans and policy at the Federal Communications Commission (FCC) in the United States.

"If local telcos were to rebuild from scratch today, they would do so mostly with radio, at a cost of about $800 per subscriber," say Peter Huber, Michael Kellogg and John Thorne in "The Geodesic Network II", a 1993 review of competition in the industry in the United States. Mobile telephones will increasingly compete head-on with fixed systems. But the most important innovation is likely to be a digital wireless link to a small fixed radio antenna in the home, which can make extraordinarily efficient use of the radio spectrum: unlike a mobile phone, the antenna is always tuned precisely to the correct base station.

Such systems of wireless local access are now being developed by several companies including Hughes in the United States and Ionica in Britain, but are not yet in commercial use in OECD countries. Nevertheless, calculations by Analysys, a British consultancy, bear out the enthusiasm of Mr Huber and his colleagues for fixed wireless access as potentially the least expensive way to make the final link to the home.

If cable companies can supply bandwidth – the capacity to send lots of information – and if wireless telephony will do almost everything else that wire connections can do more cheaply, what will that do to the established telephone operators? "Technological change always presents a problem for the owners of the old technology," says Philip Sirlin of Wertheim Schroder, analysts in New York. "Capital intensity worsens the problem, and the telephone industry is certainly capital intensive." The big operators still have immense advantages. But are they now doomed to be the railway magnates of the 21st century, saddled with vast fixed costs for a network of dwindling value?

Certainly they will have to restructure their tariffs. Once costs are no longer distance-sensitive, a premium becomes harder to maintain. In Sweden, it costs the same to call from Malmo to Kiruna, 1,400km (870 miles) away, as to Helsingborg, some 80km away. "When you tell people," says Martin Bangemann, an EU commissioner who has been pushing for reform, "they think it is a fairy tale."

But why end the fairy tale at that point? When many parts of the network are no longer constrained by capacity, why charge subscribers by the number of seconds they spend on the telephone? Why not simply charge them a regular fee based on the speed and capacity of their line, and something extra for any fancy services they buy? The pressure for such a change will grow as charges decline and billing becomes an increasing burden.

That pressure is being reinforced by the growth of the Internet, most of whose users pay a flat-rate subscription to cover unlimited use, plus the cost of a local call to get connected. As more and more people communicate by Internet across continents for next to nothing, they will ask why telephone calls should be different.

Their question is now being answered by a New Jersey company, VocalTec, which is offering the software to enable telephone calls to be made over the Internet. Early versions of the software required both parties to have a computer and to speak in turns, as with citizens' band radio, but this has changed with the launch of "one-end-only" software and the technology to allow ordinary two-way conversations. As Bill Gates, chairman of Microsoft, said recently: "I'm not sure what the Internet is good for commercially, but I don't know why you would want to be in the long-distance market with that thing out there."

If the Internet were to become a serious rival to long-distance telephony, the increase in traffic would require a vast amount of additional investment – which probably only the existing telecoms operators could provide. But even with a tiny share of traffic, the Internet's impact on prices may be large. That presents the operators with a problem.

Until now, tariffs have been based on a cat's cradle of cross-subsidies. Although a high and rising share of the costs of a network are fixed, charges in most countries are still based mainly on use. Moreover, the price of local calls is widely subsidised from long-distance and international calls, where tariffs have long been kept deliberately high. In many countries local calls are free or extremely cheap. Everywhere, too, domestic telephone users are subsidised and businesses overcharged.

Such cross-subsidies from business to domestic users – and presumably voters – have suited governments down to the ground, putting a lid on political enthusiasm for deregulation. Once competition hits the more profitable markets, cross-subsidy becomes untenable.

The end of monopoly

FOR years, telecommunications was considered a natural monopoly. Just in case it was not, governments almost everywhere hedged it about with regulations to discourage competition. Gradually, and more quickly in some countries than others, competition has been allowed to creep in. To flourish, it needs not just the acquiescence of governments but their willing support.

New entrants come from three directions. Some have built networks of their own. Others have found ingenious ways to use infrastructure leased from other businesses. And some are using new kinds of infrastructure, mainly cable-television systems and the wireless spectrum. The effect everywhere is the same: to drive down prices and expand the range of services.

Long-distance rates and business customers – the two areas where tariffs were most out of line with costs – have felt the effect of competition first. Large business customers often begin by putting together their own internal networks, to link office telephones and personal computers. The European Commission reckons that there are now around 700,000 private networks in the United States, but only 14,000 in the less competitive European Union. The proliferation of personal computers encourages companies to link them into networks which can cover anything from a single office to the whole world. Examples of global networks include those used by the banking and airline industries, or the Internet, the largest of them all.

These networks may be purpose-built, or they may run on leased lines (of which some 20m are now in use). Once such networks are constructed, spare capacity on them can be resold to other businesses and operators, local legislation permitting. For example SITA (Société Internationale de Télécommunications Aéronautiques), the airline industry's immense global network, has plans to offer voice services to multinationals.

Many other businesses have suddenly noticed either that they have rights of way along which they can easily run fibre-optic cables, or that they already have networks for their internal communications. For example, a group of European railways has set up an organisation called Hermes to carry telephone traffic across Europe's many international borders; in France, Générale des Eaux expects telecommunications to provide 10% of its turnover by the end of the century; and in Japan a group of regional electricity utilities is building a network. MFS,

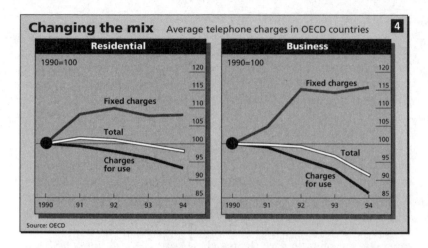

Changing the mix Average telephone charges in OECD countries **4**

Residential

1990=100

Fixed charges

Total

Charges
for use

1990 91 92 93 94

Business

1990=100

Fixed charges

Total

Charges
for use

1990 91 92 93 94

Source: OECD

an American company, has built 46 fibre-optics networks in the business districts of many big cities around the world, most recently in
Frankfurt and Paris.

The market is still patchy. Marc Destrée, in charge of international
development for MFS, complains about the cost of buying long-distance
capacity in Europe: roughly ten times what his company pays in the
United States. But the important thing about the market is that lines
are usually charged at a fixed fee, not priced by the amount they are
used. That creates an opportunity for arbitrage against the tariff structure of the big operators.

Everywhere, but especially in Europe, the big operators have fought
a furious rearguard action to prevent space on the networks being
resold, or to confine resale to closed-user groups such as the branches
of a hotel chain or a bank. But as the market develops, they have as
much interest as anyone in selling their spare capacity. In the United
States in particular, this wholesale market is huge, with long-distance
carriers such as MCI selling large amounts of spare capacity to specialist companies which have sprung up to take advantage of the pricing
constraints imposed on the big companies.

As restrictions are loosened, these resellers will enter the domestic
market too. With freedom to price on the basis of plenty rather than
shortage, they will undercut the dominant players. There will be many
more companies such as the bizarrely named 10297, which advertises
itself in the United States as a long-distance wholesale club. It buys
capacity in bulk from AT&T, MCI and Sprint and retails it to individu-

als, who need only dial the five digits that make up the company's name before calling any number to get price discounts of up to 50%. Such "systems integrators", as Eli Noam of the Columbia Institute of Tele-Information calls them, will proliferate, using their bargaining power to bring individuals benefits hitherto available only to companies, but not actually running the facilities themselves.

Foreign gold

Even before that, the market in spare capacity will have a dramatic impact on international tariffs. International calls produce only 12–15% of the revenues of the big operators, says the International Telecommunication Union (ITU), but generate 30–40% of profits. Margins are high everywhere, but especially in continental Europe. The share of operators in high-cost markets has come under increasing pressure from the use of calling cards, which allow callers to charge calls at lower rates, and from the call-back market.

Call-back services have been so effective in keeping a lid on international rates that some countries, including China and Singapore, are trying to ban them. A caller in a high-cost country, say Germany, telephones a number in a low-cost country, usually the United States. A computer identifies the caller without answering the telephone, rings back and connects the subscriber to a third country, say France. "All over the world," says Howard Jonas, head of IDT, a New York call-back company which he says is the world's largest, "countries 500 miles apart have rates double or triple or quadruple the cost of calls from the United States. Rates are not so much distance-sensitive as politically sensitive." Used mainly by small and medium-sized companies, the call-back market is not huge – perhaps $300m a year, guesses Mr Jonas – but its impact on rates is disproportionately large.

Some governments are now trying to use the spare-capacity market to break the complex settlements system for splitting the proceeds of international calls among an oligopoly of big operators. Already, sales of spare capacity between the gateways at which international tolls are collected mean that international calls take increasingly complicated routes, making the settlement process harder to police. Some governments have turned a blind eye to a bit of bypassing. But now the United States, Canada, Australia, New Zealand, Britain, Finland and Sweden specifically allow resellers of capacity to bypass the gateways. This has caused rates between these countries to be slashed. For instance, after Britain's agreement with the United States, BT's transatlantic tariffs promptly dropped by a third.

As their fattest margins are squeezed, the large operators will be forced to charge domestic subscribers more realistic prices. Up to now, the combination of high costs and cross-subsidies has made local distribution the least attractive part of the system for would-be competitors. It has also been the part guarded most fiercely by telephone operators. As a result, fewer than 1m people worldwide have any choice in the fixed-line telephone they can have. The remaining 650m or so subscribers have to take what the local operator offers. But restructuring not only encourages more rational local pricing; it also makes many governments keener to see competition in the local loop. That is likely to come from cable companies and from wireless.

The big pipe

WOULD people rather have bandwidth or mobility? The answer will determine which of the two main competitors to the telecom giants will come out on top. Cable – provided by the cable-television operators – offers the bandwidth; wireless – used by the mobile telephone companies – the mobility. The global test-bed for cable is Britain, where cable companies have been offering public telephone services in their own right since 1991, longer than anywhere else.

The cable-television operators have much in common with telephone companies. They tend to have a local monopoly; they have a fixed link with their subscribers; they bill their customers, and they know quite a lot about their habits. The main difference until now has been that their system is designed to pump information in one direction only, while the telephone companies send it two ways, and can switch it among many different subscribers. Yet the coaxial cable traditionally used for cable systems provides much more bandwidth than the telephone network's copper wires.

Now these differences are starting to matter less. Cable companies are rebuilding their systems with optical fibre, and their costs are coming down further as switching capacity gets ever cheaper. Doug Regan of TeleWest, Britain's biggest cable company, says that adding telephony increases the capital cost of a cable system by 20–25%, but boosts revenue per customer by over 50%. Customers who take the telephone service are also less likely to drop out than those who take television alone, which means the cable company saves on disconnecting customers and selling to new ones.

Mr Regan's arithmetic shows why, wherever they are allowed, cable-television operators are offering telephone services as well. Not only is the market much larger, but the double set of revenues makes it easier to justify the vast cost – some $10 billion of investment in Britain, only half of it spent so far – of digging up the streets. Britain's cable operators are now investing as much annually as BT. In some parts of the country they are signing up one-third of BT's customers. But not one of them is yet making an operating profit. Moreover, they now face a nasty squeeze on their margins. BSkyB, the satellite-television company that provides most of their programmes, has been pushing up its charges. At the same time, BT has begun to cut its prices aggressively. The cable companies have to follow suit: the main selling point of their telephone service is that it costs 10–15% less than BT's.

Is Britain's experience a cautionary tale for cable companies elsewhere? Not necessarily: Britain has been building a cable network from scratch. Besides, one of the main attractions of cable television in the United States – the quality of transmission – counts for nothing in Britain, which has high-quality terrestrial coverage. And because the cable companies depend heavily for their programming on BSkyB, which already supplies a well-developed market for satellite television, the quality of their entertainment has not been a big selling point.

In some other countries cable telephony may well be more competitive. In Hong Kong, for example, where the local monopoly of Hongkong Telecom expired in June 1995, Alex Arena, the director-general of telecommunications, licensed three new local telephone carriers. One of them, New T&T, is owned by the Wharf group, a large property conglomerate which also owns Wharf Cable. In June 1993 this company won a 12-year licence to provide cable television, with a guarantee of no competition for the first three years. Up to now, it has distributed programmes mainly with a microwave link. The group is now running an optical-fibre loop around Hong Kong's subway system, a stone's throw from the basements of most of the island's tower blocks. Servicing tower blocks that house perhaps 500 families a time clearly costs less than digging up Britain's suburban streets.

Competitors offering cable television and telephone together are springing up in more and more countries. In Japan, two consortia of Japanese and American companies are amalgamating the fragmented cable-television companies. One of them is Jupiter, which hopes to launch a telephone service by the end of 1996. Its president, Yasushige Nishimura, notes that NTT, the former state monopoly, charges ¥72,800 (about $750) for installing not just the first line but each and every subsequent one as well. "If you can offer a second line for free, that is attractive in a country where grown-up children tend to live with their parents until they marry," he points out. As the company's capital expenditure per customer connected is less than ¥72,000, the economics makes sense – for the moment.

By running telephony on the back of existing cable-television networks, systems operators in several countries can offer telephone services more cheaply than the established telephone operators. But to win a big chunk of the market, they will have to offer something more than price competition.

In the United States, the move into cable telephony will be led by a group built around Tele-Communications Inc (TCI), America's biggest systems owner, and two other large cable operators, Cox Cable and Comcast, which have allied themselves with Sprint, the third-largest long-distance carrier. Their path will be smoothed if 1995's telecommunications bill becomes law: it will then become much harder for a state to veto cable telephony. With 60% of households subscribing to cable television, and almost all homes within easy reach of a systems operator, the cable companies are keen to get going.

They still face formidable obstacles. "The great weakness of the cable industry is its fragmentation. Every one of the regional Bells is bigger in its region than all the cable operators in that region combined," admits Brendan Clouston, executive vice-president of TCI. Moreover, in America "the cable industry does not have a great perceived reputation for service. And it has no national brand."

Interactive too

Bandwidth is the key advantage the cable companies have over the telephone operators. It allows them to offer any number of fancy interactive video services – and even more once they carry digital broadcasting. TeleWest's Mr Regan talks of providing 700 channels once his customers have boxes to decode the digital signals coming into their homes. That might happen in 1997. Such capacity will not only offer more television programmes than the most ardent fan could conceivably want, but also allow the interactive use of the screen, with messages or pictures being sent to and from the home or office.

Not many telephone operators can yet rival that. One that may do so is Hongkong Telecom, where William Lo is exuberantly inventing new services to offer on the company's state-of-the-art fibre-optic, digitally switched network. He has already set up a trial based on 400 households, offering them digital video on demand: by clicking a mouse, they can order a film, pause or rewind it. In time, they will be able to shop, bank, draw money from their account by swiping a smart card through a set-top box and perhaps even gamble: the Royal Hongkong Jockey Club is one of the partners in the scheme. Mr Lo plans to have the service commercially available by July 1996. "If we cannot make this work in Hong Kong, with the great interest in new products and the low cost of additional investment, it cannot work anywhere," he says.

How much will customers, or the companies that want to reach them, pay for such novelties? Enough, maybe, to justify the relatively small extra investment that existing cable companies have to make; not

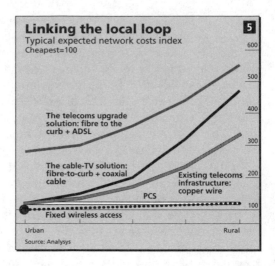

Linking the local loop `5`
Typical expected network costs index
Cheapest=100

The telecoms upgrade
solution: fibre to the
curb + ADSL

The cable-TV solution:
fibre-to-curb + coaxial
cable

Existing telecoms
infrastructure:
copper wire

PCS

Fixed wireless access

Urban   Rural

Source: Analysys

enough to reimburse the telephone operators for replacing their copper wires. So the telephone companies are racing to find ways of cramming more into their present networks. These include Asynchronous Digital Subscriber Line or ADSL, a technology which allows television pictures to travel along copper wires. At present this is expensive, and the quality of the pictures is not as good as the alternatives. Meanwhile, many telecoms operators are pinning their hopes on ISDN (Integrated Services Digital Network) as a stopgap to expand the capacity of copper wires.

If their stopgaps work, and they can squeeze more bandwidth out of their elderly networks, what will the telecoms operators do with it? All are desperate for ways to charge their customers more than they can for a plain old telephone service. "Rich people in Nassau County spend well over $100 a month on magazines and videos," says Ivan Seidenberg, boss of Nynex, the Bell in the New York region. "They spend only one-third as much on Nynex services."

To extract more, Nynex and two other Bells have set up their own television venture; other Bells formed an alliance with Disney, in the days before Disney itself owned a television network. MCI bought a 20% stake in Rupert Murdoch's News Corp. All may find they have wasted their time and money. It is difficult to imagine America's telephone companies as future media moguls.

More fruitful may be the attempts by some to become Internet service providers: the personal computer and the Internet are more likely to be the model for future interactive services than are fancy experiments with television sets. Undoubtedly, demands for bandwidth will increase as more people own computers with modems, and want to use them to contact each other. The launch of Microsoft's Windows 95, with its built-in capacity for Internet access, will give a boost to this market. But it will be many years before on-line services or the Internet make much money. France has the world's nearest approximation to a mass-market interactive service with its Minitel, which offers 26,000 services. The most popular, after directory inquiries, is train timetables. No wonder Minitel has taken ten years to turn a profit.

In the contest with the cable companies, the telecoms operators can point to considerable strengths. Frank Biondi, chief executive of Viacom (which is getting out of operating cable systems to concentrate on content), points out that the telecoms operators tend to be bigger and richer than the cable companies. They cover large regions, whereas the cable companies tend to cover only patches. The telecoms operators have the cash, the skills and the customer base to develop new software applications and charge extra for them.

But they are still vulnerable. Moreover, their grip on the local loop faces a potent threat from another direction: the wireless spectrum.

The frequency of the future

THE advent of mobility is by far the most striking change in telecommunications in the past decade. It amounts to the introduction of
an entirely new product, with huge new potential. Many people working in telecommunications assume that mobility poses no threat to the
existing networks. They are almost certainly wrong. But wireless technologies will also change the economics of fixed networks, providing
another inexpensive way of linking up with customers.

Worldwide, one new telephone subscriber in six gets a mobile
phone. At the moment, wired and wireless coexist, often owned by the
same big operator. Almost all the world's 50m cellular subscribers also
have a fixed-wire telephone. But Simon Forge of Cambridge Strategic
Management Consultants, author of an influential study of "near-zero
tariff telecommunications", argues that mobile telephones may in time
do to the public networks what the railways did to the canals. The
canals initially saw railways as feeder lines, bringing them traffic rather
than competition. The railways, in turn, initially thought the roads
would increase their total traffic. Both were cannibalised. Owning a
network counts for little if others can build a better one.

Not everybody in the telecoms business is complacent about the
impact of mobility on their business. Sir Iain Vallance, chairman of BT
(which has a stake in Cellnet, a mobile service), accepts that most conversations will eventually shift from fixed to mobile telephones: "It has
already begun in Scandinavia, driven by all those second homes."

In Sweden one person in six has a mobile phone. Indeed, fixed-line
connections are now declining: flighty young people choose to have a
mobile phone when they leave home, rather than pay for a new fixed-
line connection every time they move. Signs of head-on competition
are emerging elsewhere. In parts of Asia, the cost of a long-distance call
between mobile subscribers is well below the cost using the public network, which has boosted mobile connections. In Europe, a proposed EU
directive allowing mobile operators to use leased capacity could produce the same result.

In most parts of the world, mobile phones still represent a triumph of hope over experience. Britain's Consumers' Association
claims to have been inundated with complaints from mobile-
phone users, mainly about the terms of the contracts they had to
sign. And quality of reception is often maddeningly poor. "Cellular is full of holes, but consumers buy it anyway," says David

Goodtree of Forrester Research in Cambridge, Massachusetts.

At present, few countries allow more than one or two mobile operators. Regulation hamstrings demand. Jerry Hausman, economics professor at the Massachusetts Institute of Technology, has compared American states that regulate prices and terms for cellular telephony and those that do not. He has found that in the regulating states prices are about 17% higher and the use of cellular phones lower. For the state of California, he estimates the overall annual loss to consumers caused by regulation at about $1.4 billion a year. "Even imperfect competition", he concludes, "usually provides greater consumer welfare than regulation."

Japan, notes Alistair Grieve of Cable & Wireless in Tokyo, had the world's first public cellular service in 1979. Yet by the start of 1994 it had only 2m subscribers. In April that year, the rule preventing customers from buying their telephones was dropped; two more competitors entered the market; differentiated tariffs were introduced; and prices fell. Within a year the number of subscribers had doubled.

Competition will grow as new sorts of wireless telephone evolve. Eric Gan of Goldman Sachs in Japan envisages a sort of pyramid, rather like that in the airline industry. At the apex, the Concorde equivalent will be expensive global satellite systems that will allow subscribers to cross national borders. The next layer, akin to club class, will be cellular services, used mainly by businesses. In the United States, for example, *Fortune* 1,000 companies account for only 5% of subscribers but 19% of revenues, estimates Forrester Research. In time, digital services will lure customers away from analogue, solving three of the system's most irritating shortcomings: crackle, lack of security and fraud (but not fade-out). Operators will also be able to cram more services into the same spectrum.

Enter economy class

"What you are missing in the mobile-telecoms market is the equivalent of the airlines' economy class, where they make 70% of their money," says Mr Gan. That is now about to arrive. In the United States, the FCC, in a move of great importance, is auctioning an immense amount of radio spectrum: "Vastly more", says Peter Huber, "than is currently allocated to local television stations. And the transition to digital will eventually expand its carrying capacity between tenfold and a hundredfold."

The aim is to encourage the growth of Personal Communications Services (PCS), a new generation of wireless telephones that will be combined in all sorts of flexible ways with cordless and fixed-wire telephones. Other countries are following suit: in Hong Kong, for example, up to six new PCS licences are being made available (but not auctioned).

In Japan, a promising economy class is already up and flying. The "personal handiphone system" (PHS) was launched in July 1995 by two operators, an affiliate of NTT and DDI Personal Pocketphone. A third service, Astel, was launched later in the year. Using small, low-powered base stations sited close together in large cities, it offers a telephone about the size of a powder compact. The best-selling model has 400 hours of battery life on standby, and five hours of talking time. Its air-time charges are only a fifth of those of cellular systems, and local calls cost less than calls from payphones. They are priced to compete with pagers and aimed at a new market: teenagers and housewives. Sachio Semmoto, DDI's ebullient co-founder, remarks modestly: "As it costs ¥72,800 to get a phone installed by NTT and only ¥7,200 to join the PHS, a student might prefer our system."

Inevitably there are snags. The monthly subscription, at ¥2,700, is higher than NTT's ¥1,900. And the PHS cannot be used in fast-moving cars. That should not stunt its popularity in the dense cities of Asia, where Japan hopes to promote it, but it will be a handicap in countries such as the United States, where car use is high and density low.

But the handyphone has one enormous advantage that may catapult it to the top in Asia. Unlike conventional cellular telephones, which use lots of their bandwidth to switch quickly among base stations, its many base stations mean it uses bandwidth extremely economically. The PHS will have enough bandwidth to transmit moving pictures as well as sound. By 1997 users should be able to use it to download games software. Fitted into a personal stereo, it will allow parents to contact roaming teenagers. Attached to a notebook computer, it will allow the transmission of slow-moving pictures or digital fax. Small wonder Mr Semmoto describes his little device as "wireless multimedia", and boasts that DDI will one day be larger than NTT.

At the very bottom of the pyramid, the pager offers the equivalent of the airlines' charter class. Although it may one day be driven out of business by Mr Semmoto's gadget, for the moment it is flourishing. Hong Kong's 6m people carry more than 1m pagers, provided by 37 companies. Anybody who wants a vision of the mobile-telephone market of the future will find it here. Companies enter and leave the business all the time, endlessly innovating, chasing different markets. Ask Peter Tsang, managing director of New World Telephone, one of the

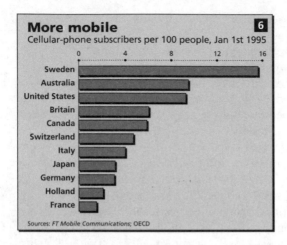

More mobile `6`
Cellular-phone subscribers per 100 people, Jan 1st 1995

Sources: *FT Mobile Communications*; OECD

three new local-service licensees, how he expects to make money in a city where a residential telephone line costs HK$62 ($8) a month and local calls are free, and he points to the pager market. "It's because services are so cheap that we expect to make money," he says. "People want more value, and don't mind paying."

Mr Tsang helped to set up New World Paging in 1990, even though 700,000 people already had pagers. He offered Asia's first secretarial paging service. Calls to the colony's myriad owners of small businesses can be routed to a communal switchboard which tells callers that Mr Chan will call them back. Mr Chan, bleeped by his pager on a street corner, can pretend that he has been summoned from a meeting to return the call.

If wireless is a potentially devastating competitor for the telephone companies, it could also be their saviour. They, too, can use it, to connect subscribers to the network much more cheaply than with copper. As that realisation has dawned, television stations have become hot properties in the United States, valued not for their viewers but for their spectrum allocation.

Two of America's long-distance carriers are using wireless to build direct links with their customers. In 1994 AT&T spent $11.5 billion to buy McCaw Cellular, which made it America's largest mobile operator. It spent a further $1.7 billion at the FCC's spectrum auctions. It is following the same strategy abroad, buying stakes in wireless operators in a number of countries, often in exchange for equipment it manufactures.

Sprint and its three cable partners invested $2.1 billion in the March

1995 auction for wireless spectrum, making the consortium the biggest successful bidder. It now has enough coverage to provide a national digital service on a single-frequency band. It will also be able to use wireless to connect customers who do not have cable television.

Increasingly, what the vast majority of customers will want most from their telephone will be portability. They will be able to get a single device, containing what would now be two or three different sorts of telephone (say satellite, cellular and PHS), capable of switching automatically among systems and allowing a subscriber to be reached at any time on a single number.

Mobility will create all sorts of new gadgets and applications. Already, says Forrester's Mr Goodtree, a Ford car contains some 50 tiny computers: link them to a mobile phone, and they could be used to tune an engine or do spot maintenance, in effect servicing the car by phone. Other car-borne telephones, linked with global positioning devices, are being developed by Germany's Mannesmann to direct a driver to a less congested route, track stolen cars – or, perhaps, charge a motorist for driving down certain streets.

For the big telephone operators, the development of wireless represents an opportunity. But it forces them to confront a harsh reality. Their most valuable assets are not their copper wires, but their customers, their billing ability and their brand names. There is nothing much that a fixed network can do that wireless will not, quite soon, do as well and more cheaply. An established, capital-intensive business with high costs and an entrenched culture will find it hard to make the most of a rival technology. It was neither the 18th-century canal magnates nor the Victorian railway bosses who built this century's successful trucking companies.

Dealing with dominance

COMPETITION in telecommunications may appear to be thriving wherever governments have allowed it. But it is an odd sort of competition. A new entrant must be able to connect to the existing network. A telephone is useful only because it connects to other telephones, and the larger the network, the more useful it is. Yet the network is owned by the very operator with whom the new entrant plans to compete. It is as if a supermarket had to use its competitor's in-house distribution system.

So the key to opening markets lies in the terms on which a new entrant has access to the existing network. How much (to use the supermarket analogy) does it pay for distribution? Can it use its own drivers, and paint its name on the vans? If so, who pays? And how are disputes settled? By the existing supermarket's board?

Bizarre as such questions may seem, they are central to telecommunications policy. The power of the incumbent operator to fight off would-be rivals is so great that governments have to intervene to restrain it. As a result, competitors – whether they be America's MCI, Britain's Mercury or Japan's IDC – frequently owe their existence to government-imposed constraints on their larger rivals.

Using such asymmetry to kickstart competition is a Faustian bargain. In Britain, the government has found itself trying to shelter the cable-television companies – most of them subsidiaries of large, mainly American telephone companies – from possible inroads into their returns. "They are building an alternative local telephone network," goes the implicit bargain, "so we should limit the risk to their investors."

The greatest threat to the investment made by new entrants everywhere is that their competition will achieve the very goal that governments hope for: a sharp drop in the tariffs charged by the main operator. If competition succeeds, a regulator may eventually have to persuade or compel the incumbent to moderate its price cuts, going against both its own interest (the pursuit of greater market share) and that of its customers (cheap calls) for long enough to allow rivals to get established.

Without intervention, though, the big operators can be guaranteed to make life difficult for would-be rivals. They benefit from a familiar brand and (usually) a protected cash flow to finance new products. A would-be telecoms company in France grumbles: "It's hard to compete with a company that uses the France Télécom name to advertise

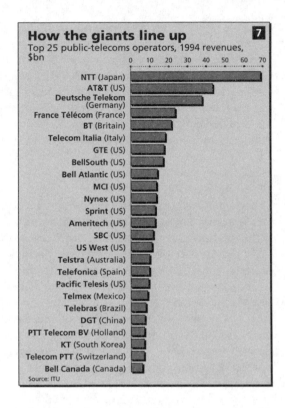

How the giants line up `7`
Top 25 public-telecoms operators, 1994 revenues, $bn

NTT (Japan)	
AT&T (US)	
Deutsche Telekom (Germany)	
France Télécom (France)	
BT (Britain)	
Telecom Italia (Italy)	
GTE (US)	
BellSouth (US)	
Bell Atlantic (US)	
MCI (US)	
Nynex (US)	
Sprint (US)	
Ameritech (US)	
SBC (US)	
US West (US)	
Telstra (Australia)	
Telefonica (Spain)	
Pacific Telesis (US)	
Telmex (Mexico)	
Telebras (Brazil)	
DGT (China)	
PTT Telecom BV (Holland)	
KT (South Korea)	
Telecom PTT (Switzerland)	
Bell Canada (Canada)	

Source: ITU

mobile services." Bernd Jäger, a telecoms consultant in Bonn who advises potential new players, argues that Deutsche Telekom has used revenue from its monopoly services to halve the cost of services which have been liberalised, such as data transmission. The result has been to confine competitors to a 10% share of these markets. Even without such cross-subsidies, DT's brand name, experience and ownership of a largely depreciated network give it huge power. "The first winner of liberalisation is always the former monopoly," observes Mr Jäger.

In most countries, one of the strongest cards in the hand of the former monopoly is numbering. Customers are often reluctant to switch to a competing telephone company if it means changing their telephone number. They may risk losing business. Hong Kong's telecoms watchdog, Mr Arena, calculated that even discounts of 10–15% were not enough to compensate. He therefore took over the allocation of numbers from Hongkong Telecom, the island's erstwhile monopoly, and insists that customers who change operators should automatically be

41

given the option of keeping their number. The luckiest numbers will be auctioned for charity, just as lucky car numbers already are.

As ever, regulation in the face of a truly determined dominant player is not straightforward. In 1994 Don Cruickshank, Britain's director-general of telecommunications, removed responsibility for numbering from BT and demanded portability. After much wrangling, the Monopolies and Mergers Commission is now adjudicating on who should foot the bill. Mr Cruickshank believes that "the true cost is very low." BT disagrees.

Only interconnect

Important though numbering is, the fiercest battles have always been over interconnection, and in particular over the rates charged for access to the local network – the hardest part to make money out of (see chart 8). As almost every call either starts or finishes on the fixed network, such charges set a floor to the price competitors can offer.

That competitors who share the network should pay some part of its cost seems, on the face of it, entirely fair. But how big a part? Most of the costs of the network are capital: the electrical pulses that new entrants send down the wires do not add to the wear and tear. In most countries, much of that capital has been stumped up by taxpayers. Even where it has not, there is plenty of room for argument over how to share the cost. A network owner who is allowed to recover his costs has little incentive to curb them. And where the operator is obliged to guarantee universal service – affordable access for every citizen to a telephone – the debate shifts to a new plane. A monopoly can cover the extra cost with cross-subsidies. But if there is competition, the most lucrative customers are picked off and offered price discounts, leaving no one to foot the bill.

In the case of universal service, most governments allow the main network operator to recoup some of the cost from competitors – who promptly complain that the operator inflates the numbers. Often with reason: studies suggest the true cost of providing a basic telephone service for unprofitable customers and areas is usually tiny. Indeed, some think it is ludicrous to regard universal service as a burden. "We say it's a franchise," says Robert Annunziata, chairman of Teleport, a company that plans to offer a telephone service in New York. He argues that serving low-income customers could be profitable, and would like to see a negative auction in which companies would bid to serve a high-cost area at the lowest subsidy.

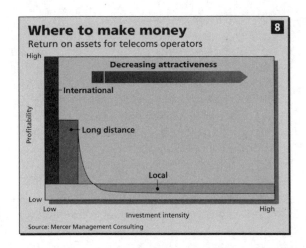

Where to make money   **8**
Return on assets for telecoms operators

Large operators are not usually keen to help new rivals (or regulators) by providing them with the basis for their calculations. It was just such a point that persuaded America's Department of Justice to order the Bells to be hived off from AT&T's long-distance operation in 1984. AT&T had been haggling over the proper price of access to its network ever since 1969, when Microwave Communication Inc (now MCI) was given permission by the Federal Communications Commission to build a microwave link between Chicago and St Louis and sell space on it to outsiders.

But while the split created competition in long-distance traffic, it left a monopoly in the local network. So the arguments about interconnection go on. AT&T and its long-distance rivals, MCI and Sprint, complain constantly about having to pay 40–45% of the cost of a call over to the Bells. "Local access is our largest single cost," says Mike Rowny, vice-president responsible for MCI's strategic planning. That may merely reflect the true cost of the local loop: but as long as local access is, in effect, a monopoly, it remains a grievance.

America's proposed telecommunications bill is, in part, an attempt to promote competition in the local network. If adopted, it will remove the regulatory barriers that have kept the long-distance carriers, the Bells and the cable-television operators from competing for each other's business. Once the long-distance carriers take calls directly from customers, perhaps by wireless links, the argument about interconnection will change: in time, perhaps, no single carrier will dominate the network.

In Japan, the three long-distance carriers sound just like Mr Rowny when they talk about NTT. They pay some 40% of their revenues to NTT in interconnection charges. Although Japan has allowed competition in every area of telephony since 1985, NTT has kept its grip on the local network mainly by its power to set access charges. The government has set up a review and aims to decide by spring of 1996 whether to split up NTT.

At the Ministry of Posts and Telecommunications, Kouji Hamada, director-general of the telecommunications business department, admires the American model of deliberately setting a number of companies at each other's throats. The break-up of AT&T, he says, has created several world-class companies in place of one. Splitting NTT into a group of local companies and a long-distance carrier would allow it to team up with one of the international companies and compete in the global market, from which ("like Gulliver", says Mr Hamada) it is now largely barred. In fact, the best reason for splitting NTT is rather different. If NTT's local and long-distance activities were separated, the local company would almost certainly have to raise its charges to reflect the real cost of local distribution. Since local calls cost next to nothing in Japan, that prospect makes politicians quail.

Splitting the network is one way to bring clarity to the argument about costs. Jonathan Solomon and Dawson Walker of Cable & Wireless have recently argued for separating the provision of telecommunications services from the operation of the infrastructure. The network owner would manage the wires and exchanges, offering access on the same terms to providers of services of all kinds. At present, the owner of a local network has every incentive to make it hard for competitors to use it. But separation would create a powerful incentive to fill the pipe rather than keep traffic away.

Better unbundle?

In the United States, a few companies are already voluntarily "unbundling". Ameritech is planning to split into a network business unit, levying a non-discriminatory access charge, and a dozen retail units marketing capacity. In New York state, Rochester Tel has split itself into a network and a competitive retail arm. One reason for that, say critics, is that the company wants to deter others from building rival networks. Another approach has been used in Stockholm, where the city has set up a company to build a fibre network which rents capacity to all comers.

Should unbundling be imposed by law? The difficulty with the

Solomon-Dawson version, say critics (including, not surprisingly, BT), is that separating the network from services is technically difficult. The more intelligence is built into the network, the harder it is to disentangle the parts, and the greater the danger that mandatory separation will create new distortions.

In any case, unbundling alone does not resolve the basic issue: how should the underlying cost of the network be allocated? "The options range from supporting new entrants to protecting the established monopoly," argues Professor Noam. An instance of the first approach would be to adopt an Internet model, basing access charges not on length of use but on a flat fee plus some charge for maximum capacity, and letting the company that sent the calls keep the proceeds. This would work in favour of new entrants, since they would send far more calls to the main network than vice versa. But it would leave the question of capital costs unresolved, as they are for the Internet itself.

This kind of solution turns the problem of asymmetry on its head. If the true cost of putting an extra call over a network is almost zero, will any charging structure allow a network operator to make a living, especially if he cannot discriminate between customers by price? With such a model, the regulator's job may one day be to protect the network, not its users. In most countries, though, that day is an aeon away.

Welcome to the world

TO CALL Penzance from London during the working day costs 9.9p (15 cents) for a minute; to call Paris or Bonn, a similar distance, 35.5p. The members of the European Union (EU) treat each other, from a telephonic point of view, as lands sufficiently distant to justify a premium tariff. The European Commission wants them to behave like the single market they say they are. Nothing illustrates more clearly the political, as well as the economic, gains that could flow from making charges insensitive to distance. Moreover, if the commission triumphs, the whole structure of international call rates will change.

At present, international calls are often a monopoly or at least a cartel. Usually only one operator – the national giant – has the right to hand calls across the international gateway that separates one country's telephone network from another's. At the gate, predictably enough, it pockets a charge.

This lucrative custom is backed up by the system of international accounting rates, which allocates the cost of a call between countries. The two operators agree on a price for handling the call and split it, usually down the middle. If one operator puts through more calls to another than it receives, it hands over a settlement payment to even things up.

For some developing countries, such payments are an important source of hard currency – more important than foreign aid. They allow Guyana, for example, to make a tidy living as a base for sex-chat lines. But most settlement payments go to rich, overpriced markets. The system is biased against countries that send more calls than they get because they have relatively low tariffs. In countries where prices have fallen fastest, the rates at which operators are now having to settle are above what they charge their customers. The system particularly irritates the United States, which has a deficit of some $4 billion, aggravated by a lively charge-card and call-back business. "It is a way for carriers to extract monopoly profits," says Scott Harris, chief of the international bureau of the FCC. "We want to drive them down to cost."

Nowhere do these arcane rules appear more anachronistic than in the EU. Prodded by the commission, the EU countries have committed themselves to opening every market for telecoms services – voice, mobile and satellite – at the start of 1998. Except for the poorer countries of southern Europe, which can delay a bit, every market should then become even more open than those of Britain, Sweden and Finland already are.

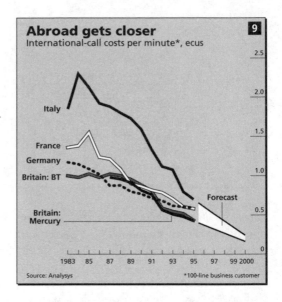

Abroad gets closer 9
International-call costs per minute*, ecus

- Italy
- France
- Germany
- Britain: BT
- Britain: Mercury

Forecast

1983 85 87 89 91 93 95 97 99 2000

Source: Analysys   *100-line business customer

In theory. But Europe has set off down this path before, and been waylaid. On paper, many of these markets were opened by the 1990 telecommunications services directive. In practice, progress has been patchy. The two EU commissioners steering the latest attempt, Martin Bangemann and Karel Van Miert, are only too aware of the gap between agreement and implementation. Mr Van Miert cautiously argues that "the mentality in the Community has changed considerably in the past four to five years." But the main reason for the failure of the 1990 directive, he says, was that the market in infrastructure was not open: would-be competitors could not acquire spare capacity to carry their calls. This time he is determined to avoid that mistake.

He is therefore threatening to push through a directive that would allow alternative infrastructure to be used from January 1996 for services that are already liberalised. That essentially means everything except public voice telephony (which, however, still constitutes 85–90% of the market). Moreover, mobile operators can either own or lease the infrastructure they use. Mr Van Miert is using article 90 of the Treaty of Rome, which does not require the agreement of the Council of Ministers, but he knows that he needs to carry member governments with him.

If Mr Van Miert succeeds, the implications for long-distance tariffs could be tremendous. All over Europe, companies with distribution

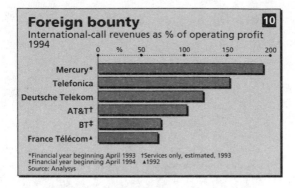

Foreign bounty `10`

International-call revenues as % of operating profit 1994

	0 % 50 100 150 200
Mercury*	
Telefonica	
Deutsche Telekom	
AT&T†	
BT‡	
France Télécom▲	

*Financial year beginning April 1993 †Services only, estimated, 1993
‡Financial year beginning April 1994 ▲1992
Source: Analysys

networks in businesses other than telephony have been laying fibre-optic cables along their routes. At present, they cannot lease out capacity at will, as they could in the United States or Britain. But once traffic is allowed to travel across borders along capacity that does not belong to the established operator, the forces for change will become irresistible. Mr Van Miert's proposal would mean that, from the start of 1996, BT and its partner Viag, a German utility group, could build their own network and deliver calls directly to large business customers.

Even more significant changes could follow once public voice telephony is liberalised. From the start of 1998, says Andrew Entwistle of Analysys, BT will have an incentive to deliver the international traffic it pipes into Germany not to Deutsche Telekom, as it does now, but to Viag – which would then deliver the calls to Deutsche Telekom, which would not know whether they came from Birmingham or Bonn. Until now, Deutsche Telekom with its high rates has done well out of the international settlement system because Germany has tended to receive more calls than it makes. But if BT and Viag were to bypass the settlements system, DT would become a large net exporter of calls. The stability of the settlements system would be threatened.

Will it happen?

At first the telephone companies might hold on to some of the cash they now hand over in settlements. But as competition on international and long-distance routes in Europe hotted up, rates would have to come down with a bump. In continental Europe, these tariffs are even further out of line with costs than they were in America when that market was liberalised a decade ago, says Mr Entwistle. And the floor in Europe would fall faster as all those fibre-optic cables come on stream, causing a capacity glut just like that in the United States.

It is easy to find sceptics, especially in the companies that have most to lose. Reform in Europe always takes longer than expected. The telecoms giants have considerable opportunities for obstruction, which are being brutally exploited in Germany. Gerd Tenzer, a board member of Deutsche Telekom, is adamantly opposed to the liberalisation of infrastructure in 1996. It would, he complains, pre-empt the decisions needed to translate the broader liberalisation of 1998 into German law (which is, of course, precisely why the commission wants it). The German government plans to privatise DT next year in what will be the country's largest ever flotation; its officials are torn between a desire to open the market and anxiety about the effect.

Yet the benign impact on European unity of eliminating distance from Europe's telephone tariffs will surely be greater than anything else the EU has ever done. If calling from Tipperary to Thessalonika cost no more than ringing next door, the squabbling Europeans might at last begin to think of each other as neighbours. Certainly Europe's businesses would think again about location.

If Europe liberalises, can the rest of the world be far behind? In Geneva, a committee chaired by Neil McMillan of Britain's industry ministry is racing to meet an April 1996 deadline to open global markets in telecommunications services. Now that the countries of the European Union, which negotiate as a block, have agreed to open their markets to each other, they could – if they wished – agree to do the same to the rest of the world.

If the Geneva talks were to succeed, as they may well do, unrestricted competition on the larger routes would take effect by the end of 1996. That would probably deal a fatal blow to the system of accounting rates. Countries might move towards one of two systems. One, "sender keeps all", would copy the Internet model. The other, favoured by the OECD, would impose a single access charge: whether France Télécom took a call from BT or AT&T, the sender would pay the same.

Either way, inflated international tariffs and a goodly slice of telecoms operators' profits would vanish. With so much of their revenue under threat, what is the future of the old giants?

A giant effort

A T THE start of the 1980s, the international airline industry was booming. Ten years later, after privatisation, deregulation and cut-throat competition, it was in deep trouble. In 1990–92, it arguably lost more money than it had made in profits in all of the first 60 years of its history. Only recently have airlines in the United States begun to creep back into profit. Elsewhere in the world the shake-out continues.

Over the coming decade telecoms, an industry now at least twice as big as the airline industry, faces even greater upheavals. Airlines have not had to cope with the relentless onrush of technological change in telecoms that is destroying old barriers between industries. Liberalisation will attract new entrants lured by huge returns on capital, especially in Europe. If America's telecommunications bill becomes law, the competition it will trigger will be just a foretaste of what lies ahead elsewhere. Companies as diverse as America's Microsoft, Japan's Toshiba and Germany's RWE all expect a slice of a business now in the hands of a relatively small number of giant oligopolies or monopolies.

Such competition will carry considerable risks. "In a business with small variable costs and huge overcapacity, a price war would be nuclear annihilation," says Wertheim Schroder's Mr Sirlin. "Serious price competition in telecommunications would make the airline business look terrific."

Even without an all-out price war, the industry will head in two different directions at once: fragmentation and consolidation. The first will follow from the sheer range of activities covered by the term "telecommunications". A host of smallish companies will flourish, especially in the areas closest to the customer, trading on their skill in buying commodity transmission capacity and adding value with ingenious new services.

For the big established operators, life will be rougher. They will have to cut costs, shed thousands of employees and innovate as never before. To survive, they may have to bring in fresh blood. "We have found a direct correlation between corporate success and managers who don't have phone-company backgrounds," says Robert Morris, director of international equity research at Goldman Sachs in London. He points to the examples of Alex Mandl, a former shipping-company boss now at the helm of AT&T Communications Services, and Michael Hepher, who came from the life-assurance industry to BT. Deutsche Telekom's new boss, Ron Sommer, used to work for Sony Europe.

Where an established operator is well run, it will still have huge advantages. In a business with massive overheads and very low marginal costs, notes MIT's Professor Hausman, the number of competitors is likely to be small. The winners will tend to be vertically integrated and have good access to the customer. Size will also make it easier to carry the costs of developing ever more fancy services: not necessarily entertainment or home shopping, although those will come, but more ingenious ways to integrate the technology of the telephone into everyday products and services. "This is essentially a consumer-services business. The product is the software that sits on the switch," says Mr Morris. But software development costs AT&T or BT the same as it costs Mercury or US West. What is different is the size of the customer base over which the development cost can be spread.

The incumbent giants have other strengths, such as their billing skills and their financial muscle. They also have a well-recognised brand, which AT&T has taken great care to preserve. Victor Pelson, chairman of the company's global operations team, says its highly successful credit card was launched because "we were concerned that we didn't have a direct link with our customers. They got their bills from the local exchange company. We found that a customer with an AT&T card was much more likely to stay with us as a long-distance carrier." According to a review of prospects for the Bells by Salomon Brothers in New York, two Americans in five still believe that AT&T is their local phone company.

The benefits of size will encourage mergers. Ten years from now, America's 11 large telephone companies – the successors of the seven Bells, GTE and the three long-distance carriers – are likely to have taken on a different shape. Some will have merged with each other; some will have found new lives in adjacent markets such as television, computer services, finance and travel. For some other countries, mergers will raise political problems. Will they be willing to accept part or full foreign ownership of their national giant, or will they prop it up in the same way as they have subsidised national airlines?

Going global

The economies of scale and scope in the transmission of information are such that, by the second quarter of the next century, only a handful of really big international providers may be left. Most national operators will shrink and mutate as their peripheral business is picked off by competitors. The big operators in the rich world are getting ready to

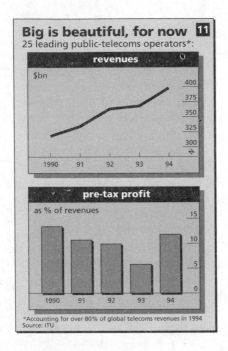

Big is beautiful, for now 11
25 leading public-telecoms operators*:

revenues

$bn

400
375
350
325
300

1990 91 92 93 94

pre-tax profit

as % of revenues

15
10
5
0

1990 91 92 93 94

*Accounting for over 80% of global telecoms revenues in 1994
Source: ITU

grab a share in the global market by forming alliances with partners in other countries.

Global business is still only a tiny teaspoon of most operators' revenues, but many hope that it will provide tomorrow's jam. As the operators' business customers become more global, says Ted Schell, head of corporate development at Sprint, "they will want one global provider to integrate services such as voice mail and electronic mail." Several international alliances, such as AT&T's WorldPartners, hope to win contracts to run big companies' global telecoms networks.

Some of these groupings – such as Unisource, a bunch of operators in some of Europe's smaller countries – consist of national networks tacked loosely together. Some, such as Atlas, an alliance between France Télécom and Deutsche Telekom, and Phoenix, their joint alliance with America's Sprint, are awaiting approval from suspicious regulators. Others, such as Cable & Wireless's minority stake in Germany's Veba, amount to little more than a memorandum of understanding.

Can such cross-border alliances really work? One of the more coherent ones is led by BT, which has chosen second-division players as allies. It now has a 20% stake in MCI Communications, and marketing partnerships with Viag in Germany and with a couple of banks in Italy and Spain. "We reckoned", says Sir Iain Vallance, "that the joining of any two major players would be fraught with regulatory difficulty." Concentrating on banks and utilities brings access to large networks, large customer bases and lots of money. It also allows BT to insist that its partners accept its network architecture. Even so, some customers claim that BT and MCI quote them different prices for the same services.

For the time being, rich-country telecoms giants have this business to themselves. They are also pouring money into the world's fastest-growing markets – in the developing world. "Half the world's population has never made a phone call," says Richard Klugman of PaineWebber in New York. While operators in the rich world worry about getting more people to use their systems, poor countries worry about their immense waiting lists. "Almost without exception, there is huge unmet demand, even at the prices the incumbent monopolies charge," says Björn Wellenius, telecoms adviser at the World Bank.

For the rest of this decade, demand will grow fastest in Asia. Andrew Harrington, director of research at Salomon Brothers in Hong Kong, expects the region to install 15m–20m new lines annually for the next half-dozen years: three to four times as many as are being added in the United States every year. China alone is now adding the equivalent of a new Bell a year. By 2000 it hopes to have 140m lines, which would put it not far behind America's figure of some 160m today.

The boom in the developing world is a golden opportunity for the telecoms operators of the rich world – for the moment. It has been seized eagerly by those operators whose domestic markets are most competitive, and therefore most under threat. Thus Nynex is one of the most active foreign companies in Asia, with stakes in Thailand and the Philippines, a small joint venture in China and a bid for a fixed-wire licence in India. Telstra of Australia, one of the first foreign companies to invest in Asia, is active in Vietnam and Cambodia. Among other things, it has installed payphones in Phnom Penh. Bell Atlantic, together with a large Mexican cellular operator, hopes to install a fixed-wire network in Mexico; Bell South has stakes in several cellular operators in Latin America; US West has permission for a build-operate-transfer scheme in southern India.

What if, as privatisation and liberalisation progress, the concept of national operators becomes an anachronism? Odd though it may seem for one country to provide the telephone service of another, there are precedents: for example, the service in the Maldives (as in many other small countries) is run by Cable & Wireless. If C&W in the Maldives, why not Nynex in Belgium or AT&T in Britain? And if some global giants emerge from the rich world, might the developing countries not grow their own? Already China makes many of the world's telephones. By the late 2020s, might it not handle many of the calls too?

Communicating freely

WHAT will it be like to live in a world where it costs hardly any more to make a phone call to another continent than to the house next door? Some countries will be well on the way to such a world before the end of this century. And what will happen when the cost of communications comes down to next to nothing, as seems likely some time in the first decade of the next century?

The death of distance will mean that any activity that relies on a screen or a telephone can be carried out anywhere in the world. Services as diverse as designing an engine, monitoring a security camera, selling insurance or running a secretarial paging service will become as easily exportable as car parts or refrigerators.

Already, first glimpses of this world are beginning to appear. India has built a flourishing computer-software industry around Bangalore. Its exports more than doubled between 1990 and 1993, to $270m. India is now attracting back-office work from airlines such as Swissair and British Airways. Some of Hong Kong's paging services are manned from China. In Perth, in Western Australia, EMS Control Systems monitors the air-conditioning, lighting, lifts and security in office blocks in Singapore, Malaysia, Sri Lanka, Indonesia and Taiwan. Telecom Ireland has been trying to build itself up as the main call-centre for Europe, handling toll-free 0800 calls from all over the continent. Last April it launched an intercontinental service to allow companies to link their European and American call-centres and to take advantage of the time differences between them.

All this will expose white-collar workers in rich countries to the same competitive pressures that have already squeezed manufacturing workers. But it will also offer educated workers in poor countries the chance to attain a standard of living that they can now get only by emigrating.

Countries that want to take a share of such markets have a huge incentive to make telecommunications as inexpensive as possible. That is a lesson few developing countries have yet learnt. Among the exceptions are some Asian countries such as Malaysia and South Korea, which are installing state-of-the-art telecommunications networks and have a relatively high density of telephone lines.

As prices fall, companies will change the way they do business. Detlef Linssen, in AT&T's office in Bonn, remembers that when he first joined from a German telecoms company, he was amazed to discover that once a month AT&T held an hour-long telephone conference with 120 participants from all over the world. "In Germany, the one that arranges the call carries the whole cost; in the US, each participant carries his own share," he points out.

Within countries, work-related travel may decline, and so may the demand for office buildings, as people increasingly work from home. Big cities will thus increasingly have to look to a future as entertainment centres. Regional development policies may at last become effective when white-collar jobs can be relocated more easily than manufacturing ones ever could.

Many services now provided by government will be changed out of recognition. Welfare and social-insurance payments will increasingly be made by plastic card rather than by relays of officials. Monitoring crime will be made easier by remote surveillance, perhaps carried out by people in a different time zone, and by global positioning devices to track cars and miscreants.

Teaching, too, will be less constrained by distance. At present, Kentucky's National Guardsmen frequently have to be flown to retraining sessions. Richard Jay Solomon and his colleagues at the Massachusetts Institute of Technology are developing a way to use distance-learning instead. "We're going to teach them to kill people in their homes," he says jovially, "but train them in paramedicine first." Health care will benefit in similar ways. In Alaska, more than 100 villages are linked by a dedicated medical telephone network on which local health workers can have regular telephone consultations with doctors at the regional hospital.

For the old and the isolated, cheap communications will be a godsend. If a telephone costs nothing but the initial subscription, why not keep a line open all day, just as people now leave the television on all the time? For women racing from job to nursery to home, accessibility on the move will make life easier. Staying in touch will acquire a new meaning. Starting next month, customers of New World in Hong Kong can have their calls switched to wherever they want them: their mobile telephone, hotel room abroad, voice mail or computer.

Inevitably, with all these benefits will come drawbacks. Privacy and security may suffer as everybody leaves a trail of data and transactions across the globe. Theft of ideas, films and music will become ever more difficult to stop. Policing shipments of information across borders is infinitely harder than policing shipments of goods and human beings (which is hard enough). That may be all to the good when the information flow brings useful knowledge or helps political freedom, but unwelcome when it serves pornography, sedition or crime. Just as the death of distance brings far-flung communities closer together, so it undermines national sovereignty, without a countervailing improvement in global regulation.

The unknowable and the predictable

Predicting the future of a new technology is a mug's game. Marconi thought radio would be useful mainly for ship-to-shore calls. Guessing the social impact of a new technology is even more hazardous. Who would have foreseen that the invention of the post box would contribute to women's liberation – by enabling new generations of young ladies to post letters to their sweethearts without their parents' knowledge?

It is possible, then, only to ask questions. Will everyone acquire, in time, a telephone number or name for life on which they can be reached anywhere in the world? How will society regulate the intrusion of near-free communications? How will national governments, their power bounded by geography, be affected by a technology that makes distance irrelevant?

Big changes driven by technology can happen relatively quickly in the economy. Social changes lag behind. People will take many years to come to terms with many of the consequences of near-costless communications. But as they do, the world will become, on balance, a better place.

THIS SURVEY ON TELECOMMUNICATIONS WAS FIRST PUBLISHED IN
THE ECONOMIST ON SEPTEMBER 30TH 1995

3

THE COMPUTER INDUSTRY

A new age of computing will be heaven for consumers – but hell for the industry

PETER HAYNES

The third age

IF ANYTHING ushered in computing's first age, it was the Type 650 Magnetic Drum Calculator, a mountain of a machine unveiled in 1953 by International Business Machines. The Type 650 did not have the obvious makings of a winner. For a start, the "numerical, stored-program, data-processing machine" had about as much computing power as a modern video-cassette recorder. And it cost $3,250 a month to rent – equivalent to $18,000 in today's money. Small wonder that IBM was cautious. After all, just a few years earlier, it had thought the global market for computers to be five machines at best. Nonetheless, quietly confident of the Type 650's appeal, IBM designed it to make a profit if 50 were sold. Should the firm's famously aggressive salesmen make their target of 250, IBM would make a fortune.

It did. By the time the Type 650 was withdrawn in 1962, several thousand had been sold, making the primitive machine the world's first mass-produced computer. Two decades later, IBM set computers on the road from mass production to a second age, one of ubiquity. Yet the machine with which IBM managed this upheaval – a personal computer, known first as Project Chess, then as Project Acorn and finally, when it hit the market in 1981, as the IBM PC – was deemed inconsequential by its maker. Not for one moment did Big Blue imagine that its feebly powered PC would pose a threat to the crunchingly powerful mainframes that had made it one of the world's biggest and most profitable companies. Mired in its "mainframe mindset", IBM failed to see that technical change was leaving it behind.

This survey is about how computer companies cope – or fail to cope – with change. The industry is in another period of turmoil, loosely encompassed by the term multimedia, which brings together the computer, the telephone and the television. The transition to this third age of computing could make the move from room-sized mainframes to book-sized PCs look like a model of stability. Will the firms that have flourished in computing's second age, the age of the personal computer, be any more adaptable than were IBM and a host of other mainframe makers? Or will they, stuck fast in a PC mindset every bit as reactionary as that of their predecessors, be left behind too?

A tale of two errors

Ted Hoff should take at least part of the blame for IBM's undoing. In 1971 Mr Hoff, an engineer at Intel, then a three-year-old manufacturer of computer memory chips, invented the microprocessor. His brain-child incorporated two innovations: he placed most of the transistors that make up a computer's logic circuits (in effect its "brains") on a single sliver of silicon, and he made the chip programmable, which meant it could be controlled by software. Add together a handful of memory and control chips, and you had a complete computer, albeit a fairly useless one. The 2,300 transistors in Intel's first microprocessor, the 4004, were able to execute what at the time seemed an astonishing 60,000 instructions a second; but it could process so few "bits" of data at a time that it was unable to handle all the letters in the alphabet.

By 1980, Intel's microprocessors contained about 30,000 transistors and ran at ten times the speed of the 4004. That caught the eye of IBM, which was casting around for a microprocessor to use in its forthcoming PC; rather than use its own chip, it decided to opt for Intel's new 8088 model. IBM also looked beyond its own laboratories for the operating software that would make the 8088's circuits work as a computer, turning to Microsoft, a fledgling software company run by a Harvard drop-out and computer nerd, Bill Gates. In a famous ruse that was to transform Microsoft's fortunes and make him the richest man in America, Mr Gates did not mention to the delegation from Big Blue that he had no operating system to sell. Instead, he went out and bought one from a small firm just down the road, Seattle Computer Products. Polished up and renamed MS-DOS, the software was licensed to IBM.

For Big Blue the PC was a sideline, an irritating diversion from its core business of churning out bigger, more powerful mainframe computers. But it sold in millions. And because IBM had failed to secure exclusive rights to either Intel's chip or Microsoft's operating software, hundreds of "clones" of its new PC soon poured on to the market. All were based on the same Intel chips and Microsoft operating software, which together rapidly became the industry standard. The clones sold in even more millions than IBM's original. And IBM's share of what was to become by far the biggest sector of the computer industry collapsed: from close to 100% in the early 1980s to well below 10% today.

The revolution sparked by the PC has been both swift and brutal. From a standing start in the early 1980s, sales of PCs have soared to around 50m a year worldwide – a market that is now worth $74 billion annually, according to Dataquest, a market-research company based in San Jose, California. That compares with global sales in 1993 of 35m passenger cars and 100m colour television sets. By the end of 1993,

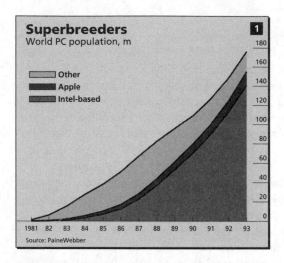

Superbreeders
World PC population, m

- Other
- Apple
- Intel-based

180
160
140
120
100
80
60
40
20
0

1981 82 83 84 85 86 87 88 89 90 91 92 93

Source: PaineWebber

according to PaineWebber, an American securities firm, 176m PCs of all kinds were in use around the world, more than four-fifths of them based on Intel's and Microsoft's standard (see chart 1). The potential global market, reckons PaineWebber, could be 700m.

This survey will focus on PCs not merely because of their popularity, but because their rise has proved so relentlessly Darwinian. For IBM was right that its original PC was no threat to its mainframes; nor to the fridge-sized minicomputers made by both it and such firms as Digital Equipment Corporation; nor to the word-processing computers made by companies such as Wang Laboratories. But these firms did not reckon with the evolutionary power of the microprocessor, nor with the iron rule of Moore's Law. Coined by Gordon Moore, co-founder of Intel, this states that the number of transistors that can be crammed on to a microchip doubles every 18 months – a process which brings with it a huge increase in power and a corresponding decrease in cost. Intel's latest Pentium chip contains 3.3m transistors and can process more than 100m instructions per second, making it 300 times faster than the chip inside IBM's original PC. A Pentium-based PC offers over 1,000 times as much number-crunching power per dollar as an IBM mainframe of the mid-1980s.

It is this combination of accelerating power, tumbling prices and open standards that has made the PC so competitive. It took less than eight years to destroy the market for dedicated word-processors, sending firms such as Wang spinning into bankruptcy. Now, mainframe and minicomputer makers are feeling the PC's heat. In 1993 alone, IBM suffered a fall of almost a third in revenues from mainframe computers, leaving it with a net loss of $8.1 billion (the biggest in American corporate history). Digital, whose minicomputers seemed the biggest threat to IBM's hegemony as recently as the late 1980s, has lost about $4 billion since 1991.

Worldwide sales of big computers have fallen by a third in the past two years; while sales of computer workstations – ultra-high-powered desktop computers which many expect to be the PC's next victim – have stalled. In 1993 four out of every five dollars spent on information technology went on PCs. It is hard to disagree with Bill Gates's conclusion that, "as the PC attains each new level of power, it simply tends to eliminate other types of computers of similar performance."

For its next trick...

This survey will concern itself mainly with American firms. Japan's computer companies, such as Hitachi, Fujitsu and NEC, have been left behind as they have focused on their ailing mainframe and minicomputer businesses, and on developing ever-bigger memory chips. In Japan's domestic PC market, NEC, the market leader, is being battered by cheap American computers made by firms such as Dell, Apple and Compaq. Overseas, only Toshiba has held its own. Of the top ten PC companies worldwide in 1993, all but two (NEC and Toshiba) were American. Big South-East Asian firms such as Acer were nowhere to be seen. And if Asian firms seem to have lost their way in the PC marketplace, European computer makers, struggling with high costs and uncompetitive products, have hardly found their way into it at all.

In the late 1980s nine out of every ten PCs were used as stand-alone word-processors cum number-crunchers, connected to the office printer but to little else. As the number of PCs in each office grew, however, users started to link them together into "local-area networks" (LANS). In America 30m PCs are now wired to such networks. And the falling price and improved efficiency of telephone modems have increased the number of PCs that are able to communicate with other PCs anywhere in the world. This has been reinforced by the number of laptop and notebook PCs in the hands of nomadic workers such as salesmen and site engineers, and by the number of users who now have a PC in their home.

As the concentration of networked PCs has reached critical mass, they have also started to be used as surrogate telephones. In America alone, around 5m computer users now (in 1994) have e-mail addresses; a further 15m–20m users worldwide are connected to the Internet, the nearest thing yet to a global information superhighway. Sitting in New York, this reporter can put a question to, say, Bill Gates by requesting a telephone interview and waiting. Or the same query can be e-mailed over the Internet in 30 seconds flat, with the possibility of a lightning response.

But the biggest change in the PC market is still under way. It is not long since the majority of homes that boasted a computer used it for just one thing: work. But as PC prices have continued to tumble, sales of home computers for education and entertainment have soared. That is especially true in America, where a third of all homes now have PCs (compared with about one in eight in Western Europe), a proportion that rises to over half in households with teenagers. Worldwide, reckons Link Resources, a market-research firm in New York, the population of home computers will climb by about 17% a year over the next five years, compared with growth of around 8% a year in the corporate market. Suddenly, PC makers are having to scramble to meet the needs of a new breed of computer user. That means new sales outlets and software. It may come as a surprise to a computer nerd, but the typical consumer does not find "the desktop" or "Windows" to be an easy way of approaching a PC.

Computer makers and software companies have little choice but to adapt: by the end of the decade, thinks Link Resources, 54% of the world's PCs will be in the hands of consumers, not businessmen, up from 34% in the mid-1980s. But how to adapt? Tumbling prices and soaring sales notwithstanding, the past decade has in one way been relatively stable for the PC business: most users have been content with a few basic components (keyboard, monitor, processor and mouse) and a handful of standard software packages (word processor, spreadsheet, database, planner). The consumer market, by contrast, offers few such certainties. For now, the CD-ROM (compact disc, read-only memory) seems the entertainment medium of choice: 80% of PCs destined for the consumer market now feature CD-ROM players, and the number of educational and entertainment titles on sale is growing rapidly. But beyond CD-ROMs the picture grows hazier.

The industry seems to agree on only one point: that today's information dirt-track will be transformed into a superhighway transmitting a communicopia of films, information, programmes and services into every household. The hard bit is figuring out the PC's role in all this.

Will today's TV sets be "interactivated" by a computerised set-top box, to become the main destination of the new highway? Or will the family of the future shun the TV in favour of the PC – a PC transformed by new easy-to-use software? Will the PC become, in the words of Avram Miller, head of corporate development at Intel, the "information furnace" of the multimedia age? Or is Ed McCracken, boss of Silicon Graphics, nearer the mark when he says that "the PC is old and creaky... washed out"?

Not surprisingly, the industry is hedging its bets by entering into every kind of alliance, joint venture and partnership with everybody from cable-TV companies to Hollywood studios. Few in the business would quarrel with Mr Gates's view that, "unless it looks forward and finds new applications in communications and multimedia, this industry will shrink like mad." Yet everything in the end will depend on what the third age of computing, the age of multimedia, actually looks like.

And the losers are...

THE end of the good times for PC makers came on a steamy June day in Houston in 1992, when Eckhard Pfeiffer declared war. Mr Pfeiffer had taken over as boss of Compaq, a troubled computer company, less than a year earlier. Once the fastest growing firm in American corporate history, Compaq had by 1991 grown fat and lazy, standing aloof while new, nimbler rivals undercut its prices. Rod Canion, Compaq's co-founder and boss, was convinced that the strength of his firm's technology would allow it to command a perpetual premium. He was wrong, and lost his job.

Mr Pfeiffer's recovery strategy was disarmingly simple: cut costs to the bone, then use Compaq's economies of scale and powerful brand to drive out the small "clone makers", which by 1992 commanded 60% of the PC market. And forget the industry tradition of 40%-plus profit margins. Mr Pfeiffer reckoned that if he could put Compaq in what he calls "cost-leadership mode", the firm could get by on a gross margin of 20–25% – and still clear a decent net profit.

Compaq executed its battle-plan with remarkable precision. In June 1992 it introduced a new range of PCs that were a third cheaper than their predecessors – and which undercut the price of many rivals. And it has continued to cut its prices by 20–30% a year ever since, forcing rivals to do likewise (see chart 2). In 1994 Compaq overtook IBM and Apple to become the world's largest PC maker, with a 10% share of the global market by volume, according to Dataquest.

As Compaq has cut prices it has vastly improved its efficiency. The firm's combined labour and overhead costs have shrunk by 75% in two years. Revenues per manufacturing employee now stand at $1.5m. The firm is not infallible: it misjudged the printer and handheld-computer markets and has suffered embarrassing product delays. But it is making money – lots of it. Although its gross profit margin tumbled from 43% in 1990 to 27% in the first half of 1994, its net profits rose sharply. In the first half of 1994, Compaq made a profit of $423m, more than double the level in the same period of 1993. Its sales soared by 47% to $4.8 billion (see chart 3).

Other firms have done less well. Sales have soared as consumers have rushed to buy newly affordable PCs, but profits have slumped. In 1993 Dell and AST Research, two big makers of Intel-based PCs, each lost money despite seeing their revenues rise by almost 50%. Apple, which in the past had managed to juggle a mix of uniqueness (it uses neither Intel's chip

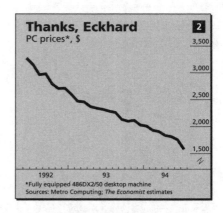

Thanks, Eckhard 2
PC prices*, $

3,500
3,000
2,500
2,000
1,500

1992   93   94

*Fully equipped 486DX2/50 desktop machine
Sources: Metro Computing; *The Economist* estimates

architecture nor Microsoft's operating software) and user-friendliness to command a price premium, saw its profits fall by 84% in 1993. But the biggest losers have been small clone makers: squeezed by powerful brands such as Compaq's, they have seen both sales and profits collapse. This year their share of the world market could fall below 40%. In Europe, on which PC companies once relied to recoup their American losses, price-cutting has driven out more than 100 small clone makers.

Big blues

And then there is IBM. Its PC company, until this year the world's biggest, sold around $8 billion-worth of computers in 1993, up by a third from the previous year. Whether it was profitable is a moot point. IBM says it was, but does not disclose the figures. PaineWebber reckons the unit made a net profit of about $150m, but this assumes "sales, general and administrative" (SG&A) expenses of 16% of revenues, little higher than Compaq's 12%. That may be too optimistic. If the IBM PC company's SG&A expenses had stood at 20% in 1993, the same as Apple's, it would have just broken even; if they were as high as Digital's (30%), the unit might have lost up to $800m.

This year, as IBM continues to lose market share to rivals such as Compaq, its PC unit is almost certain to lose money. In the second quarter of the year, its American shipments fell by 29% compared with a year earlier. In July it sacked a fifth of its 10,000-strong workforce in yet another attempt to cut costs. And in August it was forced to follow Compaq's lead once more, by cutting its PC prices by up to 27%.

The brutal truth is that IBM's PC unit has proved a disaster area. Caught by shrinking product life-cycles, it was left with $600m-worth of

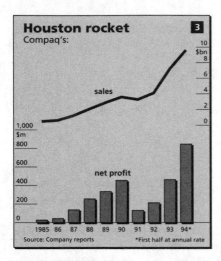

Houston rocket 3
Compaq's:

sales

net profit

1985 86 87 88 89 90 91 92 93 94*

Source: Company reports   *First half at annual rate

unsold stock at the end of 1993. In 1992, the unit launched and later scrapped its own "clone" brand, Ambra – a move that did little to boost sales and a lot to dilute IBM's brand. And in a move likely to confuse customers, IBM is launching a range of PCs based on its new PowerPC microprocessor, the fruit of an alliance with Motorola and Apple (which also uses the PowerPC in its computers). The new machines will be only partly compatible with the Intel-based computers that make up the rest of IBM's line. Meanwhile, IBM remains obsessed with its OS/2 operating software, which has never caught on. So far, only 4m copies have been sold, compared with 120m of Microsoft's MS-DOS and 60m of the same firm's Windows. OS/2 has cost IBM a fortune, and will continue to do so until the company abandons its attempt to buck Microsoft's standard.

The PC industry's troubles have now spread to software companies, for two main reasons. First, cheaper PCs have made applications software look expensive: few buyers are willing to pay $500 for software to use on a $1,000 PC. Second, applications software is becoming increasingly commoditised – one spreadsheet is much like another. So sellers are having to compete on price. In 1993 Borland cut the price of its spreadsheet software to only $50, down from $495 in 1992. Few mass-market software packages now sell for more than $150. In 1993, the price of such software fell by a quarter in America and by a third in Europe.

The price war has come at a time when the software industry's costs are rising fast. According to Datamonitor, an industry consultancy, spending on sales and marketing now stands at around 40% of big software firms' annual revenues, and may soon hit 50%. Expenditure on research and development, by contrast, has stuck at around 14%. Given the rapidly rising cost of developing new software – each generation tends to be more complex and labour-intensive than the last – that may be too little to save even some of the software business's best-known names from extinction.

Making the future compute

The industry is already consolidating. In March 1994 Adobe Systems and Aldus, two pioneers of desktop-publishing software, completed a $525m merger to cut costs and gain economies of scale. The same month, Novell bought WordPerfect for $855m and spent a further $145m on Borland's Quattro Pro spreadsheet business. More layoffs are likely throughout the industry. Lotus and Borland, which are under broad attack from Microsoft's applications software, look especially vulnerable. In the six months to June, Borland's revenues fell at an annual rate of 50%. If Borland is unable to develop successful applications for Microsoft's operating software, it is unlikely to keep its independence.

The PC industry is now looking to multimedia's multitude of new products and services for a chance of fatter profits. That profitability is some time off. Multimedia is a hit-and-miss business, with a spectacular failure (personal digital assistants, such as Apple's Newton) for every resounding success (CD-ROMs). So the industry is trying a handful of other ideas.

The least original is to copy Compaq. For most big PC makers, that means rethinking their manufacturing operations. Compaq's cost-cutting strategy is about making its existing assets work harder. That has meant adopting "design for manufacturing" techniques to reduce the number of parts in a product. Compaq now uses one-third fewer components than it did in 1989, which means its computers take 40% less time to make. "Re-engineering" Compaq's production processes is making them even more efficient: it has managed to reduce the space taken up by each production line in its Houston factory by two-thirds. And whereas many manufacturers merely claim to use "just-in-time" stock control, Compaq really does. Several suppliers have set up shop close to its factory, so that parts can be delivered within 15 minutes.

Speak to an American PC manufacturer, and there is a good chance that it will claim to be "benchmarking" Compaq's corporate strategy. Even ailing behemoths such as Digital are bewitched by the Texan firm:

Robert Palmer, Digital's boss, says he is remaking his company's PC unit in Compaq's image. "Activity-based costing" (ABC), an accounting technique that allows firms to apportion overheads accurately to individual products, was almost unheard of in the PC industry until Compaq adopted it. Now ABC is the industry acronym of choice, adopted by everyone from Dell to Digital.

One big snag with the whole idea is that Compaq is so far ahead of the curve. Compaq also had the luxury of reshaping its strategy while demand for its products was faltering. It is much tougher to restructure a firm's manufacturing operations when it is struggling to keep up with demand – as most big PC makers now are. And few of Compaq's rivals, aside perhaps from IBM and APPLE, can match the strength of its brand. IBM and Apple are for the moment using their brand strength to charge premium prices, an unsustainable strategy in such a commodity-like market.

A second strategy learnt from Compaq is for a company to beef up its management. Fast-growing, entrepreneurial firms have often skimped on management until it is too late. For instance, Dell's revenues soared by 43%, to $2.9 billion in the year to January 1994; but it managed to rack up losses of $36m during the year. Dell had done almost everything wrong. It neglected laptop computers, the hottest bit of the PC market; its stock-control and product-forecasting systems could not keep up with its growth; it had close to 150 suppliers, some good, some disastrous; and its distribution network was hopeless. Dell has now recruited more than a score of new managers, and is regaining both control of its business and profitability.

At the same time, Dell, like many other firms in the industry, is looking for new ways to sell its products. In July 1994 the company abandoned retail sales altogether, to concentrate on selling built-to-order PCs by mail. But it is also considering selling computers from kiosks situated inside video shops and record stores, in order to broaden its market and increase brand-awareness. As more PCs are bought for the home, the entire industry is seeking new, family-oriented sales outlets. Computer makers are stepping up sales through general stores such as Wal-Mart. Microsoft, for instance, already sells software in Wal-Mart and Costco shops. Computer Associates, another software company, is even considering selling software door-to-door, or at home "software parties". In the meantime, it is building market share by simply giving away software such as personal-finance programs.

As they wait for multimedia to take off, computer companies are also looking for new ways to make money. Most hardware firms reckon the safest bet is to boost sales of computer servers, the boxy machines that co-ordinate networks of PCs and currently promise much higher profit margins. As big corporate computer buyers have traded in their old mainframes for networks of PCs, the server market has boomed: this year sales could grow by 20%.

The snag for computer makers is that, as servers grow more popular, they are being dragged into the price-cutting fray – especially as main-frame, minicomputer and workstation manufacturers are all heading for the same market. So far this year the price of a typical network server has fallen by around a quarter. That is especially bad news for Compaq, which last year had a 37% share of the market, according to International Data Corporation. But at least its cost base is low enough to survive a price war. IBM, with 32% of the market in 1993, is more vul-nerable. Industry insiders reckon its server profits could be wiped out by early next year if prices continue to fall.

As they cast around for profits, PC companies have started talking about offering "solutions": which means everything from chips, com-puters and software to system consultancy and on-site maintenance. To break into this, most computer companies are looking for partner-ships. Microsoft has trained a small army of independent engineers to implement its networking software, but it is also working with estab-lished computer-services firms; Hewlett-Packard has recruited EDS, the world's biggest computer-services group, to integrate its computers into networks.

Even dinosaurs like IBM and Digital now understand that this does not mean a return to vertical integration. Take IBM's new Networked Application Services division, for instance, which hopes to offer cus-tomers solutions based on bundles of technology and services. Fernand Sarrat, its general manager, is convinced that IBM is well-placed to offer such chips-to-consultancy solutions. But he stresses that "not every piece will be IBM's. We will definitely take partners to execute some of this strategy." Big Blue, it seems, can still learn new tricks.

Ahead for now

AS THE rest of the industry struggles to eke out a living, it cannot but marvel at the profitability of Microsoft and Intel, the two giants that bestride the computer business. A mixture of clever technology, business savvy and being in the right place at the right time has landed the two companies with 80%-plus shares of the markets that have made them rich: in Microsoft's case, the operating software used on PCs; in Intel's, the microprocessor chips that power that software. That hegemony has translated into the nearest thing to monopoly that the PC business has to offer.

In Microsoft's fiscal year, ending in June 1994, the company's sales of software rose 24% to $4.6 billion. It posted a net profit of $1.1 billion, a rise of 20%. In the past five years, Microsoft's revenues and profits have risen at an average rate of over 40% a year each. Intel's performance has been equally spectacular. In its most recent fiscal year, to December 1993, Intel's sales were up 50% to $8.8 billion; and its net profit more than doubled, to $2.3 billion. Year-on-year growth in Intel's revenues slowed a little in the first half of 1994, to 31%, and net profit increased by only 13% – a consequence of heavy investment and fierce price-cutting. Yet Intel's past five fiscal years have seen the company's revenues rise by an average of 26% a year; and on average, each year delivered a 45% rise in profits.

These numbers should be put in perspective. The companies' products cost a small fraction of their selling price to manufacture. Microsoft had a gross profit margin of 84% in its latest financial year; Intel's was 63%. The two firms' net profit margins are even more impressive: in their latest financial years, Microsoft cleared 25% and Intel 26%. That makes them two of the world's most profitable publicly quoted companies: a highly efficient computer maker such as Compaq scrapes by on a net margin of 8%. Equally impressive is the amount of revenue Microsoft and Intel squeeze out of their employees, which averages around $300,000 apiece. Compare that with Digital's employees, who generated only $162,000 of revenues each in the year to June.

Yet both Microsoft and Intel are looking increasingly challengeable. In the case of Microsoft, PC operating software may have been the basis of Bill Gates's $7 billion-plus fortune; but, increasingly, Microsoft is deriving sales from applications software. Word-processors, spreadsheets, databases and so on now account for 63% of Microsoft's revenues, up from 42% in the year to June 1989 (see chart 4). This change is

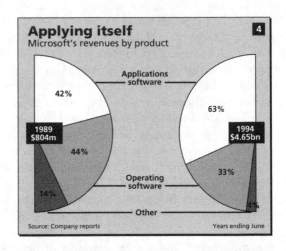

Applying itself
Microsoft's revenues by product

4

Applications software

42%

63%

1989
$804m

1994
$4.65bn

44%

33%

Operating software

14%

4%

Other

Source: Company reports

Years ending June

deliberate. Whereas independent applications developers have struggled to convert their software to work with Windows, MS-DOS's successor, Microsoft has unveiled Windows-based applications of its own. It has since snatched leadership of the word-processing market from WordPerfect (causing the applications maker to collapse into the arms of Novell), and done much the same to Lotus Development and to Borland in the spreadsheet and database markets respectively.

This strategy is not without drawbacks, however. For a firm that owns the industry standard, operating software is a perfect product, because it costs almost nothing to market and sell. And because there is little real competition – Apple's System 7, Novell's DR-DOS and IBM's OS/2 are at best niche products – there is little pressure to cut prices. Microsoft may have to hustle to establish the next generation of Windows, to be called Windows95, but the product will eventually sell itself. Analysts forecast that Windows95 will generate $1 billion of extra revenues for Microsoft in its first year.

Applications, however, are a different matter. They cost more to develop than operating software. They need selling, which means hefty advertising and marketing budgets: a shift to applications software is the main reason why Microsoft's selling and marketing costs now average around 30% of revenues, up from just over 25% seven years ago. And at the same time, the price war in applications software is hotting up. To win market share, Microsoft has had to match the fierce price-cutting of what Steve Ballmer, the firm's executive vice-president, calls "desperate competitors." Desperate, yes, but which company made them that way?

And then there is saturation. Most PC users already have a word processor, spreadsheet or database. And while many new applications-software packages come on to the market every month, it has been years since the industry came up with a "killer app" – industry jargon for massive sellers such as the Lotus 1-2-3 spreadsheet. Selling applications-software upgrades to existing customers is unlikely to make up the shortfall. Mr Gates once predicted that three-quarters of his firm's revenues would eventually be generated by upgrades. That now looks optimistic, partly because the price of applications is collapsing, and partly because PC users are proving reluctant to upgrade. Small wonder that, at every opportunity, Mr Gates is eager to emphasise that his firm's net margins may in the long run fall towards 15%.

To shore up those margins for as long as possible, Microsoft is diversifying, albeit with only limited success. In the rapidly growing markets for "groupware" and the software to run big corporate computer networks, Microsoft is meeting fierce resistance from Lotus and Novell. And it is being hammered by smaller rivals in some of the niche markets it has tackled: for instance, Intuit, a tiny Californian firm, has trounced Microsoft with its Quicken personal-finance software.

That is why Microsoft has set its long-range sights on the multimedia market. The company's consumer division, which comprises around 600 of its 15,000 employees, saw its sales more than double last year, making it Microsoft's fastest growing business unit, even though its revenues are for now small – $300m in the year to June. Mr Gates expects the division to be Microsoft's biggest within five years. Already it is the world's fourth-biggest publisher of CD-ROMs, with products ranging from "Encarta", a multimedia encyclopedia, to "Complete Baseball". But fourth place in a market worth well under $1 billion last year is a far cry from leadership of the $20 billion global applications-software market.

That neatly sums up Microsoft's dilemma. Mr Gates is busily snapping up the rights to everything from cartoon characters' voices to famous paintings; negotiating joint ventures with everyone from cable-TV companies to upmarket British publishers; buying stakes in wireless-data specialists such as Metricom and Mtel's NWN; and snapping up tiny multimedia software firms such as Canada's Softimage, bought for $130m in 1994. But the information and multimedia business is going to be tougher to dominate than was software. Mr Gates believes that, by blending software know-how with a mass of multimedia content, he can make Microsoft a front-runner in the computing industry's third

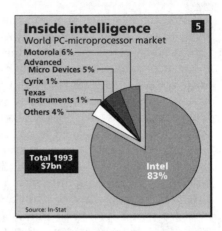

Inside intelligence 5
World PC-microprocessor market

Motorola 6%
Advanced Micro Devices 5%
Cyrix 1%
Texas Instruments 1%
Others 4%

Total 1993 $7bn

Intel 83%

Source: In-Stat

age. Perhaps. But creativity may be the missing ingredient. The reason Microsoft is number four in the CD-ROM market is not that it lacks for content or technological expertise; it is that firms such as Interplay and Software Toolworks are proving more creative.

Nor will Mr Gates's dream of Windows, or its descendants, as the operating software of choice in a multimedia age, necessarily come true. General Magic, a powerful alliance in which France Télécom, Apple, AT&T, Motorola, Sony, Matsushita, NTT, Toshiba and Philips have stakes, is one of several pretenders to Microsoft's throne in the multi-media market. All this vindicates the recent decision by America's Justice Department to penalise Microsoft only lightly for alleged abuses of its market power. Microsoft is the product of the age of the desktop PC. But as the PC moves from desktop to drawing room and beyond, Microsoft will lose control of what is likely to be a rapidly fragmenting market. Even Mr Gates senses the danger. "Microsoft could still fail to lead the way," he muses. But it is clear that he doesn't quite believe it.

Will the circuit be unbroken?

For a decade or more Intel's life has been as breezy as Microsoft's. The Californian company has grown rich from inventing and reinventing the "x86" microprocessor architecture that became the industry standard (see chart 5) thanks to the success of IBM's PC. The Intel 286 microprocessor of 1982 was followed by ever faster successors: the 386 in 1985, the 486 in 1989 and the Pentium in 1993. Each new microprocessor in effect maps out a competition-free zone, at least until Intel's rivals develop a comparable product. That is hard. To win the badge of "Intel compatibility", a competitor must engineer a chip that runs PC software in just the same way as Intel's original, without using any of Intel's proprietary chip "microcode" – or risk the wrath of Intel's lawyers.

Inevitably, this has meant that Intel's me-too rivals, notably Advanced Micro Devices (AMD) and Cyrix, two small American chip makers, have spent much of the past decade behind the curve or in the courtroom. Intel has not, however, had it all its own way. Several big PC makers have, indeed, started to break rank. Compaq, which until this year used only Intel's microprocessors, said in January that it would start using AMD's as well. AST Research and Zenith Data Systems have decided to opt for Cyrix chips in some machines; and the industry is alive with rumours that Dell and Gateway 2000, another big American PC maker, may defect as well. In 1993 AMD and Cyrix had only 6% of the world's $7 billion PC-microprocessor market; this year their slice is likely to be bigger.

At the same time Intel is coming under siege from a new generation of microprocessors based on "reduced instruction-set computer" (RISC) technology. RISC chips not only run fast; their relative simplicity makes them cheap to make. The best known RISC chip is the PowerPC; it is at the heart of a new range of PCs launched by Apple in 1994. But numerous other RISC microprocessors are also vying for a slice of Intel's market, among them Digital's Alpha, Silicon Graphics's MIPS chips and NexGen's Nx586, a hybrid of x86 and RISC architecture.

This will not be a walkover for either the "cloners" or the RISC-chippers. To persuade PC makers to migrate to its Pentium chips, Intel has cut prices sharply. The cost of a typical Pentium has been slashed by 60% since its introduction in 1993. And Intel is racing ahead with development of its next-generation x86 chip. To hedge its bets, Intel has also formed an alliance with Hewlett-Packard to develop a chip that will combine the best of RISC and x86 designs. Meanwhile, the biggest challenge for Intel's RISC-chip rivals is to get applications-software companies to develop programs: no RISC chip is designed to run Intel-compatible software. Some can run Windows and Windows-based applications using a technique known as emulation – but this slows down the chips significantly. So far only the PowerPC has attracted much software. But the chip's chances of becoming a mass-market rival to Intel have been scuppered by Microsoft's refusal to tie Windows95 to it.

This does not mean that Intel's future is secure. Both AMD and Cyrix say they will launch superchips that will easily outperform Pentium while being wholly Intel-compatible. If they deliver on that promise, more computer makers may be persuaded to loosen their ties with Intel. And, like Microsoft, Intel will almost certainly start to lose its grip on the market as the industry embraces multimedia. It is still an open question which microprocessor the handheld communicators or inter-active TVs of the future will run on.

Intel, however, remains confident that the multimedia revolution will start on the corporate desktop – and largely revolve around the PC. It is forming numerous alliances to help turn that dream into reality. One deal in particular perfectly demonstrates Intel's game-plan. In April 1994 it formed a venture with Cable News Network (CNN) to develop software that will provide a primitive "interactive" version of CNN's TV-news programmes over PC networks. But as Ron Whittier, head of Intel's architecture labs, admits, "our biggest issue right now is get-ting the PC hooked up to the communications infrastructure." It is the biggest issue for the rest of the computer industry too.

Speak to me

FOR as long as the modern computer industry has existed, seers have forecast its convergence with the telecommunications business – and been proved wrong. But fundamental changes in the way PCs are being used now suggest that the convergence-theorists' day may be at hand. The proportion of PCs that are connected to networks has soared. More than 30m of America's 100m or so PCs are now wired into corporate networks; nine out of ten big firms, according to International Data Corporation, now link their PCs to some sort of network. Once hooked up, those computers start talking to each other.

Then there is the rising popularity of laptop, notebook and sub-notebook computers. This year, forecasts Dataquest, 18% of the PCs sold worldwide will be portable, up from 15% in 1993. Inside most of those mobile PCs are telephone modems little bigger than a credit card. Thus equipped, they can send data, faxes and electronic mail via the nearest telephone socket. And in July 1994 Hewlett-Packard launched a portable hybrid PC-telephone that uses VoiceSpan, a new modem chip made by AT&T, to transmit voice and data simultaneously down a standard telephone line.

All this is making today's PCs a more useful – and productive – business tool than their stand-offish ancestors. George Gilder, an American technology writer, reckons the computer industry is ruled by what he calls the "law of the telecosm". This says that the cost-effectiveness of computers rises by the square of the number of machines connected to networks. Today, the capabilities of the typical corporate PC network are fairly limited: most allow little more than swapping data, sharing files and exchanging internal e-mail. Connect a network to external e-mail and information services, however, and its utility multiplies. Add in wireless communication, video-conferencing and interactivity, and a computer's world-shrinking usefulness soars: it can, in the words of Bill Gates, "eliminate distance". Yet as they rush to introduce such products and services, computer and telecoms firms alike are starting to wonder whether they will ever see a return on their investment.

As seen on PC

In the short run, at least, the corporate networking business looks like being a profitable niche. Computer makers have discovered that selling network servers is twice as profitable as selling PCs. Compaq, which holds pole position in what is, according to International Data

Corporation, a $5.6 billion market, may get only 14% of its revenues from servers, but it makes 28% of its profits from them. Yet not even the networking business is immune from the computer industry's relentless price wars. And falling prices are helping to nudge bits of the industry in the direction of consolidation. In 1994 two of the biggest players in the networking business, SynOptics Communications and Wellfleet Communications completed a $2.7 billion merger. Others appear imminent.

The part of the networking business that really excites computer and telecoms firms is PC-based video-conferencing. Corporate computer users, goes the theory, will lap up technology that allows them to talk "face-to-face", or to show each other documents and widgets, via their PC networks. But the ultimate goal is to make PC video-conferencing technology cheap and easy enough for ordinary consumers. The video-phone flopped because it cost too much, and too few people could be bothered to buy the necessary pair. But with computers already in a third of American homes, PC-based video telephony has a better chance.

Some of the biggest names in the computer and telecoms industries are already lining up to offer video-conferencing technology – and vying to set the industry standard. A year ago Intel seemed to be ahead of the pack with its software, which allows video-conferencing between PCs fitted with a tiny camera; the image appears in a small "screen within a screen" on the PC's monitor. In January AT&T, America's biggest long-distance telephone company, joined Intel in what seemed like an effort to establish an industry standard. But in June AT&T distanced itself from Intel by launching WorldWorx, a rival video-conferencing system for which it has already signed up IBM, Apple, Lotus, Novell and Xerox – although AT&T and Intel have now agreed to make their rival systems compatible. Others are going it alone. High-powered computer workstations made by Silicon Graphics come fitted with cameras and video-conferencing software.

There are two big drawbacks with existing video-conferencing technology. The first is cost. The special video-chip card that PCs need to run WorldWorx costs several thousand dollars, although the price is certain to fall – during the past two years the cost of digital image-processing technology has tumbled by close to 50% a year. The other snag is that transmitting real-time video images over computer networks takes up a lot of bandwidth. Most networks can either crunch numbers or transmit video images – but not both. AT&T and Intel each

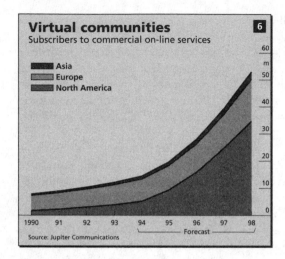

Virtual communities
Subscribers to commercial on-line services

Asia
Europe
North America

1990 91 92 93 94 95 96 97 98

└─── Forecast ───┘

Source: Jupiter Communications

claim to have at least partly solved this problem by using sophisticated "compression" techniques to reduce the amount of video data the network has to cope with. The downside to this is that the images are fuzzy, slow and jerky. Extra processing power will solve that problem – which is precisely why superchip makers such as Intel and Silicon Graphics (which owns MIPS, a maker of RISC chips) find video-conferencing so alluring.

Although PC users may not yet be able to see each other too clearly, they can at least send each other messages. In the past five years the number of subscribers to commercial on-line services – which offer everything from news and e-mail to "virtual conferences" – has more than doubled to 14.4m worldwide (see chart 6). To this virtual community can be added some 15m–20m users of the Internet. Big on-line services such as CompuServe, America Online, Prodigy and Delphi now compete for business with niche players such as The Well, Women's Wire, Pipeline and Digital Queers. At the Icon Byte Bar & Grill in San Francisco you can even log on to the Internet as you sip your coffee.

Until recently, PC hardware and software companies showed little interest in the on-line business: after all, the $500m-odd revenues of the top ten on-line companies last year were dwarfed by the almost $200 billion generated worldwide by the PC business. But as more services appear on-line, the computer industry has suddenly started to show interest. Most of the computer users now on-line are those with some technical know-how: navigating the Internet is not a task for the technologically faint-hearted. On one estimate, fewer than 3% of home-computer users are now on-line.

Computer companies reckon they can do better. In 1994 Apple launched its own on-line service, called eWorld; the software for it is now built in to virtually every Apple PC. Log on, and you are greeted by a friendly, cartoon-style "town", complete with red mail-van (to signify that a user has e-mail waiting), marketplace (to buy products on-line) and community centre (an on-line forum). So far Apple has signed up more than 100 information providers for eWorld, ranging from Grolier's Encyclopedia to Hollywood Online, which offers snippets about the entertainment world. Microsoft says it, too, will launch an on-line service, codenamed Marvel; it will be similarly easy to use, and aimed at precisely the same market.

How profitable such services will be is hard to tell. By restricting itself to Apple users, eWorld is limiting its own potential universe of subscribers. And on-line users tend to be fickle, as big operators such as America Online have discovered: it turns over around a third of its existing subscriber base each year. Most subscribers experiment intensively with on-line services at first, but end up using them mostly for low-revenue e-mail (a short on-line note generates about 15 cents, excluding the monthly service subscription charge). That may be why Rick LeFaivre, head of Apple's advanced technology group, considers the likely profitability of his firm's venture "an open question".

A wish called wander

Consider the fate of what was once deemed the industry's most promising product: the personal digital assistant, or PDA. Little more than a year ago, the PDA – a handheld combination of computer, electronic notepad, fax and diary, with a built-in cellular modem – was the hottest hope in Silicon Valley. Forecasters expected the market for PDAS to grow from $1 billion in 1994 to $8 billion in 1997. Everyone, it seemed, would be walking around with a communicative computer in their pockets.

Reality was rather more prosaic. The first true PDA, Apple's Newton, was to computing what Ford's 1958 Edsel was to the car industry. Its ability to recognise a user's handwriting was abysmal, making it the butt of industry jokes. It lacked wireless communications, and for any other sort of connection it needed a relatively bulky external modem. And, at $700, it was far too expensive. Buyers stayed away in droves. Apple sold only 85,000 of the original Newton (a Mark II version has since been launched), most of them in the three months immediately after its introduction.

Other companies have had to rethink their PDAs too. Compaq, which had intended to launch its own Newton-like PDA, is now redesigning the device – with help from Microsoft and Intel – as more of a pocket-sized extension of a desktop PC. Motorola has delayed its forthcoming Envoy PDA, while an offering from IBM and BellSouth, known as Simon, has got off to a slow start. But the most spectacular failure has been that of EO, a small Californian company whose star-studded investors included AT&T. After investing $50m in EO and selling only 10,000 PDAs, AT&T closed the company down in July 1994.

The industry is still convinced, however, that there is a treasure-trove in wireless, portable computers. Microsoft's advanced technology group is developing software for PDAs; it is also designing its forthcoming on-line service with hand-held devices in mind. Hewlett-Packard, too, is experimenting with a mix of wireless technologies. It has persuaded several computer companies, among them Compaq, IBM, Apple and Microsoft, to adopt its infrared communications protocol for communications between adjacent PCs.

What the industry really needs, however, is a standard for wireless-data communications that would make it worthwhile for PC makers to fit wireless modems to all their portable computers. That looks a distant prospect. In America the likeliest contender is the cellular digital-packet data (CDPD) network on which McCaw Cellular Communications, now part of AT&T, has spent several hundred million dollars. More than 30 companies, ranging from Apple and Microsoft to several of America's regional telephone operators, have said they will support it as the industry standard. But CDPD has competition, including Nextel Communications, in which Motorola has a large stake. It is developing a wireless digital voice-and-data network that it claims will eventually cover two-thirds of America's population.

The odds are that the wireless-computer business, once the computer industry's great white hope, will continue to grow haltingly, at best. Which may help explain why the PC industry is so keen to hone its new-found interactive-communications skills in showbiz.

Screen test

THE shrine to which interactive-age worshippers pay homage these days is a glistening, low-rise campus in Mountain View, California. Sparkling water laps up to glass-walled conference rooms named after films such as "The Abyss". Shocking-pink cubist archways frame office complexes of alarming modernity. And then there are the computers: textured in crimson, teal blue, purple, with not a bland beige box in sight. It all seems fitting for a firm staking its future on multimedia and what it calls "visual computing".

Silicon Graphics is, for now, Silicon Valley's favourite computer maker, and one of its fastest growing. In the year to June 1994 its sales rose by 36% to $1.5 billion, while its net profit climbed by 60% to $141m. The firm's workstations and servers specialise in creating and manipulating 3-D images of astonishing realism: they were responsible for both the liquid-metal cyborg in "Terminator 2" and the dinosaurs in "Jurassic Park". Wherever there is interactivity, there is Silicon Graphics. It is designing a futuristic video-game player, codenamed Project Reality, with Japan's Nintendo; working with AT&T to construct the systems and networks for firms that want to sell video-on-demand; helping Japan's NTT test multimedia services such as interactive TV; and, perhaps most significantly, supplying the powerful "video servers" and (with Scientific Atlanta) set-top boxes for Time Warner's interactive-TV trial in Orlando, Florida.

Silicon Graphics's high-profile involvement with the Orlando project sets it at the heart of a debate within the nascent multimedia business. Everyone seems to agree that interactive programming – whether video-on-demand or simply the ability to download and watch "NYPD Blue" whenever you want – is going to be the bedrock on which the 21st century's multimedia industry will be built. What the industry is squabbling about is whether the tenth series of "NYPD Blue" will be viewed on the TV or the PC.

Ed McCracken, Silicon Graphics's boss, reckons that the PC has no future in interactive multimedia: "I believe that fewer than 15% of multimedia users will interact with the information superhighway via their computers; the other 85% will use the television. And the capabilities we're building into TVs will make them more powerful than any PC." It is a view supported by many of America's cable-TV and telephone companies, most of which have interactive-TV trials in the offing: Bell Atlantic in Alexandria, Virginia; Viacom and AT&T in Castro

Valley, California; Nynex and Liberty Cable in New York; and Tele-Communications Inc (TCI), AT&T and US West in Denver.

Heading the rival camp is Intel, which, alongside a deal with CNN to fire news programmes over PC networks, counts among its interactive projects a venture with AT&T and Viacom (two of the industry's fence-sitters) to deliver video programming to PC users in Castro Valley. For most home interactivities, thinks Andy Grove, Intel's boss, the PC will be the medium of choice. For a start, although 97% of American homes own colour TV sets, none is yet wired up to interactive set-top boxes. One-third of American households, by contrast, already own PCs. And most of those PCs are used far more interactively than the typical TV set, with CD-ROMs, software-based computer games and on-line services. As PC screens get larger, they can be viewed by more than one person, making them more like surrogate TVs. Add a remote-control, perhaps with a small screen to operate the computer via the icon-based software with which most PC users are familiar, and the transformation is complete.

But the PC's biggest competitive advantage, reckons Intel, is that it already contains a large dollop of computing power – easily enough for most interactive applications. "How can the TV keep up with all this?" asks Intel's Avram Miller. "It can't. You simply cannot transform the TV into an interactive device."

Most hardware and software companies are hedging their bets. Apple may be pushing its Macintosh TV – a PC that also serves as a television – but it is also supplying the set-top-box software to Bell Atlantic. The Kaleida joint venture between IBM and Apple is developing multimedia software for Scientific Atlanta. Hewlett-Packard is building set-top boxes for TCI and Comcast. Digital is making similar devices for General Instrument. And many in the industry are coming round to Bill Gates's view that the PC v TV debate is "a fundamentally stupid argument".

Mr Gates, who does not own a television, reckons that once households are connected to the information superhighway, they will use a variety of devices to interact with it: the TV in the living room, the PC in the study. Each, as time goes on, will contain elements of the other. What sort of device you use will depend on what you are doing. "For home banking, you're more likely to use something you sit close to and which has a keyboard," argues Mr Gates. In other words, a variety of information appliances will be plugged into the information superhighway.

Confident that interactive multimedia will find some way into the home, almost every computer company in America is pouring resources into developing the powerful servers and software it will need. Many of America's big-computer makers – such as IBM and Digital – see video servers as a last chance to prove the worth of their old mainframe and minicomputer technologies. Other computer firms hope video servers will help them escape shrinking niches: Sun Microsystems, eager to diversify out of the besieged engineering-workstation market, has teamed up with France's Thomson Consumer Electronics to make multimedia servers for interactive television.

Supercomputer companies, under attack from smaller, less-costly machines, are also looking for multimedia partners: California's nCube has already found one in Oracle. And as for the PC industry's success stories, they are simply teaming up in the hope of making even more money. Earlier this year, for instance, Compaq said it was forming a venture with Microsoft to develop both servers and software to deliver video-on-demand.

Virtual economics

Yet for all the activity, investment and hype, few seem to have a firm grasp on how profitable their multimedia ventures will be. Mr Gates, for one, is deeply sceptical: "People talk about video-on-demand because it's one of the few things in multimedia for which you can predict a revenue stream. But it won't generate enough revenue to pay for the infrastructure." Depending on how you do the sums, a nationwide video-on-demand service for a country the size of America would need to generate as much as $20 (perhaps more) of revenue per week from each subscriber if it were to make a reasonable return on its investment over, say, ten years.

That would mean persuading each family to watch at least, say, five or six films a week – or to spend four times as much on video-on-demand as it now spends subscribing to cable TV – and splash out perhaps as much again on other multimedia services. And there is no guarantee that people will give up going to the cinema, or even to the video-rental shop. It is likely, thinks Nathan Myhrvold, head of advanced technology at Microsoft, that many pioneer suppliers of multimedia services will go bust with breathtaking speed.

The economics of set-top boxes are just as arcane. Industry rumours persist that each of the boxes being used in the Orlando interactive-TV trial is costing Silicon Graphics several thousand dollars to make: the devices are only a little less complex, say insiders, than some of the company's cheaper workstations. To put that into perspective, the revenue calculations above assume a set-top-box price of around $500 – and even that is twice the cost many in the industry think the market will bear. Mass-producing set-top boxes will bring their cost down sharply – but not, think many analysts, by a factor of 20.

All this suggests that Silicon Graphics will have to make most of its multimedia money from selling video servers. Yet not even their profitability is assured. Given the competition, many expect the video-server business to be a price-war zone from day one. "We believe they are going to turn into a commodity far faster than anybody thinks," says Phil Corman, of Digital's interactive video group.

If this represents an accurate picture of the industry's future, Silicon Graphics may find that its lush lifestyle starts to evaporate fast. At present the company's gross profit margin is, at 52%, one of the highest in the computer-hardware business and nearly twice Compaq's. Silicon Graphics also splashes out lavishly on sales, general and administrative (SG&A) expenses: these amount to 26% of total revenues, more than double the proportion at Compaq. Mr McCracken dismisses such comparisons, claiming that his firm's ability to innovate will enable it to stick to its business model, which calls for a gross margin of 50–52%. This sounds like Apple back in 1990: it too believed that its technological prowess would allow it always to enjoy a gross profit margin of 53%, and so continue frittering away 31% of its revenues on SG&A expenses. But other companies caught up; after two of the most painful years in its history, Apple now makes the same gross margin as Compaq and spends a mere 15% of revenues on SG&A.

What Mr McCracken should perhaps be really scared of is a newly confident and innovative Apple, with a low-cost business model based firmly on Compaq's. A year ago Apple was a mess. Its profits were collapsing, Newton had flopped, John Sculley, its chairman, was about to be ousted, and the firm was gearing up to revamp its entire PC range around the untried PowerPC microprocessor. Now, its PowerPC-based Macintoshes are gradually taking off, which should secure Apple a profitable niche in the PC market. It is re-engineering its manufacturing operations to lower its costs. And it has seized the technological lead in the market for low-cost multimedia software. Ten years after helping to create the desktop-publishing market, says Satjiv Chahil, head of Apple's new-media group, the firm now aims to create a "desktop-studio" market. That may be why even the confident Mr McCracken now

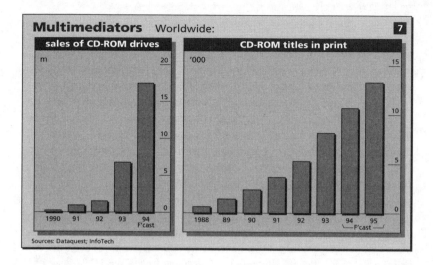

Multimediators Worldwide: [7]

sales of CD-ROM drives — m — 1990 91 92 93 94 F'cast

CD-ROM titles in print — '000 — 1988 89 90 91 92 93 94 95 F'cast

Sources: Dataquest; InfoTech

picturesquely concedes that "Apple may come up our tailpipe."

First, the almost interactive age

Perhaps the worst headache for the fledgling multimedia business is that the hype has got so far ahead of reality. Forrester Research, an industry consultancy, thinks that truly interactive television programming will not arrive for another decade. And the failure of a number of big ventures – notably the gigantic Bell Atlantic/TCI multimedia merger – has made many would-be participants both nervous and sceptical. So, for now, the industry is focusing its efforts on what Bill Gates terms "one of the harbingers of the information superhighway" – the CD-ROM.

This may be a smart move. For one thing, sales of computers equipped with CD-ROM drives are soaring. This year, according to Dataquest, 17.5m CD-ROM drives will be sold worldwide, up from 6.7m in 1993 (see chart 7). By 1996, Dataquest believes, 37% of the world population of desktop PCs will have CD-ROM drives. InfoTech, a consultancy based in Woodstock, Vermont, estimates that about 1,700 consumer CD-ROM titles will be on the market by the end of 1994, a number that rises to more than 10,700 if business and other titles are included. Global consumer CD-ROM sales for 1994 are expected to hit almost $4 billion.

Nevertheless, as a multimedium, the CD-ROM is not without flaws. The biggest is its limited interactivity. Take "En Passant", an experimental CD-ROM-based home-shopping joint-venture between Apple, EDS and Redgate Communications. It allows users to browse through numerous mail-order catalogues – some of them imaginatively animated – on a single CD-ROM. But to make a purchase, those digital window-shoppers must place a telephone call.

Microsoft's "Complete Baseball" CD-ROM comes closer to true interactivity. Equipped with a telephone modem, users can move almost seamlessly between the information on disk and the daily scores (and other news) provided by a companion on-line service. Over the coming year, says RuthAnn Lorentzen, head of marketing at the firm's consumer division, Microsoft will publish several more such "hybrid" CD-ROM/on-line products.

How large the industry eventually grows will depend on how long it takes for truly interactive multimedia to take off. As Mr Myhrvold observes: "Over time, the bulk of multimedia will be delivered down a fibre-optic pipe." But the success of CD-ROMs also depends on how willing consumers are to put up with the medium's many idiosyncrasies – slow, jerky images, crashing programs and clunky installation procedures. If today's and tomorrow's computer technologies are to become truly ubiquitous, they will have to become easier to use, and better integrated into the home. To achieve these twin goals, the computer industry will not only have to think up new ways for its machines to interact with users; it will also have to develop computers that meld seamlessly into almost every household gadget.

A smaller, friendlier future

MOST companies have a corporate Christmas tree, but few fix up their festive fir with radio-controlled microprocessors so that its lights flash to the tune of "Jingle Bells". Yet Echelon, a tiny chip designer based in Palo Alto, California, reckons that the chips which control its Christmas lights represent the future of the computer industry. Formed in 1988 by Mike Markkula, co-founder of Apple and a Silicon Valley legend, Echelon's business strategy is based on a simple premise: if computers cost a dollar apiece, manufacturers would use them in lots of products, from light switches and thermostats to burglar alarms and door locks – often in intelligent networks.

During the past few years Echelon has spent around $100m trying to realise the dream on which it was founded. This investment has spawned LonWorks, a networking-control technology based on two sorts of product. The first, the Neuron chip, is made and sold under licence by Motorola and Toshiba, and sells for $5. By next year, says Richard Kagan of Echelon, the price will drop to about $2. The rest of Echelon's product-range consists of the software, transceivers, routers and other networking equipment that link the Neurons together. It is on these peripherals, says Mr Kagan, that the firm hopes eventually to make its money; it takes only a small royalty on the chips themselves.

Echelon's technology takes the decentralisation of computing – which has its roots in the transition from mainframes to PCs – to an extreme. In a LonWorks network there is no centralised control: each chip has enough intelligence to carry out its (fairly basic) tasks and to communicate its status to other chips on the network. But adding centralised intelligence to the system, perhaps to help householders to program it, is simple: just connect a PC, interactive television or incoming information-superhighway cable.

Motorola reckons the number of these "controller chips" in use in every home, office and car will soar during the 1990s (see chart 8). So far about 1,000 manufacturers are using or experimenting with Echelon's technology, among them AT&T, Hewlett-Packard, Schlumberger, ABB and Philips. Working with Oracle, Echelon has developed systems that could control a houseful of gadgets. And IntelliNet, based in Naples, Florida, has developed a LonWorks-based network that allows home-owners to control everything from video systems to the swimming-pool temperature via a series of keypads located throughout their home.

At present 50,000 Neurons are being churned out each month, a rate

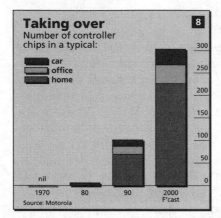

Taking over 8
Number of controller chips in a typical:
- car
- office
- home

Source: Motorola

(1970, 80, 90, 2000 F'cast)

Echelon expects to double by 1995. This year the firm will see revenues of about $20m; next year, says Mr Kagan, it should make its first profit. Outside investors seem equally optimistic. In 1994 George Soros's Quantum Fund paid $10m for a 5.4% stake in the company.

Echelon does not have the market to itself. Among its rivals are Advanced RISC Machines (ARM), a small firm based just outside Cambridge, England, which aims to establish the world standard for cheap, high-power RISC chips. How fast ARM, Echelon or their myriad fledgling rivals will expand depends on the strategies of big chip makers such as Motorola, NEC, Mitsubishi, Hitachi, IBM and Intel. Intel clearly has the market for such distributed networks in its sights. Avram Miller, head of corporate development, thinks that although a PC will be the typical household's central interface with the information superhighway, there will be what he calls wireless "I-pads" (information key-pads) in every room, allowing each home's intelligent network to be controlled remotely. It is a vision shared by James McGroddy, head of research at IBM: eventually, he believes, even powerful microprocessors will be available for as little as a dollar each.

Homes are not the only market for such distributed, or "local", computing. Many of Echelon's customers are utilities, eager to find remote and cost-effective ways to monitor their users' consumption of gas, electricity or water. Dallas Semiconductor is supplying 210,000 "touch-memory" chips to be fitted to the US Postal Service's mailboxes. Simon Forge, a high-technology consultant based in Paris, points to the numerous applications for local computing in, say, a supermarket: to update prices on shelves and communicate price data to a running list on each shopper's trolley; to order new stocks; to control point-of-sale video advertising; and to do away with almost all check-out procedures. Mr Forge notes that such applications will entail much more than cheap chips. They will also require a new era of commodity software, made up of mix'n'match "objects" costing a few dollars each. What it all represents, he says, is a relentless move from "ubiquitous" to "intimate" computing.

The quest for cute complexity

Persuading Aunt Maud to get intimate with entire networks of computers is perhaps the industry's biggest challenge. A recent survey by Apple found that 85% of respondents were terrified of computer technology – a figure that suggests the PC user who tried to use his mouse as a foot-pedal is by no means alone. For computer-literate PC users, Windows may seem perfectly straightforward; for novices it is an unnavigable nightmare. The problem is not, says Garth Saloner, a professor at Stanford University's Graduate School of Business in California, that the technology is lacking; it is that users don't have the ability to adapt the technology to their needs. Adds IBM's Mr McGroddy: "We have to hide the complexity from consumers, so that while the underlying digital world becomes richer and richer, to the user it remains simple."

At present, the most that PC makers are doing to make that happen is to add software "shells" to disguise complexity. The Navigator shell installed in PCs sold by America's Packard Bell uses winsome graphics to make Windows easier to use. Compaq's PCs employ a program called TabWorks to gather together all the computer's software into an easy-to-use "ring-binder interface". Later this year Microsoft will launch its "home interface", a shell that overlays Windows with friendlier, cartoon-like pictures. For multimedia, reckons Microsoft's Mr Myhrvold, "what's important is whether the interface is fun to use."

A coming generation of software, based on wholly pictorial interfaces, should introduce an extra degree of fun – and intuition – into the relationship between man and machine. Apple's eWorld hints at what such software will look like: its use of a red mail van to indicate that e-mail is waiting is the sort of symbolism that even Aunt Maud could cope with. General Magic's new Magic Cap and Telescript software take a similar approach. Magic Cap's "desktop", unlike those found on today's computers, actually looks like one: touch the diary and you can check your engagements. Other metaphors abound: you can "window-shop" in on-screen arcades, selecting individual shop-fronts to see what is in store. And Telescript introduces the concept of "intelligent agents". These can be instructed to wander off into the electronic marketplace to search for any goods or data a user requests. Intelligent agents, think many in the industry, are a good way to make computers seem more intuitive. As David Nagel, head of Apple's AppleSoft division, puts it: "At the moment, computers don't have artificial intelligence; they have artificial stupidity."

For richer and poorer

Computer companies like to talk of this brave new digital world in terms of the "richness" of information that will be on offer: text, graphics, sound, video, animated user-friendly interfaces, multimedia programming and eventually virtual reality, generated by everything from CD-ROMs to the giant servers speeding traffic along the information superhighway. Yet it is this very embarrassment of riches that is in danger of making some of the computer industry poor.

Rich data take up a huge amount of memory, computing power and bandwidth. Some 500 pages of *The Economist* can be squeezed into a megabyte of computer memory; a single minute of uncompressed animation, by contrast, occupies at least 150 megabytes. Start mixing and matching information types and even more space is needed. Add interactivity and, as John Sviokla, a professor at Harvard Business School, puts it: "The consumption of computing power and storage is going to get crazier and crazier."

Chip makers love this. Intel reckons it will clean up, because its Pentium microprocessor was designed to handle richer data types, and because it owns the desktop-PC standard. Rival microprocessor makers – such as Digital, MIPS and the PowerPC triumvirate of IBM, Motorola and Apple – are confident that as computing power moves from the desktop to the drawing room, they will have their chance to unseat Intel. Similarly, Echelon and its cheap and cheerful chip cohorts view the increasing need for widely distributed dollops of computing power as their chance to crack the market. And memory-chip makers see in the multimedia age an opportunity to soak up some of the massive over-capacity that has beset their business. The third age of computing could be kind to those whose strategies are set in silicon.

In theory, software companies should also be smiling. The coming of multimedia and a multiplicity of computer interfaces could loosen Microsoft's grip on their business. The snag is that, just when they need to invest heavily, today's big software firms are being starved of cash by a fierce price war. The likely outcome is a cluster of bankruptcies and a host of new competitors pouring into the market.

For the computer makers, it will be an even more hostile environment. The tumbling cost of personal-computing power is devastating the market for big computers, be they mainframes, minicomputers or workstations. PC makers, too, are feeling the pressure, as they struggle to cut costs to keep up with price cuts of up to 30% a year. To differentiate their increasingly commoditised products, PC makers are resorting to everything from extra gadgets and services to a newly rediscovered faith in brand equity. And all are trying to move upmarket, to higher-margin products such as network servers. The problem with this strategy is that this is precisely where the mainframe, minicomputer and workstation manufacturers are heading – albeit from the opposite direction. The chances are that, within the next two years, the server business will see a price war that will make the PC wars look tame.

The tyre precedent

As it enters the multimedia age, the most nagging doubt in the collective mind of the computer industry is more fundamental: just how big and how profitable is this market going to be, and when? Optimists such as John Sculley, ex-boss of Apple, reckon it will amount to the lion's share of a $3.5 trillion business, but concede that all this is unlikely to materialise until after 2000. Intel's Mr Miller also takes a bullish long-term view. Computers, he says, could one day be more important to the average person than a car.

Yet if the industry is ever to recoup the vast sums it is investing in computing, communications and interactive technology, its customers will have to spend more on multimedia than they have ever done on television, or films, or books, or CDs, or any other form of entertainment. Why should they?

Budding multimedia moguls should perhaps consider the experience of the car industry. When cross-ply tyres were replaced by longer-lasting, fuel-efficient radials during the 1950s and 1960s, many in the business believed that all those newly re-tyred motorists would drive greater distances than ever before. But they didn't.

THIS SURVEY ON THE COMPUTER INDUSTRY WAS FIRST PUBLISHED IN
THE ECONOMIST ON SEPTEMBER 17TH 1994

Postscript

Oddly, for an industry where change is a way of life, by the end of 1995 not much had changed in the computer business since this survey was written. Prices, especially of PCs, were still tumbling; Moore's Law still just about held. Microsoft remained strong, bolstered by its Windows 95 software; Intel and Compaq Computer continued to prosper. IBM, propped up by surprisingly buoyant sales of mainframe computers, had staged a mini-recovery, but its PC unit and OS/2 software continued to bleed cash.

Optimists thought that Big Blue's $3.5 billion purchase in June 1994 of Lotus Development, one of the pioneers of PC software, might herald a new era for what is still the world's biggest computer company. But given that Jim Manzi, Lotus's boss, had already quit, the signs were not encouraging. Nor were they at Apple Computer, which, despite some of the smartest technology in the business, still could not get its business model right, and seemed unlikely to remain independent. And much the same applied to Silicon Graphics, for all its success and showbiz glitz. Its high-margin, proprietary-technology strategy may yet be its undoing.

When the survey was written, it was clear that more and more PCs would find themselves connected to networks. What is now even clearer is that, for the foreseeable future, the *ubernetwork* of choice will be the Internet – and especially the World Wide Web. Since 1994, the number of Internauts had almost doubled by the end of 1995, and this momentum shows no sign of slowing – hence the stunning stockmarket debut of Netscape Communications, which makes software for browsing the Web.

All this will profoundly change the computer industry. With more and more intelligence and software on the Net, home PCs will increasingly become smart "dumb terminals". With so much of the Net's intelligence available for free (or for much less than the cost of PC software), today's successful software, chip and computer makers will have to start rethinking their business models, too. And networks will not stop there. In time, their intelligence will spread to objects that, for now, are all but brainless: door locks, thermostats, desks and telephones. Echelon's vision, then, still holds true. But it will be many years before its dream pays dividends.

4

THE INTERNET

The explosive growth of the Internet is not a fad or a fluke, but the result of a digital free market unleashed.

CHRISTOPHER ANDERSON

The accidental superhighway

FOR the past few years the titans of media and communications have waged a war for the digital future. With great fanfare, telephone and cable TV companies have launched dozens of trials to demonstrate their vision of speedy electronic networks, connecting homes to a boundless trove of information, communication, education and fun. Shambling towards their distant goal of a wired world, they have been too busy to notice the unruly bunch of computer hackers, engineers and students scurrying about at their feet.

They should have paid more attention. For while the giants have just been talking about an information superhighway, the ants have actually been building one: the Internet. For almost all of its 25-year life, this loose confederation of interconnected networks has been the arcane domain of computer scientists and academics, a private line for electronic conversations that no one else would understand anyway. It grew, fast, because it was left to its own devices and filled unmet needs. The Internet's builders laid no cables and dug no trenches; they simply leased existing telephone lines. When the Internet linked up with public and commercial networks in the mid-1980s, its growth accelerated. Yet most big telephone companies still wrote it off as nothing more than a playground for bitheads and boffins.

In mid-1993 something new happened: the Internet sprouted multimedia wings. A combination of special software and a way of connecting documents allowed users to travel the network with pictures, sound and video, simply by pointing and clicking a mouse. Suddenly the light dawned. The Internet was not just a way to send e-mail and download the occasional file. It could be a place to visit, full of people and ideas: "cyberspace". It was a new medium, based on broadcasting and publishing but with another dimension added: interactivity. Internet veterans had known this for years; they could see the potential behind the screens of plain text and baffling computer commands. But thanks to the friendly, multimedia side of the Net, called the World Wide Web, a much broader audience started to catch on to it.

In 1994 the Internet as a whole doubled in size, as it has done every year since 1988. It is now estimated to reach nearly 7m "host" computers, each of which may connect several individual users. At the same time the Web grew almost 20-fold; in just 18 months users created more than 3m multimedia pages of information, entertainment and adver-

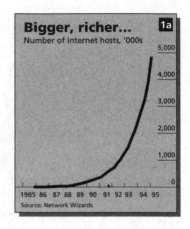

Bigger, richer... `1a`
Number of Internet hosts, '000s

tising. No one knows how many people are behind this, but a mid-1995 survey by Nielsen, a market-research firm, put the number of users at 37m in North America alone. Whatever the worldwide number is today – 40m is not an unreasonable guess – it will be at least half as big again a year from now. No communications medium or consumer electronics technology has ever grown as quickly; not the fax machine, not even the PC. At this rate, within two years the citizens of cyberspace will outnumber all but the largest nations.

What does that mean? This survey will argue that the Internet revolution has challenged the corporate-titan model of the information superhighway. The growth of the Net is not a fluke or a fad, but the consequence of unleashing the power of individual creativity. If it were an economy, it would be the triumph of the free market over central planning. In music, jazz over Bach. Democracy over dictatorship.

As a result, the information superhighway will arrive sooner, but it will be a very different kind of road from the one the giants intended. Cable and telephone companies will still build their high-speed networks to people's homes, but what will pour through them will be the Internet, not just the network providers' canned content. This will be a grown-up version of the Internet, made much easier to use. It may even be called something else. But the basic ingredients of success will be the same: openness and interactivity, making it a combination of community and marketplace.

Some people argue that the Internet already is the information superhighway; it simply looks different from the television-based version promoted by the cable and telephone companies. Others say that

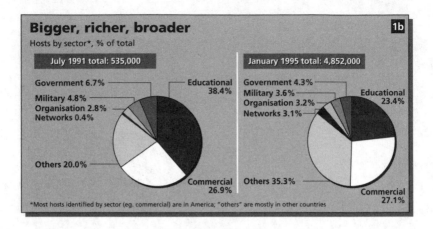

Bigger, richer, broader `1b`

Hosts by sector*, % of total

| July 1991 total: 535,000 |
| January 1995 total: 4,852,000 |

July 1991 total: 535,000

Government 6.7%
Military 4.8%
Organisation 2.8%
Networks 0.4%
Educational 38.4%
Others 20.0%
Commercial 26.9%

January 1995 total: 4,852,000

Government 4.3%
Military 3.6%
Organisation 3.2%
Networks 3.1%
Educational 23.4%
Others 35.3%
Commercial 27.1%

*Most hosts identified by sector (eg. commercial) are in America; "others" are mostly in other countries

some important features are still missing: the real superhighway will combine not just computer networks but all sorts of other communications links, from telephone to wireless and satellite. It will be fast where the Internet is slow.

Yet the Internet already offers, albeit in embryonic form, most of the services and technologies that cable and telephone companies are still a decade from delivering. You can make a telephone call on the Internet; watch a video; listen to an audio broadcast, or broadcast yourself; shop; learn; and, of course, communicate. Every day the Internet delivers more of the features of the fabled superhighway. It may be doing these things clumsily, unreliably and slowly, but it is doing them, now.

Electronic potholes

Sceptics abound. The Internet, they say, is chaotic, frustrating and intimidating. Only those lucky enough to be able to afford a high-speed connection can really enjoy its multimedia side; for those using a modem, it simply takes too long. Finding what you want can be maddeningly slow: in an ocean of information, sense and understanding is often lost in a flood of random facts and rhetoric. Moreover, you need a computer equipped with some telecommunications link to use the Internet in the first place, which excludes most of the world's homes. Even in America, where a third of all households have a PC, only about half of those also have a modem connected to a phone line.

All true, the believers concede, but just wait. Already the Web is making the Internet easier to use, and hundreds of companies are developing software to make it easier still. Hundreds more are developing software and services to make sense of the sea of data on-line. At the same time the equipment is becoming much more widespread. Private consumers were expected to buy some 15m PCs worldwide in 1995: the home is now the fastest-growing market for such computers. And the cost of high-speed data links is falling.

This survey will argue that the Internet's fans have a better case than its foes. The Net will suffer plenty of growing pains, and it may not change the world as much as the cyber-Utopians would have us believe: compared with the richness of real life, even the best on-line "virtual spaces" are cartoons. But it is here to stay, and it will allow people to exercise one of their most basic desires: to communicate. This they will be able to do on an unprecedented scale: globally, openly, to one person or many. In that sense, the Internet will almost certainly have a stronger impact than the PC alone. PCs put computing power in the hands of ordinary people; the Internet gives them something compelling to do with that power (other than play games). How important this revolution will eventually turn out to be is as yet impossible to say. A reasonable guess might put it ahead of the telephone and television but behind the printing press and the motor car.

Such a ranking is clearly subjective. But Marc Andreessen, the main creator of Mosaic, the software program that made the Web easy to use and thus launched the mainstream Internet revolution, suggests a mathematical reason why it may be quite near the mark. Computers owe their growth and impact to a phenomenon dubbed Moore's Law (after Gordon Moore, the founder of Intel), which says that computing power and capacity double every 18 months. This exponential growth has led to the digital revolution, and it has only just begun.

Networks have their own growth rule. According to Metcalfe's Law (named after Bob Metcalfe, the inventor of the Ethernet standard commonly used in PC networks), the "value" of a network – defined as its utility to a population – is roughly proportional to the number of users squared. An example is the telephone network. One telephone is useless: whom do you call? Two telephones are better, but not much. It is only when most of the population has a telephone that the power of the network reaches its full potential to change society. The Internet owes its extraordinary growth and impact to its ability to harness both these laws at the same time. The world has never seen a technology like this before. "Data dialtone" – networking as widespread as the telephone – suddenly seems not only possible, but likely.

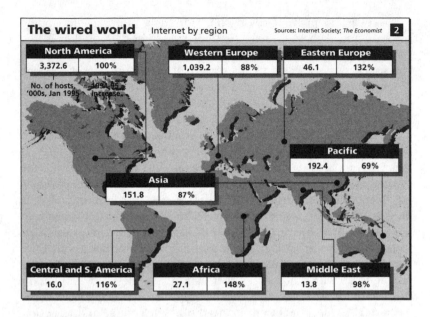

The wired world   Internet by region   Sources: Internet Society; *The Economist*   2

North America		Western Europe		Eastern Europe	
3,372.6	100%	1,039.2	88%	46.1	132%

No. of hosts, '000s, Jan 1995 1994-95 increase

Pacific	
192.4	69%

Asia	
151.8	87%

Central and S. America		Africa		Middle East	
16.0	116%	27.1	148%	13.8	98%

The fish-tank phenomenon

This is the sort of brave talk one hears about all sorts of plans for the information superhighway. The difference is that the Internet is already there. Today a handful of cable TV and telephone companies are conducting interactive television trials, giving a few thousand homes a limited taste of video-on-demand, games, home shopping, advertising, education and information. Yet if those same homes have a PC, they can get all this (bar video-on-demand, although that too may come) and more on the Internet. It is not yet as fast, but there is infinitely more of it: a whole world of content, from the glossy digital facades of the *Fortune* 500 to thousands of "home pages" created by people who have assembled some unique information – or just want to show the world their fish tank.

Of the two, the fish tank is actually the more profound. In its audacious uselessness – and that of thousands of ego trips like it – lie the seeds of the Internet revolution. The Internet allows everything: anyone can be a publisher, and publish anything he wants. Set up a home page to show all comers what you are watching on TV at that moment, and it will stand side-by-side with IBM, competing equally for visitors.

That is why the Internet has exploded past commercial on-line services such as CompuServe and America Online (although they, too, are growing quickly, in part because they offer Internet access). Many of its users are not just information consumers, they are producers as well. For them, the Internet serves as personal printing press, radio station and billboard, all in one. No commercial service can ever hope to rival the quantity and quality of the output of 40m people. True, much of what they produce is rubbish; but much is astoundingly creative, sometimes even useful.

This is a lesson the PC revolution should have taught us already. PCS toppled mainframes and changed the world because they put power in the hands of individuals, bypassing centralised control. The same is true of the Internet. Yet a remarkable number of those who rode the PC revolution to greatness missed the significance of the Internet. Even Microsoft underestimated its impact. The company designed its forthcoming commercial on-line service, the Microsoft Network, around a proprietary network technology. Only in 1994, when the Web took off, did Microsoft adopt the Internet standard as well. Now, humbled by the speed at which the Internet has passed commercial networks, it is moving away from the stand-alone model entirely.

The big names on the Internet are not Apple, IBM or NEC (at least not yet), but a motley collection of young companies, university students and entrepreneurs. Netscape Communications, started in 1994, rules the Internet software market; Cisco Systems (1987) and Sun Microsystems (1982) sell the most hardware. The World Wide Web was invented by a software engineer at a physics lab in Switzerland, and the software that popularised it was written by an undergraduate at the University of Illinois. Almost anything that made a difference on the Internet was produced by people whom the corporate world might consider nobodies.

Equally, it was not the telephone companies that built the Internet, although it uses their networks. They carry its data for a fee, just as they carry data from thousands of other sources. The companies that lease this capacity to bring the Internet to users around the world are mostly newcomers: Performance Systems International, Netcom, Pipeline, UUNet, Demon, Pipex. America alone has more than 600 of them. Almost all of them are under five years old.

This is what Tony Rutkowski, executive director of the Internet Society, calls "bottom-up information infrastructure". In the late 1970s, telecoms and computer titans tried to chart the future of communications for decades to come. They planned to build their own digital highways and sell videophones, Videotex and other such wonders. It never happened – consumers were not buying. Instead, the PC arrived, spawning office networks. Once telecoms competition had lowered the cost of connecting these networks, the makings of a highway of a very different kind began to emerge.

Mr Rutkowski recalls visiting America's Federal Communications Commission in 1990 and seeing an official excitedly waving two charts. One, from the FCC, showed the traditional telecoms investment, worth several billion dollars and growing at the same rate as for the past few decades. The other, from the Commerce Department, showed all network infrastructure investment – including office PC networks and private long-distance data networks. It had started at about the same level as the telecoms investment a few years earlier, but had grown exponentially to double that figure by the late 1980s. The gap was widening rapidly, representing something altogether new; something, the FCC official admitted, "we know nothing about".

It was the foundation for the Internet, even though the true importance of that development did not become clear for another decade. The Internet not only challenges the traditional way of building networks; it is so chaotic, decentralised and unregulated that it also defies conventional understanding of such networks.

Like a flock of birds

MOST people imagine that anything as complicated as, say, an economy or a global computer network must be designed and run by some central authority. Take the Internet. Those who know little about it usually reckon it is run by a company to whom you pay a subscription fee and an hourly charge to use the network. The way it works, they think – if they think about it at all – is that once you are in the system, your computer sends requests or messages to a central data centre. Big computers in this centre send out information in answer to your requests or pass your messages to other users. If you want to put some of your own material on to the network, you approach the company and strike a deal.

It all sounds perfectly plausible, but it is completely off the mark. In his book "Being Digital" (Alfred Knopf, 1995), Nicholas Negroponte, the director of MIT's famed Media Lab, gives an example of the "centralised mind-set" fallacy that leads to such expectations. We usually assume "that the frontmost bird in a v-shaped flock is the one in charge and the others are playing follow-the-leader. Not so. The orderly formation is the result of a highly responsive collection of processors behaving individually and following simple harmonious rules without a conductor."

Parcelforce

This is as good a description of the Internet as any. For collection of processors, read all the computers and wires that make up the thousands of smaller networks connected by the Internet; for harmonious rule, read a method of transferring data called TCP/IP, stemming from the Internet's military origins (see next article). The rule says simply that data shall be broken up into chunks called "packets", and that the first part of each packet shall consist of the address it should go to. That is all. What happens next is not laid down in any master plan. There is no central computer; indeed, there is no centre at all. Far from being a hub with spokes, the Internet is more like a spider's web, with many ways of getting from point A to point B.

Physically, it has little substance: most of it is simply leased space on existing telephone networks, with some dedicated computers at connection points. Forrester Research, a consultancy in Cambridge, Massachusetts, estimates that total sales of Internet-specific hardware in 1995 will be only $50m; like a parasite, the Internet uses the multi-billion dollar telephone networks as its hosts and lets them carry most of the cost. That makes it largely a "virtual" network, running on top of the physical network of the telephone companies.

This works because the Internet does not need what telephone companies consider to be their main assets: the centralised mainframes and big switches they use to control their network. Instead, the Internet uses distributed intelligence, taking advantage of the telephone companies' lines while bypassing their tollgates.

Imagine you wanted to make a telephone call from New York to Los Angeles without paying the long-distance charge. If you had the right kind of telephone and knew enough people across the country, you might call someone at the western limit of your local zone, who would call someone at the western edge of their local zone and patch you through, and so on across the country. This may be an impractical method of making telephone calls, but it hints at the way the Internet uses the telephone networks without being controlled by them.

All the content on the Internet is held in computers known as "servers" at the edges of the network, usually owned and operated by the companies and organisations that want to distribute the information. Microsoft has servers; so do thousands of other companies (including The Economist). In response to a request, the machines parcel up data in a lot of packets with an address on each one, and send them blindly down the nearest connection to the Internet.

When they arrive on the network, they are read by a computer (called a "router") that has a rough idea of where things are on the Internet. It reads the addresses and sends the packets in the right general direction, using the best path available at that moment. The same thing happens at the next intersection, and so on until the packets reach their destination. The network's best path from A to B at any one time may bear no relation to real-world geography. At the moment this paragraph was written, for example, the best path from London to Amsterdam, using one Internet provider, was via New Jersey. Other providers might have used different routes.

None of the routers has a map of the whole Internet; it just knows the best way to the next router at that time. That makes it impossible to predict what path a particular packet will take. It all depends on what is available at that moment; the individual packets making up a single message may end up taking different routes, only to be sewn back together again at their destination.

Free-for-all

This is the power of networked intelligence. The Internet does not need any particularly smart computers to run the show, just a lot of dumb-but-fast ones that know how to work together. The secret of its success is an idea of breathtaking simplicity. Think up a universal way for networks to share data that will work with any kind of network, of any size, carrying any kind of data, on any sort of machine. Let anyone use it, for free, with no restrictions or limitations. Then just stand back.

Networks want to connect. As Metcalfe's law states, the value of a network increases geometrically with the number of people who use it. Local area networks linking PCs within offices have been widespread for years, but isolated from each other. The Internet broke that bottleneck. It offers a standard method of transmitting data that works equally well for anything from voice to e-mail. Most importantly, it is in the public domain. Nobody owns it and nobody charges a fee for its use.

Proprietary networks using different data standards can be part of the Internet as long as they package their data to the TCP/IP standard when they meet each other. But increasingly they use TCP/IP internally, too, because otherwise they miss out on the thousands of Internet software programs. These allow the Internet to be used for things its founders never imagined, from telephone calls to live rock concerts. An open standard means more users speaking a common language, and hence a potentially huge audience, which makes it worthwhile producing such programs.

But software is just the beginning. Internet content – everything from classic books to underground music – is exploding even more spectacularly. This same critical mass of users has stimulated a creative outpouring not seen since the arrival of the PC (another open standard). Without any prospect of profit, thousands of individuals have put millions of pages on-line – anything from complete libraries of technical information to day-by-day personal diaries or mini-directories to their favourite part of the Internet. Some of them do it because the Internet has the remarkable power to make an ordinary person an on-line celebrity; it bypasses distribution channels and public-relations machines. Others do it because they see a new world emerging on the Internet, and want to contribute to it. Still others do it simply because the Internet is there, and nothing stops them. If the site is interesting enough, it might be visited by hundreds or thousands of people a day.

All this activity keeps the wires humming and attracts millions of new users each year. It also puts a great deal of pressure on the network; the companies that provide access and store data are often swamped by the relentlessly rising tide of traffic. In theory, the solution is simple: buy more and faster equipment. But that takes more money, and therein lies a problem. The Internet's economics are still stuck in its non-commercial past.

A changeling's tale

SAY Internet, and you instantly conjure up a picture of creative anarchy. Yet, incongruously, that cheerfully chaotic child was fathered by cold-war paranoia and born in a military laboratory. It started life in 1969, as ARPAnet, named after its sponsor, the Pentagon's Advanced Research Projects Agency. The aim was modest: to allow computer scientists and engineers working on military contracts all over America to share expensive computers and other resources. As an afterthought a few researchers cooked up a way of sending messages, too. "E-mail", as it became known, quickly turned the network into a new communications link.

The Internet owes its main technical advantage to its military origins. Splitting data into tiny packets which can take different routes to their destination makes it hard to eavesdrop on messages. And a "packet-switched" network can resist large-scale destruction, even a nuclear attack; if one route is knocked out, packets will simply travel along one that remains intact.

Until 1983 the Internet consisted of fewer than 500 "host" computers, almost exclusively in American military labs and academic computer-science departments. But the word was getting out to other academics. By 1987 the Internet had grown to include 28,000 host computers at hundreds of different universities and research labs.

Using it was still difficult and frustrating, but its power was already obvious. No other method to network universities around the world was so universal and so flexible. Internet users invented ways for many people to participate in open discussions, created software and document libraries on the network and made them accessible to all. This was exciting stuff for computer scientists and some other academics, but it remained a cloistered world.

Yet during the late 1980s, while the Internet was growing in the academic world, a networking revolution of another sort was taking place outside. Businesses realised that, having traded their mainframes for a multiplicity of PCs, they needed some way to recapture the mainframe's ability to share data and devices such as printers. So they strung wires around their offices and connected the PCs together.

These internal "local area networks" (LANs) did more than save money; they changed the way people worked. E-mail took off within offices, and soon between them, as companies created "wide area networks" to connect distant workplaces. But there it stopped. Different software and hardware standards used by different companies made creating wider networks a nightmare of incompatibility.

At home, PCs had made computer power affordable, and modems had allowed them to be connected up over telephone lines to commercial "on-line" services and "bulletin boards" – electronic discussion groups and software libraries usually set up by enthusiasts. Both of these grew steadily, but not explosively. Each had disadvantages. The networks offered by CompuServe, then the leading on-line service provider, and others that followed in its wake were national, even global, but they were closed. The providers controlled what was available. Private bulletin-board systems, which had sprung up in their thousands, were unrestricted but usually confined to a small group of users near the host computer.

Around the same time the American government was relaxing its hold on its network. The National Science Foundation, a civilian agency, was now paying for most of it, originally to connect the agency's supercomputer centres, but later as a way to allow all kinds of academic and government researchers to communicate. For the first time companies were allowed to join, although not to use the network for purely commercial purposes.

Still, that was enough. Having conquered the academic world, the Internet began to serve as a connection point for commercial networks, both to reach academics and to communicate among themselves. "The Net came at a unique time when the computers and networks that existed were waiting for a way to bring them together," says John Curran, chief technical officer at Bolt Beranek and Newman, a Cambridge, Massachusetts, technology company widely credited with creating much of the early Internet. Commercial use skyrocketed as restrictions were eased, and in 1994 companies passed universities as the dominant users. In April 1995 all remaining curbs on commercial use were lifted, and the National Science Foundation began to phase out the last direct federal subsidies for the network. The Internet had grown up.

Words inside words

THE PHENOMENAL success of the World Wide Web, the part of the Internet that has most captured the public's fancy, is usually put down to its colourful pictures, sound and video. But the real explanation is different and considerably more interesting: it is "hypertext", the ability to link documents to each other by way of a live footnote. By clicking on these "hotlinks", users can travel ("surf") around the Internet following a more-or-less thematic path from one source to another – or simply dive into one link for a bit more information, then back out to continue where they left off in the original text.

The Web, and its use of hypertext, is the brainchild of Tim Berners-Lee, who invented it as a way to organise on-line scientific information at the physics laboratory CERN. But it did not take off until Marc Andreessen, then an undergraduate at the University of Illinois, and others wrote a programme called Mosaic. That programme made using the Web as easy as pointing and clicking at pictures and underlined words.

Hypertext is not unique to the Web – CD-ROM encyclopaedias and other multimedia reference works use it, too. But the Internet takes it further. The Web is as big as the Internet, which is to say unlimited in size, not restricted to the contents of a compact disc. Following Web links, surfers can as easily (and inadvertently) find themselves in the Internet version of the Andy Warhol Museum as in the angst-ridden diary of an American Generation Xer, and a thousand places in-between.

The potential of hypertext on the Internet is only just being explored, but users seem to be captivated, too. The Web is growing at about 50% per month, with the number of Web sites doubling in size every 53 days, according to Sun Microsystems, which makes most of the computers they run on; already, the number of Web servers has grown to more than 30,000, with more than 3m pages of information.

Mr Berners-Lee left CERN in 1994 for MIT, which now hosts the World Wide Web Consortium, W3C, a group of companies that is developing the next generation of the Web "language", HTML, to let on-line text look more like a printed page.

In 1994, Mr Andreessen co-founded Netscape Communications, which has since grown quickly to dominate the commercial market for Web browsers.

Freeloading as a way of life

A SIMPLE question: if the Internet runs over telephone lines, why does it cost the same to send an e-mail message around the world as it does to send it next door? Answer: no one really knows; maybe it shouldn't. Just as the Internet has overturned the conventional wisdom on building telecoms networks, so it has challenged their archaic pricing systems. Unhelpfully, though, it offers nothing more substantial than a vacuum in their place. When Internet builders lie awake at night worrying that the whole thing might fall apart, as often as not their nightmares are about its economics.

Start with the distance puzzle. The first reason why distant messages costs no more than local ones is that the Internet, although it runs on telephone lines, uses them much more frugally than voice calls do. A voice call is an analogue signal which needs a lot of electronic space to avoid interference, so it takes up an entire line for the duration of the call. By contrast, the Internet is digital, so its data bits – ones and zeros – can be compressed.

Second, and more important, the Internet data is split up into packets, which do not need a line to themselves. Packets from hundreds of sources are mixed up by the computer and shoved down the pipe in a jumble. The router at the other end of the line receives each one, reads its address and sends it in the right direction. When you make a telephone call, you are consuming a scarce and expensive resource: a whole line. When you send a message on the Internet, you are sharing a plentiful and cheap resource: the entire bandwidth on the line. Your packets are just a drop in a passing river.

But there is a third reason: telecoms pricing is a notorious scam. A large part of the price of a telephone call (often more than 40%) goes to the recipient's telephone company for taking it the last few miles. Through a complicated accounting scheme known as "settlements", telecoms companies exchange billions of dollars each year to pay for the local component of international calls.

The Internet bypasses all this. It usually operates on leased lines, out of reach of national telecoms accounting. Even if these companies could track the traffic, they would simply find a constant stream of ones and zeros, 24 hours a day.

Digital data makes short work of all the anachronistic pricing schemes and implicit cartels of the international telecoms market. Telephone calls are priced at what the market will bear. Data transmission on leased lines is priced somewhere nearer to what it actually costs. The difference can take several noughts off the amount you pay. Talk to a friend abroad for an hour and you may be charged $50. Make the same call on the Internet, using software from companies such as VocalTec, and you pay nothing, or nothing more than the cost of a local phone call. Even after allowing for your monthly fee, the call costs just a few cents.

Forget economics, let's surf

One of the many remarkable things about the Internet is that once you have paid your monthly connection charge – say $20 – it appears to be free. Send one e-mail message around the world or send a thousand, the price is the same: $0. In fact, each e-mail message does cost somebody something, because it consumes a tiny bit of "bandwidth", the capacity of the expensive data pipes that make up the Internet. But since the Internet providers have no way of billing for such infinitesimal consumption, they have settled for a rough approximation instead. They multiply the number of their subscribers by the average network usage to calculate the capacity they need to lease, which gives them a fair idea what to charge. As long as the average usage does not change much, this works.

But usage does change. Until recently the Internet has been mostly a world of text, which is an efficient way to communicate. A million bytes can capture the text of a 700-page book, but only 50 spoken words, five medium-sized pictures or three seconds of video. Yet people are now flooding the Internet mainly for the sake of byte-hungry multimedia. The World Wide Web lets users navigate the network by simply clicking on colourful screens of words, pictures, sound and video. Already the Web accounts for more than a third of the traffic on the Internet, and will soon chew up more bandwidth than any other service. Assumptions about average use may need to be revised.

This worries some network analysts. The Internet is a shared resource, like the fish in the sea. Economic theory is gloomy about these: individuals tend to exploit shared resources, but look after private ones. Eventually that leads to depletion which ruins the resource for all its users: the sea becomes fished out, the Internet gets swamped.

At the moment users have every incentive to exploit the Internet. The more they use it, the more they get for their monthly fee. And many users would rather click on data-rich pictures than read lots of frugal lines scrolling down the screen. Some analysts, such as Hal Varian and Jeffrey MacKie-Mason, two economists at the University of Michigan, now argue that those who spend all day surfing the Internet should pay more than those who just send the occasional e-mail message. Pricing, they say, should be based on usage.

That is easier said than done. At the moment, individual usage is usually not even measured, much less charged for. Counting all those packets just means more work for some overloaded computer. Likewise, the most obvious sort of usage pricing – a charge per packet – would consume more computer capacity than is needed to transmit the packets in the first place. A simpler way to charge (which is actually incorporated in the next version of TCP/IP) is to allow each packet to carry a "priority". High-priority packets – live transmission such as voice or video – would flow through the network without delay; low-priority packets – such as e-mail – would wait for a lull. Internet providers would charge more for high-priority items.

The reason why usage-based pricing on the Internet is so controversial is that it would abolish one of the system's big attractions: the ability to surf at whim, with no meter running. Users do not have to work out if the latest picture of someone's fish tank is worth a few cents. They can have a look because it is fun, and free. Critics fear that usage-based pricing might kill the vitality that built the Internet. Where it has been tried – in New Zealand, Chile, and some universities – the growth of usage has usually slowed.

Compromises may be possible. Users may decide at the outset what level of service they can afford. A high-priority connection would cost more than a low-priority one, but it would still be charged at a flat fee. Or providers could charge on tiered usage: users would pay a fixed monthly fee up to a certain level; if they exceeded that, they would pay more. This might discourage excessive use without that ticking-meter feeling.

There is one other option: do nothing. The Internet has come this far without complicated charging systems, and although the traffic jams today are bad, they have been worse in the past. The existing system does already include a crude form of usage pricing. Big pipes cost more than little ones: a leased line that can handle up to 64,000 bits per second can cost 50 times more than a dial-up connection at only 14,400 bits. Perhaps this is enough. In competitive markets, the cost of bandwidth is dropping almost as quickly as usage is climbing. The computers that route Internet traffic are getting faster. Maybe market forces, along with the rough limits of pipe size, will set prices at the right levels. Nobody really knows.

Net profits

FOR the past two decades, teenage hackers and pony-tailed ex-hippies have been labouring in American university computer labs to build the Internet. Now it is the turn of smartly besuited young men in gleaming corporate offices to take it over. The commercial world has suddenly become serious about the Internet.

Some of those suits have set up MarketplaceMCI, a "virtual mall" created by MCI, an American long-distance telephone company. It does not look like much in the real world; just another big room of cubicles. But a few computers create a more mall-like illusion on-line. Seen from a netsurfer's screen, there are plenty of stores to "visit" (a bit like looking at a mail-order catalogue), and a mall-like range of unrelated items – from software to bathrobes – to see and buy. MarketplaceMCI, along with dozens of other new on-line shops, has proved that it is possible to market in grand style over the Internet.

The idea sounds compelling. You look up the company you want in a sort of Yellow Pages, click on its name to be taken to its Web site, and are presented with all the information you need, and usually some way to order. In reality, buying on the Internet today is still chaotic: there are hundreds of directories, each organised differently, and none lists more than a fraction of all the stores on-line.

But for many merchants, especially small ones, the Internet is hard to resist. It is inherently global, so a corner florist can become an international flower power simply by getting an Internet connection (and some good marketing). Overheads are minimal. In some businesses, distance may not even affect delivery costs because the merchant may pass the order to a regional warehouse, or ship the goods electronically. And on the Internet, no one knows whether you are a giant multinational company or a one-man band.

A handful of companies have shown that on-line commerce can work if you pick your product carefully. Software, technical books and flowers seem to do well on-line. They are easy to describe in a few pictures and text, and they suit the market: Internet users tend to be computerphiles who sometimes spend too much time in front of their screens, hence the occasional need for flowers. But what else will sell?

This is not just a question for stores. Huge consumer-goods companies such as Sony, Virgin Records and Reebok are now turning to the Internet for marketing. Newspapers, magazines and music and book publishers see the on-line world as a combination of threat and opportunity. As a new medium with almost no distribution costs, the Internet has the potential to reshape the media world, letting new competitors in and forcing established giants to evolve or die. Already sales of the Encyclopaedia Britannica have collapsed in the face of competition from CD-ROMs; the next battlefield will be on-line.

The commercial world now dominates Internet use. More than 100,000 companies are connected. Between them, they have more than 1.7m Internet hosts, each of which may support many individual users. Some of them are joining as consumers, but many are there to sell. For the moment the market is probably small: estimates put it at no more than $100m in 1994. But its potential is huge. Analysts point to the existing $53 billion catalogue and $2.5 billion TV home-shopping markets worldwide, and they wave surveys showing that the average Internet user earns 50% more than the national average and likes mail-order shopping.

A world of window browsers

But it is early days for that. Nielsen calculates that by mid-1995 about 18m Internet users in North America had used the Web in the past three months. It is the Web – with its multimedia gloss, interactivity, and emerging secure areas – that most companies would choose as their Internet marketplace. However, most Web users are in companies and universities with leased-line Internet connections; for the average home user, downloading the Web's graphics-rich pages over a modem connection is too slow and clumsy. This balance will shift as more home consumers get faster modems, ISDN connections and other high-speed links, but only gradually. Forrester Research reckons that it will take at least three more years for consumer users to pass corporate ones in America.

If Forrester is right, Internet commerce may take off a lot more slowly than the suits at MCI think. Home consumers are the key to on-line shopping. Browsing through catalogues and chasing discounts tends to be a leisure-time activity. But the technology that makes the Internet bearable usually stays at work. Cathy Medich, the director of CommerceNet, an industry consortium aimed at getting this market going, has perhaps more reason to be sanguine than most other people; yet she admits that "I don't have time to shop on-line at work, where I've got a fast connection. But at home all I've got is a modem."

Moreover, browsers are not necessarily buyers. Many Internet merchants record hundreds or thousands of visits each day, but ring up

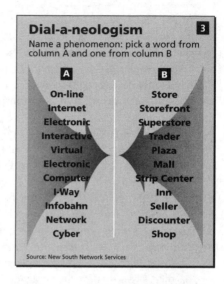

Dial-a-neologism

Name a phenomenon: pick a word from column A and one from column B

A	B
On-line	Store
Internet	Storefront
Electronic	Superstore
Interactive	Trader
Virtual	Plaza
Electronic	Mall
Computer	Strip Center
I-Way	Inn
Infobahn	Seller
Network	Discounter
Cyber	Shop

Source: New South Network Services

only a few sales. This is not a problem unique to the Internet: commercial on-line services such as CompuServe have had electronic marketplaces for more than a decade, but total retail sales have never exceeded $75m annually.

There are good reasons for consumers' reluctance. Compared with the security and ease of telephoning a company they know and placing an order, buying on-line is still mostly for the brave and curious. For the average home Internet shopper, for example, finding a particular music CD on the Internet can easily take half an hour. And even when the would-be buyer has eventually located the goods, he may hesitate. After all, anyone can scan in a few pages from a CD catalogue, register an Internet address and start taking credit-card numbers. By the time buyers realise that they are not getting their wares, a crook may have collected hundreds of credit-card numbers. If he lives abroad, he may be hard to bring to book.

Then there are technical problems. Internet merchants are just starting to adopt encryption techniques that allow credit-card numbers to be sent safely, but the competing standards may take a while to sort out. Netscape, maker of the most popular Web browser software, as well as CommerceNet, Microsoft (with Visa) and others are working on ways to check the identity of both the merchant and the customer to limit fraud, but results could be a year or more away.

Other forms of payment seem even further off, from the on-line accounts offered by First Virtual, which aggregates purchases from merchants and bills the buyer's credit card, to the futuristic "digital cash" of DigiCash, CyberCash and others. None has made much headway so far. "We have a business model," Dan Lynch, a co-founder of Cyber-Cash, recently told a conference, "but we don't believe it. We don't know what we're doing, and the other guys don't either."

Selling bits and pieces

But home shopping is just one of many commercial possibilities on the Internet. Companies selling news and other information, such as financial data and research, may well hold greater appeal for those with fast corporate Internet links. The same is true for services that make the Internet easier to use, such as InfoSeek, which lets subscribers search its database of Internet content. And many firms are exploring the Internet as a way to conduct electronic transactions with suppliers, which at the moment take place over expensive private lines.

The biggest market for the Internet, however, is advertising and marketing; and here business is already thriving. Most of the corporate "home pages" on the Web amount to little more than the usual marketing gloss, polished to an extra shine by electronic means. But the best ones offer something potentially useful as well. Federal Express offers a way to track the status of a package. The site for Zima, a drink, offers links to bar and restaurant directories across America. Holiday Inn offers direct booking for its hotels, and Visa lets visitors search for the nearest hole-in-the-wall cash machine.

Companies are starting to include the address of their Web sites in their traditional print and television advertising. Others are paying to place a link to their home page on a popular site, such as the on-line version of *Wired* magazine (which is said to have made $2m from selling such placements in 1994). Some firms sponsor on-line magazine articles or an entire publication. The advantage of Web advertising over the traditional variety is that consumers are free to explore as little or as much of the information as they want, instead of having all of it shoved down their throats. "If the remote control was the great equaliser in the battle between advertiser and television viewer, [the Web] and the mouse may shift power completely to the hands of the consumer," writes Gerald O'Connell, of the Internet advertising firm ModemMedia.

But this increasingly sophisticated Internet advertising carries a cost: a return to domination by the traditional giants. It takes money to stand out in the Internet's sprawl. Big companies can pay to promote themselves in the most popular sites. Little companies may not be able to afford to advertise their Web page anywhere but locally. Suddenly the Internet is beginning to look a lot less like the much-hyped global-village market.

Paradise by the modem lights

NEW technologies tend to create new cultures. Early radio pioneers had to learn Morse code and soon developed their own language and conventions. A similar mystique grew up around the earliest computers and the PC. Eventually these technologies all entered the mainstream, relegating the insider culture of their infancy to fringe groups. The Internet is still in its pioneer phase, and its culture is still like nothing else on the planet.

The network's main language, inevitably, is English: the Internet was born and raised in America. At the beginning of 1995 America still had twice as many users as the rest of the world put together (see chart 4), although other countries are now slowly catching up. Most of the Internet's key resources – not only software but things like directories and information libraries – are in English. And e-mail, newsgroups and other text areas are generally limited to roman characters, forcing more of the world to use fiendishly complicated phonetic versions of their languages.

Although the Internet is global in reach, much of its content is surprisingly narrow and local in focus. Anyone with an Internet connection can go to Amsterdam's Digital City, but they need to speak Dutch to get around: this is a local outpost, built by and for natives. The same is true for hundreds of local discussion groups, from German "help wanted" to New Zealand politics.

But despite the local variations, there is a recognisable flavour about the way Internet users talk among themselves, accentuated by a highly developed insider's language. The Internet dialect is full of mysterious abbreviations. Some of them – FTP, PPP, IRC – refer to technologies and services. Others take some of the labour out of typing: BTW (By The Way); IRL (In Real Life); IANAL (I Am Not A Lawyer). Yet more characters, called emoticons, try to compensate for the limited "emotional bandwidth" of text communications by using letters to sketch a facial expression sideways on; a wink, for example, becomes ;-).

The content of the messages is often as distinctive as the language. The classic user takes a libertarian stance, is suspicious of government, disdainful of politicians, and actively hostile towards those who would screw up his paradise with indiscriminate advertising, stupid questions and "newbie" (naive newcomer) behaviour. But the Internet attracts people of all leanings: liberals welcome it as a tool of empowerment for the disenfranchised; conservatives love it as a free marketplace.

Who's wired 4
Internet use, hosts per '000 population, January 1995

Country	Hosts	Growth Jan 1994 to Jan 1995, % increase
Finland		103
United States		100
Australia		50
New Zealand		441
Sweden		83
Switzerland		40
Norway		57
Canada		96
Holland		98
Denmark		181
Britain		112
Austria		92
Israel		96
Germany		77
Hong Kong		52
Belgium		125
France		68
Czech Republic		153
Japan		86
South Africa		147
Spain		141
Taiwan		83
Italy		80
South Korea		101
Poland		121

Sources: Internet Society; *The Economist*

Fundamental to the Internet credo is the protection of free speech and the right of every group to be heard. This has given an international voice to cat fanciers and quilting clubs, but it has also brought out more worrying sides of human nature. As one would expect, there is lots of talk about sex of various kinds; at the same time the Internet provides a home for hate groups, from Holocaust revisionists to Turkish Armenian-bashers.

Internet debates can easily become heated to the point of mutual vilification. Just as no one needs any special permission to speak up, nobody is accorded any special courtesy either. Yet Internet users will often go to extraordinary lengths to help perfect strangers with information, tips, even research on their questions. The Internet is still a surprisingly altruistic place.

Life, but not as we know it

Enthusiasts see the Internet as a sort of digital Utopia, not because everything on it is admirable, but because it is there at all. The Internet defies centralised authority; its mantra is "do your own thing". The Internet's most passionate evangelists believe that its radical heritage is not about to be swept away by a tidal wave of conventionality and electronic shopping. Its interactive culture, they think, will take root and flourish. Once introduced to the powerful consensual illusion of cyberspace, people will surely choose to embrace it, spending hours on-line in virtual places and joining vibrant electronic communities.

In this future world, people will read not only newspapers but also books – embellished with multimedia hypertext – on-line. "Intelligent agents" will act as personal butlers, travelling the networks on their masters' behalf, bidding against other agents for theatre tickets and making dinner reservations. Users will telecommute to work, and their children will be taught on-line. Much of this is already possible; soon it will be technically easy.

To the evangelists, this is a message of hope and optimism about the future. They are puzzled that it seems to make other people bristle. Earlier this year Louis Rossetto, the editor of *Wired*, sketched out his vision of the digital future to a large audience in London. The first response from the audience was typical. "We've heard this before. This was Timothy Leary telling us the drugs were going to make this a better world. It didn't happen then; why should we believe it will now?"

By comparison with the electronic nirvana of the information superhighway prophets, today's Internet is easy to ridicule. Yes, things are quite difficult to find; yes, 90% of what is available is rubbish. True, information is not the same as knowledge. And quite right: everything takes far too long.

But while the hype of the information superhighway is setting dreamers off on flights of disembodied fancy, the Internet is already becoming ensconced in daily life in all kinds of prosaic ways. Lots of people send each other e-mail. They may follow a newsgroup or two. Increasingly, their daily routine now takes them to a few Web sites, for news or stock prices or whatever else they may want to know. Indeed, rather than Internet culture pervading the world at large, the reverse seems to be true. The centre of Internet activity is shifting from the anarchic if enjoyable chaos of the newsgroups to the commercial and more passive Web, a place of fascinating images, places and information, but little real contact with other people.

So the culture of the Internet is changing. For 20 years its users managed to maintain a world with the core values of a hippy commune.

Now Mum and Dad and the suited advertising smoothies have moved in, bringing with them their consumer culture and corporate values. For now the two cultures coexist uneasily, but the numbers are on the side of the mainstream. This is beginning to challenge many of the principles of Internet culture. Calls for more government involvement are getting louder. If one day the Internet is to become a "data dial-tone" like the telephone system, those critics argue, then perhaps the principle of universal service should apply here too – which would mean subsidising some of the poorer Internet users with revenues from some of the richer ones.

The flood of new users on the Internet is also putting a strain on its egalitarian principles. When everyone is talking at once, how can you tell sense from noise? Increasingly, the old filtering prejudices are creeping back, creating new hierarchies that mirror those of the real world. If an open discussion triggers hundreds of e-mail messages, even Internet junkies must start weeding. Predictably, comments from big companies (microsoft.com), the government (senate.gov) or prestigious universities (mit.edu) tend to get read. Those from some obscure free library connection in Cleveland fall victim to the "delete" key.

Lawless

"THE net interprets censorship as damage, and routes around it." This quote from John Gilmore, a founding member of the Electronic Frontier Foundation, often appears on the Internet. It reflects its users' confidence that their electronic world, designed to resist nuclear attack, can also shrug off government regulation. By nature of its global reach and its decentralised design, they believe, it is unpoliceable.

They may be mistaken. On April 27th 1995 the US Congress held a hearing on terrorism in the wake of the bomb that killed 167 people in a federal building in Oklahoma. Senator Edward Kennedy waved a 76-page "Terrorist's Handbook" that his staff had downloaded from the Internet, and explained that it contained instructions for building different types of bombs, including the ammonium nitrate bomb used in Oklahoma: "Right now we're considering a telecommunications reform bill in the Senate that is trying to do something about porn on the Internet – we should do something about this terrorist information, too."

The telecoms reform bill the senator mentioned would do more than something about pornography on the Internet. It would criminalise the sending of any content deemed (by some unspecified definition) "obscene, lewd, lascivious, filthy, or indecent". It passed, in modified form, in late 1995. In Washington state the legislature has passed a bill that would make Internet access providers liable for any obscene content going through their lines. At least a dozen other states have proposed similar legislation.

Internet activists claim that such legislation puts unconstitutional restrictions on free speech. But that would not stop it from becoming law before it is challenged in the courts. Since screening for all obscene content is impossible, network providers in states that passed such laws might have to shut down. Even the Internet cannot route around that.

Internet providers have so far ducked responsibility for what they transmit by claiming "common-carrier" protection. They argue that they are not like publishers, who can be held responsible for the contents of their publications, but like telephone companies, acting simply as a conduit for messages they have no knowledge of.

The current round of congressional hearings indicates that the common-carrier exemption is not enough. Somebody has to take responsibility for protecting vulnerable groups from obscene material. Usually this would be the person who had put the material on the network in the first place. But that person may live in a place where such material is perfectly permissible. And besides, it is quite easy to put material on the Internet anonymously. This leaves the Internet community with two broad options: to regulate itself or be regulated. Most Internet users prefer self-regulation, but the nuts and bolts of that are a technical nightmare.

The problem is that pornography on the Internet can appear under an infinite number of guises. Some of them are obvious, including newsgroups with names such as alt.binaries.pictures.erotica.children, along with Web sites put up by Penthouse, Playboy and a host of amateurs. Others are harder to find: live "keyboard sex" on Internet Relay Chat channels; secret libraries known only to porn traders; even a live video-sex service, where real women obey the typed commands of paying viewers. Cutting off the more obvious pornography newsgroups is easy, but that will merely make them adopt a heavier disguise. More generic filters are bound to fail. No computer on earth can recognise an obscene picture.

One possible self-regulating solution seems to be voluntary "tagging" of adult material, so that specially configured software on users' computers can screen it out. Parents could set the software to view such material only with a special password. Several companies are already selling software that allows this. Smart kids can no doubt get round it; but users hope that such gestures may yet save the Internet from being regulated to death.

Inadvertent criminals

But it is not just pornography that concerns the would-be regulators: they also paint the Internet as a haven for piracy and crime. There is something in that. Software programs by the hundreds are illegally copied on-line, and hackers are having a field day breaking into poorly guarded sites. But some of the problem also has to do with the failure of legislators to keep up with new technology.

Copyright law is having particular trouble with adjusting to the new age. It has not been able to come to terms with a unique property of digital information: the ease of making an infinite number of perfect copies, essentially for free. Copy an article, casually post it to a newsgroup, and at a keystroke you may have robbed a company of thousands of sales. For publishers who still see a threat in the photocopier, the Internet looks like the end of the world.

The problem with copyright law is that it is unable to distinguish between abuse and ordinary use. On the Internet, any number of normal activities may inadvertently break the law. The simple act of reading a document on-line often makes a copy of it in a user's hard disk. Internet providers often keep copies of popular Web sites on their local servers so their subscribers do not jam their long-distance lines. Then there are innumerable deliberate, but essentially innocent violations without a commercial motive: copying an interesting electronic article and e-mailing it to a friend, or putting it on a company LAN.

In the end copyright laws must change to reflect this new digital domain. Publishers need some assurance that their work will not be pirated to the point where they have nothing left to sell, yet a way must be found to avoid criminalising normal use.

Cyberspace has no respect for trademark law, either. An arm of the Internet Society issues "domain" names – mcdonalds.com, for example – to companies on request. But it does not usually check to see if the person requesting it owns the trademark; indeed, when a journalist took mcdonalds.com as a prank, the company had to threaten to sue him to get it back. Worse, different companies may own the same name in different countries, yet an Internet domain is inherently global. As the writs fly, groups such as the International Trademark Association are desperately trying to find some solution.

Crime is another mess. The trouble is not so much that criminals will use the Internet, but that the police will not be able to keep track of them there. Techniques for encryption – scrambling messages so that only the intended recipient can read them – are now so advanced that they can be virtually uncrackable, even with the biggest computers. Encrypted messages make Internet wiretapping nearly impossible. This is why the American government has banned the export of strong encryption technology, and law-enforcement agencies want to set up a system which allows them to decode messages sent within the country. Internet users, fearing invasion of their privacy, have mounted the virtual barricades. But the battle has slowed the deployment of encryption technology in general, ironically making it even easier for criminals already on-line to steal information.

Crime, the maintenance of public decency and the protection of intellectual property are the problems of any mature and complex society. No doubt the Internet will find solutions to them in time; but meanwhile they act as a reminder that building a real electronic nation involves a lot more more than laying down the pipes.

The shape of nets to come

IN THE early 1970s, a new communications network began to take off in America. It bypassed traditional links and grew from the bottom up. Millions of people joined it to communicate and share information. It developed its own culture and language. Visionaries saw it unleashing creativity and opening the door to an egalitarian future. It was CB radio. By 1980 it was almost dead; it had collapsed under the weight of its own popularity, its channels drowned under a sea of noise and chaos. Could the Internet go the same way?

For parts of it, the answer seems clearly yes. In some newsgroups and mailing lists the "signal-to-noise ratio" – the fraction of messages that are even remotely interesting – is becoming quite unrewarding. Sensible people will go elsewhere and those newsgroups will die.

But as a whole, the Internet seems safe from CB radio's fate. Where CB radio had just 40 channels, the Internet has an infinite number. Broadcast chatter is just one of its many forms of communication; the Web, moderated mailing lists and private e-mail are not as easily swamped. Technically, there is some concern about the system's ability to make the leap from a few thousand computers to tens of millions. But so far nothing has emerged that experts feel they cannot set right.

Most important, the Internet has commercial potential. A critical mass of companies have now bet heavily on it. Already some of the world's biggest telecoms companies are developing "industrial-strength" parts of the Internet for such businesses. AT&T, MCI, BT – along with some of America's regional Baby Bells, and smaller networking companies such as BBN and PSI – are rolling out services with lots of bandwidth, security, reliability and a help desk to call when things go wrong.

There is plenty of scope for growth. At the moment perhaps 100,000 of the many millions of businesses around the globe are on the Internet. Even in America, the most wired society in the world, less than 20% of the population is connected up. And yet the network seems to be straining at the seams already, with long delays during the American business day.

For a while, more users will continue to strain the network. But much of the congestion that users chafe at is not within the network itself, but at its periphery: in the hundreds of thousands of servers owned by companies, universities and local Internet providers. This is where the Internet content is stored, spread among many private computers. Firms can reduce the queues by buying more and faster servers, or bigger links to the Internet. If they want people to come back to their sites, they will spend what it takes to keep up with demand.

Even if the jams can be avoided, though, some users fret about information overload. They see themselves surfing a sea of random facts, half-baked thoughts and blabber. But the Internet is not a database. It is a world with many facets: information of varying quality, entertainment, people and places. Just like the chaotic real world, the on-line world contains too much information to make sense of. But this is evidence not of its unmanageability, but of its vitality. Like newcomers in a foreign land, people will have to find their place on the Internet. But they will get plenty of help. Entire industries will grow up to make sense of the information available on-line, just as a plethora of guides do in the real world.

The empire strikes back

Today no one in particular owns the Internet; which is to say that hundreds of companies own small parts of it. Over the next few years a shake-out seems inevitable. A dizzying number of companies are clamouring for a share. Beyond the big telephone companies, America alone has 600 small Internet providers. Cable TV companies have suddenly realised that the Internet has bypassed their fitful interactive TV trials. Led by TCI's @Home effort, they are racing to offer Internet and other data services on their own networks.

In this new world, the commercial on-line services – mostly Compu-Serve, America Online, Prodigy and the Microsoft Network – have an uncertain future. At the moment, the Internet explosion means that their business is booming. They can provide their subscribers with a safe home from which to explore this teeming jungle.

But already hundreds of other companies are developing software to make the Internet easier to use. Until now, the commercial services have made their money by keeping their subscribers within their own service, paying for something that they alone can offer. But content providers are looking for a better deal. There is little incentive to limit their clientele to the 4m subscribers that, say, CompuServe can offer when they can get at least 10m on the Web. Forrester Research projects that the commercial services' growth will peak around 1998; after that the growth is all Net.

Providing Internet access may soon become a tough commodity

business. The companies that will continue to make money are those who offer more. Users will need – and be willing to pay for – Internet directories and guidance. Businesses will pay Internet companies to run their on-line storefronts, as some already do.

Yet the best business prospects lie not in carrying other people's bytes or running their stores, but in having something to sell yourself. Telephone companies agree, which is why so many of them are getting into the content business. In May 1995 MCI committed itself to investing up to $2 billion in News Corp, following the path taken by Bell Atlantic, Nynex and Pacific Telesis (which invested $300m to start a new content shop), Bell South, SBC Communications and Ameritech (which put $500m into a deal with Disney), and US West (which bought a quarter of Time Warner for $2.5 billion). Microsoft is investing more than $400m in news ventures with NBC.

In the meantime, the telephone companies are fighting to regain the pipes. The explosive growth of the Internet may have caught them off-guard, but they are now believers. "A year ago," says Lance Boxer, MCI's data services chief, "we thought of the Internet as an interesting model, but not as a necessary model. Now we're probably investing more in the Internet than any company has in history. We've never had an opportunity like this."

Or a threat? If the Internet does become a "data dialtone", regular dialtone might find itself out in the cold. It is already possible to make telephone calls on the Internet from specially-equipped computers; the spread of multimedia PCs and faster Internet connections could make this commonplace. At the same time companies are turning an increasing amount of their telephone traffic into digital data and sending it through private data networks, saving up to half their telecoms costs. Regulation permitting, this traffic could eventually move to the Internet. For the telephone companies, "the only decision is whether they participate in the cannibalisation of their revenues or watch it happen," says William Schraeder, president of PSI.

At the moment, neither the Internet, nor any digital network, could handle all the world's telephone calls. But MCI predicts that by the turn of the century the Internet will be carrying as much data as the voice networks. When that time comes, the Internet may have to grow up in a hurry. It will be too important to stay in the grey market of borrowed wires and back-of-the-envelope economics.

Growing up could be painful. Mr Schraeder suggests one way things could go wrong: at some point in not too many years the telephone companies have enough customers within their own parts of the Internet to launch an attack on the network. They want to go back to the telephone model that has earned them so much for so long: settlements, usage-based pricing, the works. They cut off independent networks that refuse to go along. The Internet splits in two, leaving a high-priced, orderly business network and a cheap, chaotic consumer network, with minimal interconnection between them. Thus balkanised, the Internet as we know it fades away, leaving the field to commercial networks. The cable TV and telephone companies' vision triumphs.

But there are more ways in which that vision might fail. If enough consumers choose the more chaotic, but more open, independent networks, the telecoms giants would be unable to cut them off. Or the telephone companies could simply accept the new world and the inevitable decline in voice revenues it foretells. They could, as some are doing now, embrace it and look for new ways to make money.

Ironically, in these rosier scenarios the Internet might also fade, but in a different way: it just keeps on growing, absorbing other networks of all sorts until it becomes so ubiquitous that it is simply woven into everyday life, carrying not just data, but telephone calls, television, everything. This is the information superhighway writ large – and small. In this vision, we plug into the data stream as casually as we plug into an electric socket today. Content and transmission are disaggregated; the network has turned into an open road.

This, indeed, may be the more likely future. Despite the racing pace of the Internet today, it will not happen overnight. After all, the PC, more than 15 years after its launch, is still nowhere near being considered an appliance. But ubiquitous, open networking seems as fundamental to civilisation's needs in the first half of the 21st century as ubiquitous, open roads did in the first half of the 20th. The lesson of the Internet is simple and lasting: people want to connect, with as little control and interference as possible. Call it a free market or just an efficient architecture: the power of open networking has only just begun to be felt.

THIS SURVEY ON THE INTERNET WAS FIRST PUBLISHED IN
THE ECONOMIST ON JULY 1ST 1995

5

MANUFACTURING TECHNOLOGY

*Manufacturing companies face a
bewildering range of technologies.
The ones that matter will be those that let firms play
most fruitfully with information.*

OLIVER MORTON

On the cutting edge

THE machines that dominate the factory floor thrill the senses. Their tools whirl under the workers' sharp eyes; some are being taught what to do, while others, having learnt, go through the motions with inhuman speed and precision. Mechanisms as big as houses arch protectively over metal they are cutting to an accuracy of a few ten-thousandths of an inch. Smells from lubricants and the cutting fluids that splash across the tools hang in the air, as though the great machines marked their territory with scent like crouching animals. Work as shifting and complex as the aromas flows through the whole building.

The Ingersoll Milling Machine company is one of the last machine-tool businesses left in Rockford, Illinois, a town that once proclaimed itself the machine-tool capital of the world. Its machines produce more machines; they in turn produce machines for consumers to buy and use. The floor of its main works looks just as it should, a factory that would be recognisable as such throughout the world. In its research laboratory across the road, though, there is something quite different.

The octahedral hexapod does not look like any machine that you have seen before. It is a bit like an illustration in a geometry book, a bit like a sculpture, a bit like a time machine. Steel cylinders are joined in a framework with eight open, triangular faces: a top and a base held apart by six triangular sides, half of them pointing up and half pointing down. The three topmost corners are shoulders; from each of them, two arms reach towards a platform that they hold in the centre of the framework. On the platform is a light motor and a machine tool capable of cutting, drilling or boring. When the six arms expand and contract – they do not bend – the platform moves; it is like the pointer on a ouija board, picking up messages from another world. Its cutting edge can be positioned anywhere within a metre or so, pointing in any direction.

The hexapod is exceptionally strong and rigid. It can be installed anywhere, with no special foundations. It can be made cheaply. At heart, though, it is there to do the same thing as the hulking machines next door, and the key technology is the same: computer control. For making complex machines, machines controlled by computers are now essential; they are becoming more and more common in all kinds of manufacturing. The computer has taken over the tool. That has a profound effect on the way jobs are done and on the ways in which firms compete, an effect profound enough for the computer's arrival to be heralded as a new industrial revolution. But there is more to come.

A tale of two worlds

New machines permit revolutions, but they do not start them. The changes going on in manufacturing are not all about machines; but their rate and nature are influenced by the extraordinary range of new manufacturing technologies now available. That is what the revolutionaries are looking at. However, they do not all see the same thing. There is no old Indian proverb about seven blind men trying to make sense of one barricade, but there should be. The revolutionaries do not know what they will get, nor do they agree on what they want. But they do agree that the hour for revolution has come.

It has been brought about to a large extent by trade. Manufacturing industries in rich industrial countries are facing more and more competition from the rest of the world. Rockford's workshops were overtaken by Japan's; Japan now sees the industrialising Asian countries moving into its machine-tool markets. Manufacturing has entered an age of global competition that is forcing it to change. Low wages elsewhere are forcing companies to seek higher productivity, often through automation. And the basis of competition has changed, too. In the 1980s, in response to Japanese excellence, higher quality shot to the top of corporate wish-lists across the world. Managers put huge efforts into achieving it.

At the same time, another change became apparent. Markets are fragmenting, both in size and in time. Product cycles have grown shorter, making total production runs smaller and reducing the time that any manufacturing system designed for a single product could be useful. And consumers are asking for products that fit their needs as if designed for them alone. The age of mass consumption may be drawing to a close; if it does, the age of mass production must end too.

Many companies are responding by seeking to produce exactly what the customer wants, paying as little regard as possible to the question of whether anyone else wants it and whether the firm has ever made it before. Mass production in lots of one: that is the aim. Automated machines that can turn their handlessness to many tasks are seen as the answer, offering perfect, personalised products cheaply in double-quick time. This is the sort of equipment that a bespoke machine-tool company such as Ingersoll hopes to make its living from, now that the commodity machine-tool business has gone.

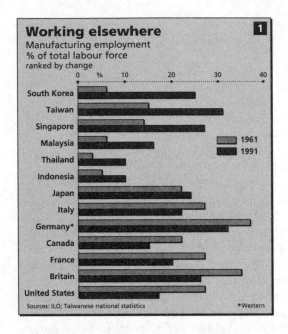

Working elsewhere 1
Manufacturing employment
% of total labour force
ranked by change

Categories: South Korea, Taiwan, Singapore, Malaysia, Thailand, Indonesia, Japan, Italy, Germany*, Canada, France, Britain, United States

Legend: 1961, 1991

Sources: ILO; Taiwanese national statistics   *Western

It is not an impossible aim; some companies are already doing it. Not all the revolutionaries will reap such benefits, though. A highly automated system can make a limited range of shoddy goods, and that sad eventuality is quite likely to be visited on companies that fail to grasp the nature of the revolution. It is not, in its essence, about quality, though in the right circumstances computerised machining can provide quality better and more dependable than even the most skilled human. Nor is it a revolution about flexibility, though computerised machines can go from making sprockets to poltroons and back in the time it takes to click on a screen with a mouse. Nor is it about time, though today's machines work quickly and ceaselessly. It is a revolution about information.

The cutting edge of a computer-controlled machine is the point where information is made flesh, without human intervention. The two worlds that meet are very different. The immaterial world of information allows perfection that dull earth cannot match; pure forms, absolute certainties. Matter is awkward, cussed, unpredictable, flawed. But matter is solid, workable, graspable; information is fluid, hard to grip or control. It is easy to share, potentially boundless; matter is limited, which is its strength as well as its weakness.

There has been, until recently, only one place where the two worlds could be seen to meet: in humanity. People live in both worlds, creatures of thought and deed, and have always used their thought to make their deeds better. They have found ways to make the material world carry information around, not just explicitly, as writing or recordings, but also implicitly. A well-designed tool embodies information, even if it has never been near a computer. Now, though, the information can flow free of mind or matter, liberated in the perfect realm that exists within and between computers. This freedom offers great potential; knowledge can be shared more freely, can be multiplied endlessly, and can be changed ceaselessly, without cost. The computer lets manufacturers try out new ideas and play with hypotheses in ways they never could before.

The challenge is to make this new realm of thought compatible with the old world of deed when thought and deed are not combined in the one body. Sometimes this means limiting the awkwardness of the material world. A computer-controlled cutting tool is useless unless exactly the right part is held in exactly the right place; a robot cannot pick up a slightly misplaced component. The machines are too much part of the information world to have the thoughtless dexterity that the human mind picks up through years of stopping its body running in to things. At other times, it is the world of information that must be restrained, its freedom and perfection limited; computer programs must be made to behave more like the objects in the material world that they refer to. This survey will look at how such approaches can be used in the places where the worlds still have much to offer each other that has not yet been realised; in design, in modelling, in planning.

The technological details differ from industry to industry. The tools used for making Tupperware and printing newspapers are not at all similar. Technical advances are introducing new products, new materials to make them from and new tools to apply to the materials – something that would not be possible without the new information technologies, which is what they have in common. Semiconductor manufacturing, for example, uses a suite of technologies largely developed within the past 30 years to build products undreamt of before that time; it is the basis of computing, but would also be impossible without it. Increasingly, all the technologies of processing, creation and assembly, from die-casting to spinning cotton to printing chips, are co-ordinated by computers.

The feeling of feedback

That "by" means "by means of"; it does not denote agency. Tools, no matter how sophisticated and no matter whether made of steel or information, need users. Companies that think they can fix problems with nothing but a bit of technology – or even a lot of it – are sorely mistaken. General Motors invested billions in fruitless automation in the 1980s. When technology changes, the work changes. And when work changes, the company should change, too.

Work has been changed through technology since long before the spinning jenny. In the information age, though, the changes made when incorporating a new technology have become strangely reflexive. When companies were people, plant and product, the information infrastructure lay mostly in the organisation of people. Companies arranged themselves in functional groups and management hierarchies designed to get the appropriate information to the right level for decision-making, and to transmit the resulting commands.

Now that information has been freed from the confines of material manifestation in ledgers and files, and can flow along preset channels without human intervention, much of that structure needs to be looked at afresh. Manufacturing companies that were structured to transfer and control information can now be rebuilt around the production process. The information technology used in that process can help the rebuilding. It is information technology that forges the link between engineering the product and re-engineering the company.

Think back to the octahedral hexapod. It looks weird, but its purpose is the same as that of the huge arched milling machines in the factory next door. The difference is that those machines had ancestors that were controlled entirely by men. Although they are now controlled by men indirectly, for the most part, their origin is still evident in their structure. In this, they are like living things. The information that gives them form is embedded within them, like a creature's genes; this embodied history imposes constraints on the forms that life can take.

The hexapod, on the other hand, has no ancestors. Its designers tried to work out how they would build a computer-operated milling machine if there had never been any other sort. The idea that informed their design did not come from previous machines. It was not inherited, like a gene; it was invented. The octahedron is a platonic solid straight out of the realm of ideal forms – information made flesh, again.

The future of manufacturing will be played out in a similar way – through contrasting fits of evolution and invention. At the moment manufacturing looks relatively unchanged, as do many machines; a deceptive surface above depths that have changed quite profoundly. New technologies that tie shop floor to shopping mall more tightly than ever before could change that. Some companies will reach their new shape by evolution; some will reach it from a *tabula rasa*, unconstrained by history. Their structure will reflect the strengths that come from incorporating information technology into the design of a business from the beginning, all the way from the corporate strategy of the board to the cutting edge of the tool.

The arsenals of progress

TO SEE historical constraints at their most concrete, visit the factory of Fabbrica d'Armi Pietro Beretta in Gardone, northern Italy; thousands of feet tall, they hem it in. The factory is not particularly large, but it clogs the narrow valley in which it sits. The mountain torrent that runs down from the hills and the main road that runs up to them both pass through the middle of the labyrinthine sheds and halls; it is not convenient. But because of the iron ore in the hillsides, gun barrels have been made there since the Middle Ages, and despite the fact that the ore now comes from far afield, they still are.

The Beretta family has been in the business since 1526 or so, and claims to be the world's oldest industrial dynasty; it is now a highly automated, flexible manufacturer, a clever user of up-to-date technology. Its barrels, still the company's pride and joy, are hammered from cold steel by a machine that can be programmed for shotguns or rifles of all sorts. In its evolution from craft guilds to global company, it has witnessed revolution as dramatic as any its guns have been fired in.

The greatest drama came in America at the turn of the 19th century, when the shape of modern manufacturing was laid down. In New Haven, Eli Whitney put into practice his idea that that if gun parts were machined accurately enough, guns could be assembled from the first parts that came to hand, rather than from parts tailored to the individual gun, as was previously the custom. The city engineer of New York, Marc Brunel, saw how to break down the job of making wooden blocks used in the rigging of men-of-war into a series of specific shapings. He took the idea to England and commissioned 43 specialised machines for the tasks from Henry Maudslay; with them, ten men could do the work of 100.

Whitney's concept of interchangeable parts was the basis of the "American system" of manufacture, which soon spread from the arms business to farm machinery, and then to almost all mechanical production. It required ever more precise machining to work; and ever more precise machining became available, thanks to Henry Maudslay's lathes, among other things. Brunel's notion of cutting up work, and creating specialised tools for each of the atomistic functions this division produced, eventually led to 20th-century mass production, brought to its peak in the second world war, when Ford's production line delivered a B-24 bomber every 63 minutes – and was still criticised for being slack.

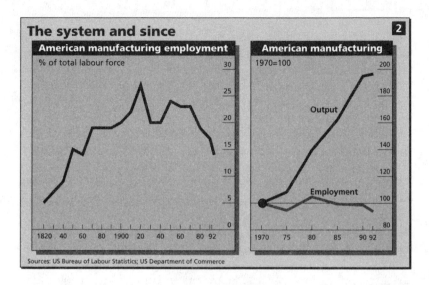

The system and since [2]

American manufacturing employment
% of total labour force

1820 40 60 80 1900 20 40 60 80 92

American manufacturing
1970=100

Output

Employment

1970 75 80 85 90 92

Sources: US Bureau of Labour Statistics; US Department of Commerce

Only new types of companies capable of large investments and strict control over workers could reap the benefits of these technologies. Beretta was more or less pushed into this; Napoleon outlawed the guild system at the end of the 18th century, forcing the forge owners to become modern capitalists. Before then, the gunmakers' crafts passed from father to son, except on the numerous occasions when the son was shot first; the citizens of Gardone showed an alarming propensity for using their wares to settle personal and business disputes.

In the new companies of the 19th and 20th centuries, the relation between men, machines and work was transformed. The change was not a matter of more machinery; in 18th-century Gardone, and throughout Europe, the age of the machine was already at hand. Machines were helping men make things better; and men were beginning to think of themselves and their world as mechanical. Clocks had taken time from the skies and put it in houses and pockets, while Newton had turned the skies themselves to clockwork; Descartes had done something similar to men. The pieces of a man were like the pieces of a machine. The image of the machine pervaded the enlightenment, from its philosophy to its pornography.

The science of mechanics, the study of force and matter, was in the ascendant. Everything seemed soluble: Laplace, France's leading physicist, talked of a supreme intellect that could understand the entire cosmos, and predict its movements indefinitely, as a way of celebrating the powers of the mechanistic approach. Not surprisingly, this mechanism was reflected in an intense interest in the study of machines. When he was not touring Italy picking out art for his friend Napoleon to plunder, Gaspard Monge, a colleague of Laplace's, developed the mathematics of descriptive geometry, applying them to the tasks of describing machinery. His work is the basis of modern technical drawing, and made possible the blossoming of the American system. It allowed people who had never seen a given part to make it with tolerances that were close enough to what was required. Previously, people learnt what a part should look like by seeing one.

Soon they were to learn what a part was like by being one. In the 19th century, it was the factories that were like machines: their occupants became more like components. Monge's pupils developed mathematical descriptions of work, transforming what had hitherto been a human activity into a mathematically calculable quantity in the science of machines, a quantity defined as the product of force and distance. As work was quantified it became a commodity. People were becoming not just parts, but interchangeable parts. The trend reached its first peak at the beginning of the 20th century with Frederick Taylor and his precise measurement of the capabilities and tolerances needed for the smallest sub-divisions of labour: the scientific management of the production line, in which man was a source only of work and individual error.

Fruit of the loom

The most spectacular working wonder of the early 19th century was Jacquard's loom. Developed in 1804, it could be programmed to produce different designs according to which punched cards were fed into it. It chewed up information and turned its abstractions into realised patterns. To men like Laplace and Monge, it was a marvel. The state awarded Jacquard a pension; the workers rioted, fearing for their jobs. When Charles Babbage tried to build the world's first computer in England, a mechanical embodiment of Laplace's ideas, he used Jacquard's cards for the programming; in a sense, all subsequent programmable machines are the fruit of the loom.

It was the technology of the Jacquard loom, with its ability to turn abstraction into physical patterns, that inspired early forays into the automation of machine tools after the second world war. It was not the only technology available. It was possible, for example, to record the movements of an expert machinist and then play them back, rather

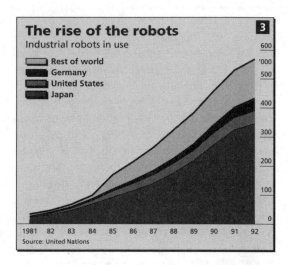

The rise of the robots
Industrial robots in use

- Rest of world
- Germany
- United States
- Japan

Source: United Nations

than conceive of the movements as mathematical perfections, encode them on to a storage medium (a numbing task before cheap computing power), and get a machine to realise them. But it was numerical control, not record/playback, that won the backing of America's military-industrial complex. It allowed them to do things they could not trust to machinists, making finely worked pieces of material for new high-performance aircraft, for instance. It also allowed them, they believed, to replace skills on the shop floor with programming skills. The technology of Jacquard's loom was always conceived of as a technology to free capital from labour.

The numerically-controlled (NC) tool transmuted itself, reasonably painlessly, into the computer-numerically-controlled tool (though there are hangovers; the people who work with them still call CNC programs tapes). At the same time a new sort of automation started to emerge: industrial robotics. Here computer control took on a new importance. It was not just mimicking human control of a tool; it was mimicking, poorly, a human. While there were tools before automatic control, there were no robots. They are pointless without some inhuman source of information to animate them.

However, robots have not displaced men and women (robots often do assembly work traditionally left to women) entirely, despite the fact that their advent gave rise to yet another wave of speculation about the workerless factory. They have a role in manufacturing, and have been used well in Japan, where they have helped bring about large increases in productivity. The Japanese have understood that, if work is designed properly for robots, they will do it well – but they are not able to replace people at jobs that have evolved to need a human's innate ability to fit the world of ideas and intentions to that of deeds and objects.

That does not mean robots cannot do things that people do now. At the Fraunhofer Gesellschaft's research institute in Stuttgart, robots do things previously unthinkable. They wire up lights, attach jacks to the end of printer cables, fit rubber padding around car doors, string tennis rackets. The robots can do this not because they are clever, but because the people behind them are. The cleverness lies in the tricks that let robots do their tasks in ways quite unlike those of people. The aim is to save jobs, not lose them – at least, not locally. With robots, hopes Jens-Gunter Neugebauer of the Fraunhofer, German factories can become productive enough to keep such work as tennis-racket stringing from moving to cheap-labour countries. There may be fewer jobs in the factories, but the factories are more likely to stay in Germany, and new service jobs will be created to support them.

Beretta uses only a few robots. However it saw the possibilities of NC reasonably early, and invested at a time when the payback was fairly slow. It went as far as buying an NC machine-tool maker to understand the technology better. It reorganised its production to take advantage of the increases in accuracy, reproducibility and flexibility that the machines offered. The reward came in the 1980s, when it was able to offer better guns at lower prices and win a sidearms contract for the American military. Eli Whitney would have been impressed.

Beretta has captured the benefits of past industrial revolutions. It can deliver huge numbers – the American military contract was for roughly half a million. Its accurate tools and its corporate attitude provide extremely high quality. It offers a wide range of guns, with each specific model available in a bewildering number of versions, in part because of computerised flexibility. But there is still progress to make, not in machining, but in handling information. Beretta has only recently started to exploit computer-aided design, for example. It is time to assess the benefits this could bring.

The mind's eye

IN THE biggest factory in the world, the first Boeing 777 is being put together. In April this year (1994), it will roll out of the doors and, fairly soon thereafter, lift itself into the air over Seattle. Boeing and its customers hope that this twin-engined long-haul airliner will be a remarkable machine in many ways. In some ways, it already is. Normally the company would build mock-ups of a new aeroplane to make sure that its millions of parts fit together. The workers have not assembled any trial 777s, though; the first produced, the one now being assembled, will be a functional flying machine.

But a mock-up exists elsewhere: in trillions of bytes of information stored in the company's mainframe computers. The development of the 777 has been the biggest single trial of computer-aided design (CAD). Using the computer's representations of the aeroplane's parts, engineers and their programs checked that the whole thing would fit together before any pieces were made. Their checking appears, so far, to have been pretty good. When the wings of the first 777 were attached to its waist, the port wing tip was out of position by a thousandth of an inch; the starboard wing was positioned as accurately as the gauges could measure.

When computer graphics can give verisimilitude to dinosaurs, turn actors into androids and make even the most tedious news broadcast a kaleidoscope of shifting imagery, it is easy to underestimate the power of the simple images CAD programs put on to screens. They are not spectacular. But CAD makes it possible to transmit designs directly to machines that will follow them perfectly; it gives the designer new tools; and it allows companies to change the way they organise design.

Good design is the key to manufacturing. It is the difference between a product that does a great job reliably, is easily fixed if damaged and is made cheaply and quickly; and a pile of junk. As chart 4 shows, half the life-cycle cost of a product is fixed by the original design; 80% may be set by the time that production actually begins. The designer needs all the help he can get.

Changing the parameters

The classical advantages of automation are time and accuracy; both are provided by CAD. Technical drawing is a time-consuming task. If CAD screens were nothing more than high-tech drawing boards, they would still be useful; studies show that they can cut the time it takes to draw

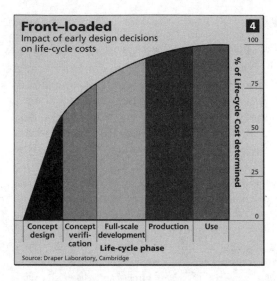

Front–loaded
Impact of early design decisions on life-cycle costs

4

% of Life-cycle Cost determined

Life-cycle phase

| Concept design | Concept verifi- cation | Full-scale development | Production | Use |

Source: Draper Laboratory, Cambridge

a design by as much as 90%. Perfect copies are made at the touch of a button, changes incorporated quickly and easily.

A design made with CAD can be transmitted perfectly from one place to another, if they both use the same system, and passed without much fuss into CNC tool systems. So subcontractors know exactly what is wanted; and if they make it accurately, as their CNC tools should, the parts will fit perfectly. The impact of CAD's ability to provide "digital pre-assembly" are felt in big things, like slotting in the 777's wings, and in lots of small things too.

Aeroplanes are built in slices, but there are many systems – the air supply, the heating, the plumbing and the electronics, for example – that permeate the whole. (The data pathways are, in the case of the 777, particularly impressive, which is another aspect of the information age – where would an airliner be without 100 channels of television in the back of every seat?) Normally the conduits and tubing required for these things are added during assembly. Now, though, the slices of aeroplane come with all their stanchions, tubing and what-not already attached, and it all lines up as it did on screen. When new floor space was added to Boeing's Everett plant for the 777, it came with power outlets for hand tools, normally needed to trim and shape the parts during assembly. They have hardly been used.

Such gains in precision are seen in all sorts of automation. Take spot welding. Designers used to put in more spots than were needed, because the space between spots varies when the welders are people. Robots get it spot on, and so, on top of any other advantages gained, there is a 10% decrease in the amount of work.

The advantages of CAD mean that large complex engineering tasks now depend on it. If big companies work with CAD, subcontractors need to be able to receive designs as CAD data and feed them into their computer-controlled machines. This can be a problem. There are many different CAD systems available, and transmitting data from one to another and into manufacturing systems is not as easy as it should be. According to Mitchell Fleischer at the Industrial Technology Institute in Ann Arbor, Michigan, as many as 25% of designs transmitted to small tool and die shops as CAD files have to be printed out as blueprints and re-entered into the computer because translations between programs are so poor. In these circumstances, lead times and costs go up, not down, with the installation of CAD. To simplify things, many companies impose their choice of CAD on subcontractors. That means some subcontractors end up with many systems. Mr Fleischer knowns of one with 17.

There is a standard for CAD transmission, IGES, but different systems can approach it in different ways, which causes problems. STEP, a new standard, should be less vulnerable to that. And not only is it better than IGES, it also offers far more. IGES is a standard for technical drawings, and describes things in terms only of geometry. Its creators have designed STEP to go beyond a vocabulary of figures to provide a way of describing parts in terms of what they are to a designer, and to include all sorts of other data about the product. In this it reflects the change in the CAD industry which has turned CAD systems from computerised drafting boards to the seeds of something far grander.

There are still a lot of computerised drafting boards around, offering simple CAD capabilities to people with personal computers. But at the high end, advanced systems are increasingly capable of working with features, not just with geometry. A designer can point at one of a part's faces, tell the machine that he wants a hole in it – and the hole will appear. He does not have to specify its geometrical relations to all the faces concerned, or even draw it. If he wants a knob, or a flange, then a knob or flange will appear. By using such natural concepts, the tool gets closer to the designer's thoughts.

Parametric Technology of Waltham, Massachusetts, has led the way in a particularly fruitful application of this technology with their Pro-Engineer software. If a feature of the design has to be changed for some reason, the program will make the change, and then make further changes to keep things consistent. The impacts of the change ripple through, and the design remains a consistent whole. The system works by remembering the history of the design on the screen; when the change is made, the program goes back to the point in the part's history where the feature being changed first appeared, makes the change, and then runs forward through history, amending everything that has to do with the changed feature.

This technology has been the basis of Parametric's impressive growth. Other companies have taken it up, although some in the field distrust it and are using other techniques to achieve the same end. The new systems provide the designer with one of the greatest advantages of the world of information: the ability to ask "what if" and look at alternatives without actually trying them out. All that is used is processing power, the costs of which are increasingly negligible. They also provide flexibility. Make a late change on a parametric system, and as soon as the numbers have been crunched, it is as if the change had been made early on. Look again at chart 4. The curve dictates the cost of making changes; the flatter the curve, the higher the cost. Modern CAD tools can reduce the costs of late changes and straighten the curve.

The ideal, though, is to avoid late changes by getting everything right early on. The effort to increase the quality of products and, most of all, to reduce the time to market has led to "concurrent design". Traditionally, design and production are separated by a metaphorical wall. The finished design is thrown over it, at which point the designers go on to the next thing and the production people realise they cannot make the current one. The idea of concurrent design is that designers should work closely with everyone else who will at some point have a stake in the product; what used to be done at length should now be done in parallel, with manufacturing people having their say all through the design process, and building up the manufacturing capability early on.

Until the 19th century, there was no need for concurrent design; everything happened in one mind. The designer would build the product, or at least be a master of the building craft. The increasing complexity of products is one reason that stopped; but information played a role, too. Companies were cut into divisions, to ease the flow of information; and the advances in drawing started by Gaspard Monge made designs portable.

The aim of a good concurrent design team is to recreate a master craftsman's mind and see all aspects of the process at once. For that to happen, the divisions that give structure to the company have to be overcome. That is why concurrent design requires the time and effort of management. Boeing put people into the 777 design teams according to the section of the aircraft they were working on, rather than their functional division within the company. Manufacturing and maintenance were represented all along – as were customers. British Airways, for example, spotted a way to get four more seats on by rejigging the aft toilets and galleys: a 1% increase in capacity for no extra cost.

Mimicking a mind, though, is still a hard thing for a team to do, even if the structure is right. It has to know what it is thinking about, to be able to communicate its thoughts clearly and unambiguously, to know when a change has been made and what its implications are. That is what CAD systems provide. They allow designers to see the effects of suggested changes in ways that were previously impossible except for those with exceptional mental abilities; they give everyone the spatial awareness and rigour that only freaks of nature had before. And they make these acutely perceived visions portable. As well as a design tool, CAD is a communications technology, tying all the knowledge in the team together. It is the team's common imagination: the mind's eye looking into the world of information.

Living in the material world

THE thoughts that float on CAD screens may be fathers to the deeds of manufacturing; but a lot of pregnancy and labour separates the two. During this, a concurrent-design team needs more than visualisation. Parts are not just physical objects – they are problems for manufacturing engineers, they are fulfilments of specifications, they are objects of consumer desire. The design process has to take all this on board too, and for that it needs a model of the product that contains all sorts of information beyond its shape.

Steve Gutierrez, who works on Hewlett-Packard's advanced CAD software, talks about the product model as a wheel. Its hub is a database that holds all the necessary information about the product. Its rim is the CAD representation of the product. The spokes are other types of software, which advise on ways of cutting sheet metal to make the parts, or look at how the product will deform if you hit it, or allow the electronics to be sorted out. The spokes all do their job in the context of the CAD model, and depend on it; in turn, they give it solidity, and connect it to the rest of the world. The different parts of the model can come from different suppliers, as long as they can communicate. The STEP standard should let them do so.

Frank-Lothar Krause, of the Production Technology Centre in Berlin, offers a goal for such a product model in terms of chart 4, which showed how much cost depends on design. You can add a second set of curves that show how much is known about the product (see chart 5). Today, lots of life-cycle cost is defined when hardly anything is known about the product; CAD improves that a bit. Detailed product modelling might improve it a lot, pushing the knowledge curve above the cost curve. Mr Krause suggests that knowing how to make product models could soon be as important as making the product, and might be the ability companies most need to develop. George Kuper, head of Ann Arbor's Industrial Technology Institute, sees the transformation of data into information as a process equal in importance to the transformation of raw materials into a product.

Fumihiko Kimura of Tokyo University offers a vision of what such models could be: "virtual manufacturing" systems so realistic that they can simulate everything that matters about both a product and the processes that produce it. Imagine a simulation of a car that can be assembled in the computer by a simulation of the production plant, that safety engineers can crash in the computer and customers can test-

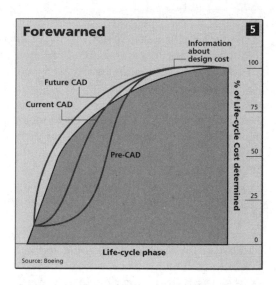

Forewarned [5]

Source: Boeing

drive in it. Researchers around the world are developing virtual-reality systems that will let designers walk around their products and computer-generated dummies try them out for comfort. In America, the army is now using flight simulators to provide feedback for helicopter designers. The pilots tell them where the controls should be best placed.

Flight simulators and virtual reality are enticingly sexy but they are not enough; there is more to virtual manufacturing than visualisation. It needs programs that can model all sorts of aspects of the real world. Some of this modelling cannot yet be done; some of the modelling that can be done is hugely expensive in computing time. Computers deal easily with the mathematical perfection of geometry. That is what made simple CAD possible in the dark ages of two decades ago. The physical world, though, is very different. Working out how a product will bend in a crash, or how heat will flow through it, is hard. The best computers can do is to cut up a model into tiny little bits, and use rules derived from physics and chemistry to predict the effects that stress, heat or whatever will have on them, and how the changes in each will affect its neighbours. This soaks up ever more computer power as the analysis becomes more detailed.

Such computerised analysis is widely used to test designs, especially in products that are expensive, produced in small numbers or pushing the boundaries of the possible. However, it is often unwieldy and time-consuming, and it is less versatile than other information technologies.

Tools that analyse the material world this way seem to take on much of its intractability. They describe how a part will behave, but they do not help to make it behave better. They are not good for asking "what if" questions, because each answer takes too long.

Get real

The alternative to using a computer to model the physical processes of the real world is to get direct access to them with a prototype. This is perhaps the fastest changing area of manufacturing technology. There are new technologies around that will build almost any part a CAD system can dream up in hours. They are, as yet, limited in the materials they can use: but they are getting better all the time, and they already offer capabilities that appear magical, opening new doors between the material world and the realm of information.

Most of these rapid prototyping technologies work by building a three-dimensional structure out of a pile of two-dimensional cross-sections. Selective laser sintering, for example, works with layers of fine powder. A computer system takes a CAD representation and cuts it into thin slices. Then a laser beam draws the outline of one of those slices on the powder, and its heat makes the particles in the powder join together: it sinters them. The outline completed, the laser scans back and forth within it, sticking together all the powder so that it forms a solid slice. A new layer of powder is spread over the top, the outline of the next slice is drawn, and the process continues.

Laser sintering can produce models in wax or nylon. If the powder particles are thinly coated specks of metal, it can make metal parts; the coating is removed after the part is made, leaving a foamy metal that is then infused with liquid copper to fill up the spaces. Similar techniques can make things layer by layer using liquid plastics that a laser can solidify, or using layers of paper that a laser can cut away, or using a technology more like photocopying to produce each layer. There are also ways of building a model drop by drop, and others, descended from ink-jet printers, that bind together powders with finely-controlled sprays.

All depend on CAD; you could not bring a new design from the world of information to the world of matter unless there were ways to put the information in the right form. But the idea of turning CAD into matter has been treated as a new challenge, and solved in several different ways. The new technologies have been invented, not evolved.

According to a report produced by Quo-tec, a British consultancy, on the basis of a trip to America by European experts, there are about 500 such machines now in use. All but one of the companies that build them are American, as are most of the users – only the laser-in-a-bath-of-plastics method, the oldest, is widely used outside America. They are based there because rapid prototyping is a computer-based innovation – at which America excels – rather than a new variation on old production machines, which are equally advanced in Europe and Japan.

The systems are, as yet, far from perfect. They are quite expensive, though prices may fall quickly, especially for the machines based on ink-jet printing technologies. Perhaps the biggest drawback is the narrow range of materials available. The systems make CAD data real in geometrical terms, but they often do not produce real parts, just models in the wrong material. That limits the scope for physical testing. But models are still useful. If a product involves mechanical linkages – trains of gears and cogs, for example – physical models can show that the pieces will all move together the right way more convincingly than a computer rendering can. And prototypes plonked on desks can make things seem real to a non-technical mind – a finance director's, perhaps – in ways a CAD file cannot.

Perhaps virtual manufacturing within computers will one day be so good, and so widely used, that there will be no need for any parts of the process to move from the information world into the material one. But that day is not one to seek for its own sake. The reason for doing as much as possible in the world of information is that changes are made more easily when intractable matter is kept out of the way. If movement between the world of information and that of matter becomes easier, and physical artefacts become part of the process without slowing it down, fine. If it is easier to build a model of a wing and put it in a wind tunnel than to simulate the air-flow in a supercomputer, then developers will do it. The world of information is only preferable when it offers real advantages.

Even if everything is done in a virtual environment, though, parts must at some point be made for production. Devotees of rapid prototyping technologies are already aiming at that point; to show that they are not limited to approximate models and stop gaps, they are rechristening their craft free-form fabrication (FFF). For some mould-making, an FFF model is as good as anything used today, and available far more quickly. A metal FFF part can work as a tool on an existing machine. It may not be as tough as a traditional tool, but it does not need to be if it can be reproduced perfectly. Ceramics can be made with FFF printing technologies, in which powders are glued together and then cast; and ceramics are increasingly sought after.

Though virtual products and FFF may look like different solutions to the problems of rapid design, they could be complementary solutions to the problems of rapid manufacture. That, at least, is what Arlan Andrews of America's Sandia National Laboratories hopes. Sandia has developed a multi-user virtual environment for design, in which people can put together and test any contraption they can think of. Any problems with analysis are alleviated by the fact that Sandia has some extremely powerful supercomputers. But the system does not need supercomputers; and anyway, supercomputers are becoming cheaper to buy and, thanks to high-speed data links, easier to gain access to.

On the other side of the corridor, Sandia is working with FFF systems, both to fill in the detail that for the present eludes the most super of computers, and to see how much final manufacturing can eventually be passed on direct to FFF systems. For some materials, machining may soon be a technology completely superseded. The raw material will be transformed into a finished part, with no chips or tailings left over. Such processes may never be quite as fast as mass production, but they have the much-sought-after attribute of flexibility built in from the very beginning. They are far more flexible than today's computer-controlled machine tools could ever be. And they need no factory, no supply chain; just the raw material, the design and, perhaps, an operator. Some types of product – personalised porcelain, perhaps – may go all the way from design to department store in the world of information.

Putting it all together

COMPANIES want products designed well and quickly; information technology can make that easier, if the commitment to design is there. They also want a wide range of products, and they want them produced at exactly the right time. Traditional automation – production lines with tools and fixtures built into them – cannot do this. It offers high efficiency only with constant output and a small range of products, so it makes sense only for large product runs. The advent of programmable machines was meant to change that by providing flexibility.

Gather computer-controlled machine tools together, give them robots to fetch and carry, and put computers in charge of the whole thing: you now have a flexible manufacturing system, and can use the abbreviation FMS to prove it. That abbreviation is dangerous. It suggests that flexibility is a single quality, that can be bought in the form of machines and programming. In fact, flexibility covers a multitude of virtues and some sins as well; and those virtues reside in the whole company, not just in the machines on the shop floor. The good news is that once flexibility is understood, computers may be able to help more than sorry past experience gives any reason to believe.

Daniel Whitney of the Massachusetts Institute of Technology identifies a number of different types of flexibility. There is flexibility about inputs, which lets the same thing be done even when the parts needed are presented in unusual ways. There is flexibility within production, which allows many things to be made in different batch sizes at the same time in the same system. There is process flexibility, which allows entirely new things to be made quickly and easily. And there is flexibility as a way of having a second chance if you make a wrong decision. Many companies, he suspects, really want the last of those: but it may not be on offer. As for the first, it may not be needed in a well-run system. But flexibility in production and process can be achieved, as Dr Whitney's case study of Nippondenso, Japan's biggest car-component company, demonstrates.

The robots and programmable machines used in FMS reflect a belief in flexibility as part of the process of manufacture. But there is more to it than that. Flexibility can be part of the product, designed in from the start. With the proper design you can limit the need for flexibility in the manufacturing process and, perhaps more important, define the bounds of that flexibility in advance. The aim is to be no more flexible than necessary, given the variety of products being produced. Nippondenso achieves this largely by getting the flexibility implicit in the design realised only in the last stage of manufacture, assembly. Its assembly is highly automated, but the work involved is not complex: the robots can afford to be simple because the intelligence is in the products.

Nippondenso puts it there in several ways. One is by minimising the number of parts. A second is modularity and standardisation. If the difference between two radiators is their length, they can have a large number of components in common. With proper design, many different products can be made from lists of parts that differ only slightly. A third is the principle of partial assembly. If a half-assembled object hangs together, there is no need for special jigs and fixtures to hold it in place. Fewer jigs: more flexibility. This, too, is an accomplishment of good design.

If the same parts are used for different products, and the different products require little by way of different handling, then flexibility can be achieved without losing efficiency. The manufacturing facility is arranged to maximise such advantages. Many of the robots and other devices are developed in-house, as part of the same process as the design of the products. The robots are not designed to be particularly dexterous or smart; the work is designed not to need such skills. Developments of product and process feed off each other continuously.

Heading for heterarchy

Nippondenso deliberately minimises the role of flexibility in fabrication – the making of individual parts, which is what flexible manufacturing systems are meant to excel at. Much of this fabrication is done by subcontractors. Dr Whitney points to a tendency for Japanese companies to buy parts but make their own systems, while American companies tend to do the reverse. But the fact that flexibility can be achieved without flexible fabrication does not explain why flexible fabrication, the supposed goal of FMS, is hard to achieve.

It is not impossible, given proper design; there are well conceived flexible manufacturing systems. But there are also many that are not quite what was wanted, and the growth in FMS sales has not been what early proponents hoped for. David Upton of the Harvard Business School puts the blame on the bit of the system that is meant to provide flexibility: the computer. It is the computer that makes an FMS into a system; without it, an FMS is just a bunch of tools and robots. It is the computer that has animated the dream of going beyond FMS and integrating whole factories and companies to achieve a new kind of manu-facturing. The tools and robots on the shop floor would be just part of some grand immaterial structure that spread beyond the bounds of their world: the machines in the ghost.

Ghosts are undoubtedly fabulous things; but they have their draw-backs. They tend to stay in one spot, be overburdened with guilty knowledge, harp on about the past and never change, just fade away. Not, in short, very flexible. Traditional computer systems share many of these flaws. The fact that information (like ectoplasm) can be very fluid does not mean that the systems in which it runs allow flexibility. Quite the reverse: they are often excessively rigid. A system running an FMS has to be complex in order to keep track of everything, to recognise dif-ferent failures and to deal with them. If the range of products the FMS is making changes, this software often has to be changed too. If the FMS itself is changed – one type of mill or robot replaced by another, say – there must be more changes. The software to deal with this is complex and extremely hard to amend; in fact it is far more difficult to change than the hardware, which can just be bought and bolted in place.

These rigidities are not unique to flexible manufacturing systems. Dr Upton has found it in other places where computers have been put in charge. Take the fine-paper industry: there is a strong correlation between flexibility, in the sense of the ability to move from one product to another, and the advent of computer-integrated manufacturing. But it is negative. The flexible plants are those where people are incessantly striving for flex-ibility, not those into which flexibility has been programmed.

The problem is that manufacturing is extraordinarily complicated; and the capacity computers have for discovering perfect solutions in the world of information cannot, as yet, deal with such complexity. Most companies do not really know how they do what they are doing; their solutions have evolved unconsciously. A good manufacturing system is self-regulating: staff who can see what is going on continuously tweak and titivate, keeping it productively poised on the edge of chaos. But a centralised, hierarchical computer system of the sort that most com-panies have cannot capture this continuous functional jiggling. Lacking the ability to evolve, a system of tight controls must be invented for it, controls that constrain the system's ability to adapt. Even so, chaos some-times breaks through. Dr Upton found that computer-integrated paper plants were often more likely to have catastrophic failures.

People cannot provide the different products that producers now want at the speeds that they could manage for mass production when helped by the machinery of a production line. So Dr Upton offers a new view of automation, one that he calls heterarchy rather than hierarchy. A part comes into a factory with a chip sitting on top of it. The chip knows what needs to be done to the part, and broadcasts the first step in the process. The machines in the factory ask themselves whether they can comply; those which can, ask themselves how much work they have to do and, on the basis of that, bid for the right to machine the part. The chip listens and makes its choice. When everything has been done, the part leaves the floor but the chip goes back to the beginning, to negotiate for another part. The chips learn which machines to trust.

The charm of this idea is that there is no hierarchy. Each chip needs to know only about one thing – a product or a machine – and its needs and capabilities. Failures in the system are always local. Efficiency comes about through the invisible hand of the market. Changes are easy. Add new products and the machines will still make them, if they can, with no new programming. Add new machines and the products that need them will use them.

In the real world, where jigs and fixtures, among other things, are needed, such systems may be pipedreams. But they are useful thought experiments – and a useful metaphor for a form of computer programming that can provide similar advantages. Object-oriented computing began as a way of modelling the real world. The "objects" within it are packages of data wrapped in programming that applies to that data. An object in a factory control system might represent an automatic vehicle. The data would say what it was and what it carried; the programming would allow it to be sent hither and thither by other objects in the system.

Imagine an object-oriented solution to controlling an FMS. Instead of trying to control the state of all parts of the system centrally it would have different objects within it representing the products, the robots and the tools, which knew how they should relate to each other, and which could follow rules like those in Dr Upton's market-based factory. Change the system, and you give the computer new objects. You do not need to rewrite the program from scratch. There is no need for continuous invention; evolution is powerful in a world where information is told to behave as if it were embodied. Such programs are proving highly useful as ways of organising the factors of production, parts, labour, capital and, as important as all three, time.

The uses of time

IN THE modern world, everyone can know the time exactly and carry it with them anywhere. In the pre-industrial world, only precise observation of the heavens could provide accuracy, and time was encased in all-but immovable clocks. The difference was both brought about and necessitated by industrialisation. Greenwich mean time was taken from London to the provinces by clocks on steam engines, the better to synchronise the rhythms of the nation's work. Time's unmeasured flow became controlled, paid for, subdivided. Factory whistles punctuated it, Frederick Taylor and his stopwatches measured it exactly, punching the clock gave it value.

At present, the industrial obsession with time is focused on two issues; time to market, and being just-in-time. Time to market depends largely on design; just-in-time depends largely on working practices. In a company convinced of the value of being just-in-time, orders trigger production, rather than triggering a trip to a warehouse that is being continuously filled by the production process. It is a large part of what is meant by "leanness" in manufacturing, and much in favour. It has not, to date, had much to do with technology: it has been about management and the design of work.

The idea is to avoid tying up capital in work in progress. If the production system is thought of as a machine, work in progress corresponds to the tolerances between the parts. It is tolerance in time and money, not space: the inventory between two parts of the process represents the degree of uncertainty over the time they take, and over the speed at which the whole system may have to work. Computer-controlled machining and CAD have allowed engineers to make pieces with tolerances finer than ever before as a matter of routine. Can analogous technologies do the same for time tolerances?

According to 12 Technologies, formerly known as Intellection, they can. The Dallas-based company starts from an analysis of the weakness of the just-in-time approach. In this, the message to up the pace or slow it down travels upstream from the customer through to the component supplier like a tidal bore running up a river. If the process is simple, that is easy enough. However, if the process is complicated and many-branched – that is, flexible enough to turn out many different products – things get trickier. There are more likely to be bottlenecks in the process that distort its speed. And if the changes in the market are extremely quick, quicker than the time it takes for information to travel step by step up the manufacturing stream, then the system loses stability like a pendulum swung beyond its accustomed range.

12's solution looks simple; it is a program that plans the path of work through a manufacturing plant, saying what parts will be needed where and which machines will do what. Such programs have been around for a long time – there is a large installed base of software dealing with material-resource planning (MRP). But Rhythm, 12's product, is smarter and better at details. An object-oriented approach allows it to solve scheduling problems by looking at the starting condition and the desired outcome, and bringing the two together. Traditional programs are more idealised, starting with assumptions such as an infinite supply of components and slowly running through long loops of calculations before coming to an answer.

The result is that Rhythm can produce schedules in minutes, not days. Work can be planned by the hour rather than the week. That means the tolerances are tighter; if the system gives good results by the hour, there is no need to keep a week's worth of production around. Another advantage of Rhythm is that it can be used to schedule things machine by machine. It, and better software like it which will surely follow, can take a floor full of machines and arrange the flow of work through them so that they become "virtual cells", linking machines far apart into the sort of tight-knit unit seen in an FMS. They will not quite match an FMS in throughput, perhaps; but they can be reconfigured quickly and easily. Factory layout moves from the material world into the world of information.

Rhythm's speed allows it to reroute work more or less on the fly. Earl Mott, who has put Rhythm into the heart of Black & Decker's manufacturing division, enthuses about its ability to answer hypothetical questions. It can tell you what is gained and lost by giving an order high priority. And according to Sanjiv Sidhu, president of 12, it can do this for a whole company, not just for a factory. It can tell you whether shipping parts over from the Singapore plant is an easier way to fulfil an urgent order than building them on the spot. It allows you to commit to a delivery date with a high degree of confidence. Delivering on time is a problem for a lot of companies. Many do not even meet the date they commit to, let alone the date that the customer really wants. Improving that performance would provide a competitive edge. Mr Sidhu notes that many of his company's customers are firms that were quick to tackle quality, a crucial issue of the 1980s. They now see timeliness taking its place as the ground for competition. Quality is no longer a stake to be raised. It is the ante necessary to enter the game. Time is where the stakes are being laid.

With Rhythm, a company can go beyond simply having a flexible facility; it can know just how flexible the system is through simulations, and it can know what making use of that flexibility to prefer one job over another will cost. Remember Dr Upton's notion of a factory floor as a marketplace, where machines bid for parts, and the work ends up efficiently allocated. Rhythm provides similar capabilities; but rather than setting up a surrogate market, it allows the scheduler to let the real market in to the factory, and set priorities accordingly.

There are other technologies that can offer similar insights into how factories actually work – a whole new category of software that can be seen as fitting between traditional MRP and what actually happens, called manufacturing execution software, is forecast to grow by 20% a year through the 1990s by Frost & Sullivan, a consultancy. And there are technologies to allow computers to know what is really going on. Computers work on the idea that what should be happening is happening. Once something goes wrong, this approach can amplify the problem and widen the divide between idea and reality. Stand upstream of a robot on a production line and push the pieces it is working on out of kilter; it is fun if you enjoy watching futility. Now factories are turning towards barcodes and other sorts of labelling to keep track of reality. If the software and the people running it are flexible enough to cope with the data, this does a lot of good.

To see such technologies working together, look at Motorola's Fusion production facility. Fusion is the company's name for a family of pagers, designed to be easily customised, and the processes of design, manufacture and marketing that surround it. A customer phones in a requirement – a pager, say, of a particular size and colour (it matches his tie) that plays a particular tune. The Fusion computer system turns the specifications into a set of parts, and nips into a virtual manufacturing world to preassemble them and make sure they add up to a product. Then it releases the design as a series of routing instructions to the manufacturing facility. As the piece goes through the facility, it is continuously tracked. Nothing is made until it is ordered; mass production in lots of one.

The advantages go beyond single facilities, though. Hewlett-Packard has realised that, like many companies, it is not yet delivering to its customers at the speed they would like. A company-wide object-oriented database, showing exactly where everything is, is part of the solution; so are changes in management and in attitude. Their new technology is part of a general corporate re-engineering; the changes involved make sense only in the context of one another.

The tools turn in

Such re-engineering is all the rage, and technology is a good tool for it. What sorts of companies might eventually emerge from the makeovers that the new tools will offer?

One of the most influential visions of future manufacturing in the past few years goes by the name of "agile manufacturing". It is outlined in the "21st century manufacturing enterprise strategy", produced by Lehigh University's Iacocca Institute for America's defence department. Agile manufacturing requires companies to have more than just the fast, lean and pro-active virtues of the 1980s. Like "new men", they have to be butch but caring, ever responsive to the needs of others. They also have to co-operate. Agility resides in the provision of a product, rather than in any single company. The visionaries like to talk of virtual enterprises, ad hoc coalitions put together around a promising new idea. An idea is born, a design made, a design verified, parts built, a product assembled, marketed, shipped: a need is fulfilled. Each step could be done by someone different; the last step is the product of the whole.

There are various preconditions for success in such a venture. One is clear communication. Here the new standard for product data, STEP, will undoubtedly be useful, especially since it can carry quite a lot of data about the product on top of its geometrical form. Standards have their drawbacks; they always lag the leading technologies. The history-based approach of Parametric's CAD software, for example, which allows the far-flung repercussions of changes to be felt, cannot be communicated through STEP: when a model is moved through the STEP standard, it loses this aspect of its history. But interoperability will, in the end, matter more than pure performance, and assuring that systems in different companies work together will definitely require standards.

The precondition that matters most, though, is predictability. The essence of agility is sensitivity to time. The different companies involved have to know their capabilities exactly, and the time they take exactly. This is what new factory management technologies make possible. When a virtual enterprise is assembling itself, it has to know precisely the dimensions of its parts, not in breadth, length and depth, but in terms of such things as process time and quality. At present, few companies can accurately measure themselves in many of these dimensions.

There are hints of these virtual worlds already to be seen. The American military is encouraging them, as it encouraged NC machining. A programme called CALS will require every new piece of equipment to come with a form of electronic product model, and in so doing begin to tie the supply chain into a sort of virtual enterprise. And there are less technologically advanced models available elsewhere. One is found south of Beretta's home in Gardone: the fabric mills of Prato. In the 18th century, the old guilds were unified into vertically integrated mills. In the 1970s the mills subdivided themselves back into small units. They now provide a marketplace of capacity co-ordinated by a few brokers and served by a united retailing operation. The industry, once moribund, is now flourishing.

Dr Upton and his colleague Ramchandran Jaikumar have pointed out that there is a growing potential for this to happen elsewhere, in other industries. Manufacturing plants that can work from CAD files are spreading. The size of many manufacturers is shrinking. With a modern multi-purpose CNC tool, a man in a garage can bid for work that would have needed a job shop in the past. Versatile scheduling can give a few such machines great capabilities. The information networks needed to join such places together are almost in place, offering high data-rates to any user in an industrial country that needs them. And the software for good product modelling is being written. Without product models, such schemes are doomed.

It may be that another great change is on the way. Once parts became interchangeable, people soon followed suit. Now the factories themselves may go the same way. The parts will evolve, their histories guiding and limiting them. The new whole, the new machines of production, remains to be invented.

■

The multiplication of labour

FREDERICK TAYLOR searched for the one best way to do the job with his measures and stopwatches. But there may not be only one best way. In a flexible world, by definition, there are many ways, and many trade-offs between them. Which is best depends on what you value. The same is true of possible responses to new technology. Agility, virtual enterprises and the like provide a range of choices all of which may be correct for some, but not for others.

In his book "Die Fraktale Fabrik" (Springer-Verlag), Hans-Jürgen Warnecke, head of the Fraunhofer Institute in Stuttgart, uses an image from geometry. Not the perfect Euclidean geometry of CAD drawings and platonic forms, but the new geometry of fractals, endlessly complex shapes generated from simple mathematics that organise themselves in unpredictable but almost regular ways; their distinctive forms repeat on different scales, geometric echoes fading to the infinitely small. The image is one of worker empowerment through technology, with the local organisation of teams on the shop floor echoing the organisation of the whole company. This repeated complexity is the working out of a single corporate aim.

Fractals are computer-generated; before the advent of cheap number-crunching, such patterns remained hidden in dull equations, the outcome of which could never be seen. A fractal factory depends on computers, but also on people, and the new possibilities created within jobs that have sometimes been dull. A man working with a tool used to look inwards, managing the tool. Now that the tool takes care of the job on its own, he can look outwards, at the flow of work to and from the tool, at how the tool could be better used, at maintenance requirements. Taylorised work required men to ignore everything except what they did; computerised work makes it possible for the nature of work – its flow, its quality, its design – to be reclaimed as an area of workers' collective expertise.

Possible, but not necessary. Technology does not force; it permits. The future in some factories may be one of a newly sophisticated Taylorism, with work controlled by networks beyond the reach of the workers. John Alic, of the American Congress's Office of Technology Assessment, points out that new technologies can make work more opaque, harder for a worker to understand: alienating. However, there is research showing that in workplaces where the shop floor is given local control over new technology, the technology is better used than when it is controlled elsewhere. People offer solutions, as well as problems; they often turn out to be better at organising themselves than bosses expect. Decentralised decision-making seems an obvious corollary of decentralised information.

Perhaps machines will do this themselves one day. Engels believed that the human mind had evolved to take full advantage of the human hand; more recently, many researchers have preferred the idea that the mind is an organ evolved to allow complex social interactions. Computers will face similar challenges. The fact that solutions can always be invented for computers by humans who have already evolved consciousness may mean that computer consciousness never develops. If it does, though, it might well be in response to the tasks of the factory. Manufacturing systems, unlike other places where computers are used, offer a place to act, not just data to process; two worlds to live in at once, their border endless in its complexity.

Frederick Taylor saw no fractals. His was a mechanical sociology, a theory of the factory as machine in which the flow of information and work was embodied in material products. Workers' intelligence was largely wasted. Now it needs to be captured. Information is becoming disembodied. For the moment, at least, bridging the gaps this opens up between ideas and deeds requires people. A post-Taylorist view of manufacturing needs explicitly to understand the non-mechanical aspects of the process provided by the people within: the ability to respond and adapt, to form coalitions, to maintain a complex internal balance.

Machines cannot yet come to life. But factories and manufacturing can. The image of the machine has been projected on to factories since the 19th century heyday of mechanisation. Now biology is the dominant science. It is in the ability of living things to evolve and to create, to act and to process information that new metaphors for manufacturing will be found. A machine is more than the sum of its parts; but a living creature is far, far more.

THIS SURVEY ON MANUFACTURING TECHNOLOGY WAS FIRST PUBLISHED IN
THE ECONOMIST ON MARCH 5TH 1994

6

RETAILING

Economies of scale and information technology have given top retailers awesome power. But can they keep it?

MICHAEL REID

Change at the check-out

FOR much of this century retailing was a Cinderella business. No matter that in many countries it was – and remains – the largest single industry, employing between 7% and 12% of the workforce in rich parts of the world. And no matter that it counts almost everyone, everywhere, among its customers. Retailers were seen as simple and parochial businesses requiring little management skill, as fusty as the stock that gathered dust on their shelves.

No longer. In the past 15 years, retailing has undergone a many-sided revolution from which it has emerged as a leader in business innovation and the management of complexity. Top retail firms are now run by polished professionals. They exert enormous power and influence over manufacturers and consumers – and over urban, suburban and rural environments the world over.

Retailers have grown, first at home and then increasingly abroad, into some of the world's largest companies, rivalling or exceeding manufacturers in terms of global stretch. Wal-Mart, a discount chain that has become the world's top retailer (see chart 1), has bigger sales than any of its main suppliers; its turnover of $67 billion in the year to January 31st 1994 was the fourth largest of any American company. It is Procter & Gamble's largest single customer, buying as much as the household-products giant sells to the whole of Japan.

The retail business carries clout in many different ways. Each of Europe's top half-dozen food retailers has bigger sales than any of the continent's food manufacturers except Nestlé and Unilever. Metro, a privately owned and secretive German retail chain, turns out to be Europe's largest computer seller on top of its German cash-and-carry outlets, department stores, furniture and do-it-yourself shops. J.C. Penney, an American middle-market department store, buys its goods from suppliers spread across 50 countries. Saks, a mid-sized American department store chain, has become American Airlines' second-largest freight customer.

In America, many of the star stockmarket performers of the past two decades have been retailers. Wal-Mart's growth is legendary: for the first quarter century after 1962, when its founder, Sam Walton, opened his first discount store in Rogers, Arkansas, his company's sales and profits grew at an average annual rate of 25%. Even at its current growth rate of around 18%, Wal-Mart's sales, forecast at close to $100 billion in 1995, would double by 2000 – possibly making it the world's largest company.

The retail elite

The world's top retailers, by sales

	Main type of trade	Home country	Sales 1993 $bn	Annual average % change 1988-93	Number of stores 1993	Annual average % change 1988-93
Wal-Mart	Discount	United States	68.0	26.7	2,540	13
Metro Int.	Diversified	Germany	48.4	19.1	2,750	na
Kmart	Discount	United States	34.6	5.6	4,274	0.1
Sears, Roebuck	Department	United States	29.6	-0.5	1,817	2.0
Tengelmann	Supermarket	Germany	29.5	8.2	6,796	6.8
Rewe Zentrale	Supermarket	Germany	27.2	13.2	8,497	2.2
Ito-Yokado	Diversified	Japan	26.0	19.4	12,462	25.2
Daiei	Diversified	Japan	22.6	10.5	5,920	12.9
Kroger	Supermarket	United States	22.4	3.3	2,208	0.1
Carrefour	Hypermarket	France	21.7	16.0	647	17.9
Leclerc, Centres	Hypermarket	France	21.1	11.1	524	1.3
Aldi	Supermarket	Germany	20.9	23.9	3,435	na
Intermarché	Supermarket	France	20.7	12.0	2,890	14.6
J.C. Penney	Department	United States	19.6	4.2	1,766	-0.4
Dayton Hudson	Discount	United States	19.2	9.5	893	8.6
American Stores	Supermarket	United States	18.8	0.3	1,695	-2.4
Edeka Zentrale	Supermarket	Germany	17.9	8.2	11,670	-2.7
Promodès	Hypermarket	France	16.0	15.6	4,676	16.0
J. Sainsbury	Supermarket	Britain	15.9	12.2	514	5.8
Jusco	Diversified	Japan	15.8	15.3	2,452	25.0
Price/Costco	Warehouse club	United States	15.5	20.2	200	18.9
Safeway	Supermarket	United States	15.2	2.3	1,078	-1.2
Koninklijke Ahold	Supermarket	Holland	14.6	14.5	2,152	14.4
Otto Versand	Mail order	Germany	14.4	13.6	na	na
Tesco	Supermarket	Britain	12.9	12.0	430	2.8

Source: Management Horizons

When push turns to pull

At the heart of this retailing revolution lie two things. One is the rise in disposable incomes since the second world war, first in the industrialised countries and more recently in parts of Asia and Latin America. More people had more money with which to go shopping, so more and more shops were built to meet this demand.

The second is more recent, and arises from changes in the way goods and services reach the consumer. This distribution chain used to be controlled by manufacturers and wholesalers. The retailer's role was to buy goods from a range offered by the wholesaler or other intermediaries, and sell them on to the consumer. His main competitive advantage lay in merchandising – his skill in choosing the assortment of goods for sale in the store. He had a second potential advantage – closeness to the customer – but its only use, if any, was to beat his rival retailer across the street. For it was manufacturers who decided what goods were available, and in most countries at what price they could be sold to the public.

That distribution system is now being turned upside down. The traditional supply chain, powered by manufacturer "push", is becoming a demand chain, driven by consumer "pull". In most countries resale price maintenance – which allows suppliers to fix the price at which goods can be sold to the final customer – has been either abolished or by-passed. In America the Robinson-Patman act requires manufacturers to sell at a single price in a given market, but in practice they give large discounts, dressed up as "promotional money", to big retailers. Even in Japan, where a labyrinth of intermediaries has kept prices high and allowed hundreds of thousands of small shops to survive, more competitive retailers have begun to import products directly from manufacturers.

Retailers have won control over distribution not just because they decide the price at which goods are sold, but also because both individual shops and retail companies have become much bigger and more efficient. They are able to buy in bulk and to reap economies of scale, mainly thanks to advances in transport and, more recently, in information technology.

By the middle of the 19th century, permanent shops had grabbed much of the business formerly held by open markets, fairs and travelling pedlars in urban Europe and eastern America. But their clientele was limited to people within walking or comfortable riding distance. It took railways and urban trams to create a mass market, and it took cast-iron construction, plate glass and the Otis elevator to enable retailers to serve those new customers in ever bigger and more attractive shops. Those shops eventually turned into department stores, and later supermarkets, chain stores and shopping malls. Each of these innovations succeeded because it provided shoppers with more choice, or greater convenience, or better quality, or lower prices, or a combination of any or all of these. And each of them attacked one or more of the main costs retailers face: the variable costs of labour and stock, and the fixed costs of the store itself and the ground on which it stands.

Size is not everything. French hypermarkets, with their huge sales areas combining food and general merchandise, did not work in America. The growth of warehouse clubs – sheds selling bulk goods to customers who pay a membership fee – has slowed much sooner than most retail analysts predicted. And some small-scale shops, such as those of Britain's Body Shop, have found a profitable international niche. Even so, the trend to bigger stores with fewer staff, spreading lower overheads across a larger sales volume, is evident the world over.

Though each new retailing format has caused casualties among those who have stuck to earlier, less efficient formats, some old-established traders have survived by adapting. That might mean countering lower prices with better service, cutting costs to become more efficient, or even switching to the new formats themselves.

Information is power

The casualty rate may increase sharply from now on, because larger and more cost-effective shops are only half the story of the retail revolution. The second chapter is all about information technology and its application to store management, logistics and the distribution chain. Sophisticated computer systems installed over the past 15 years – but only now proving their full worth – can tell retailers instantly what they are selling in each of hundreds of stores, how much money they are making on each sale and, increasingly, who their customers are. Thanks to computers, a well-managed retailer should no longer be lumbered with stock that may not sell, or run out of items customers want to buy. The stock burden has been passed up the supply chain to the manufacturer.

Computers have at last enabled clever retailers to exploit the closeness to the customer and control of the shelves that have always been their strongest points. Over the past two years this has triggered a wave of plant closures, lay-offs and mergers in the food, drink and household-goods industries. And retailers are making life even harder for their suppliers by increasingly switching to goods made specially for them and sold under their own labels.

Computers have also allowed retail managers to exercise closer control over much more extended store chains. This has coincided with the lowering of trade barriers around the world, and the spread of free-market economies in Asia and Latin America. These two factors have allowed some big retailers – such as America's Toys "R" Us and Wal-Mart, Britain's Marks and Spencer, Holland's Makro, Sweden's IKEA, France's Carrefour and other European supermarkets – to start transforming themselves into global businesses.

This survey will show that scale and information technology have given retailers unprecedented power. But they must also grapple with new threats. In many countries, saturation and consumer pressure is forcing down retailers' gross margins (their mark-up). Edward Brennan, the outgoing chairman of Sears, Roebuck, reckons that over the past 15 years average gross margins in American general merchandise retailing have fallen by ten percentage points. Retail shares, after a decade as Wall Street's darlings, have underperformed the stockmarket for the past two years.

In America and in north-west Europe, the golden age of retail expansion between 1960 and 1990 was fuelled by the post-war baby boom, rising car ownership and, on the supply side, the push by specialist chain stores and department stores to expand from regional to national businesses. But now the baby boom has given way to the "birth dearth". The majority of American shoppers are over 35, and are spending more on their homes and their children's education. Consumers also feel financially less secure. In America, the ratio of household debt to income has gone up to 90% from 70% a decade ago.

Consumers everywhere are far more conscious than in the 1980s of value for money, a trend that has outlasted recession and spurred the worldwide rise of discount retailing. As they become more knowledgeable, consumers start to second-guess retailers. For example, in America and Britain many of them delayed buying Christmas presents in 1994, forcing weaker retailers into early mark-downs. With more women working outside the home, consumers are spending less time in stores; shopping is becoming more functional and less social. And lower inflation means that retailers no longer gain much from the lag between being paid by customers and paying suppliers. All this means that retailers must work much harder to turn their market power into profits.

Stores of value

TO DISCOVER how information technology has changed retailing, the obligatory starting point is Wal-Mart. Its success is due not just to computers, but many other things besides: the late Sam Walton's entrepreneurship; his strategy of avoiding early competition by putting "good-sized discount stores into little one-horse towns which everybody else was ignoring"; his insistence on saturating one area with stores before moving on to the next; his drive to keep costs down and sell at "everyday low prices"; and his policy of "empowering" staff while keeping trade unions out.

Equally, Wal-Mart was not the first to harness computers to retailing. American bookshops and supermarkets installed EPOS (electronic point-of-sale) systems in the late 1970s, as did European food retailers such as Holland's Ahold and Switzerland's Migros. Britain's Sainsbury began to automate its back-office ordering systems around the same time. The attraction of EPOS systems is that they instantly record each sale, using a laser scanner which reads the bar code on the product, so retailers no longer have to wait for a periodic stock-take to find out what they need to re-order. But Wal-Mart went further than installing a few computers. Its real innovation was its integrated use of computer systems to transform the way it did business.

That the greatest innovator in recent retailing history should emerge from the backwoods of Arkansas is perhaps less surprising than it might seem. Many of Wal-Mart's strategies were born of necessity. Its very obscurity prompted disdain from suppliers. "Sometimes it was difficult getting the bigger companies – the Procter & Gambles, Eastman Kodaks, whoever – to call on us at all, and when they did they would dictate to us how much they would sell us and at what price," Walton said later. This forced him to set up his own distribution system. In 1969, with just 32 stores, he built his first warehouse so he could buy goods in volume.

In the past each store manager would order goods to replace those sold, relying on suppliers to deliver them direct to the shop – a hit-and-miss system that took up potential selling space for storage and often left shops out of stock. As Wal-Mart developed its distribution centres in the 1970s, it introduced two innovations. The first was "cross-docking": goods were centrally ordered, delivered to one side of the distribution centre, and then transferred to the other side for delivery to an individual shop, along with other goods that shop had

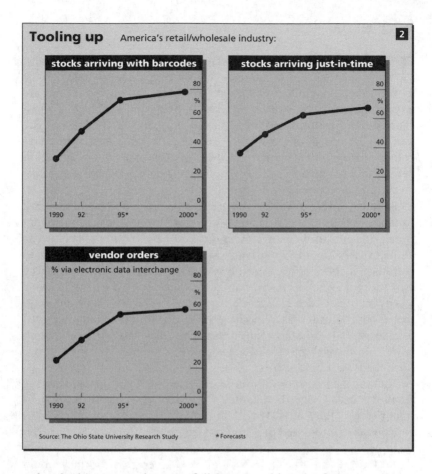

Tooling up America's retail/wholesale industry:

stocks arriving with barcodes

stocks arriving just-in-time

vendor orders
% via electronic data interchange

Source: The Ohio State University Research Study *Forecasts

ordered. This meant that one full lorry would make frequent trips to each store, instead of several half-empty ones visiting less often. To make this system work well, the firm had to keep track of thousands of cases and packages, making sure they were delivered to the right shop at the right time.

That was where computers came in. By the early 1980s Wal-Mart had not only set up computer links between each store and the distribution warehouses; through a system called EDI (electronic data interchange), it also hooked up with the computers of the firm's main suppliers. The distribution centres themselves were equipped with miles of laser-guided conveyor belts that could read the bar codes on incoming cases and direct them to the right truck for their onward journey. The final

170

step was to buy a satellite to transmit the firm's enormous data load. The whole system, covering all the firm's warehouses, cost at least $700m, but it quickly paid for itself.

The first benefit was just-in-time replenishment across hundreds of stores. This has since been refined further, using computer modelling programmes to allow the firm to anticipate sales patterns. The second benefit was cost. According to Walton, Wal-Mart's distribution costs in 1992 were under 3% of sales, compared with 4.5–5% for the firm's competitors – a saving of close to $750m in that year alone.

Perhaps the system's finest hour came in 1987, when Procter & Gamble proposed setting up a "partnership" that involved not just data-sharing through EDI but joint management of the whole relationship between the two companies. P&G uses this to tailor production to Wal-Mart's demand. The two firms say they both benefit – a faster and more predictable stock-turn can help the manufacturer too. But as other retailers adopted similar distribution systems, it became clear that one of the partners had benefited more than the other: P&G went through a round of plant closures and lay-offs, while Wal-Mart's profits just kept on growing.

Wal-Mart's distribution system gave it a great competitive advantage, helping sales grow from $1.2 billion in 1980 to $26 billion in 1990 and pushing up the number of stores from 276 to 1,528. The company overtook first Kmart, its discount store rival, which had been slow to computerise, and then Sears, to become America's biggest retailer by 1991. Kmart has still not recovered from the setback; it has spent much of the past decade trying, without great success, to imitate Wal-Mart's every move.

Turning stock into flow

Many other retailers are catching up with Wal-Mart on technology. Late entrants can move straight to new-generation systems, such as client-server networks (a number of personal computers linked to a data-processing centre) that offer greater flexibility without sacrificing power. Some of Britain's top retailers, such as Marks and Spencer, Sainsbury and Tesco, waited until the mid-1980s before investing in expensive information technology. Tesco, a supermarket chain, has cut the amount of stock in its distribution chain to just two weeks' supply – the lowest for any food retailer anywhere. Studies in America suggest that supermarket stock figures there are much higher.

For Tesco, the next step is the use of automated picking and sorting systems in the distribution centres, capable of breaking down deliveries into smaller units. The firm reckons that in five years' time it could be operating with only a week's supply. The aim is to turn static stock into a continuous flow. Like Wal-Mart, Tesco is now using computer modelling derived from stored EPOS data to predict future demand.

British supermarkets, which sell large quantities of fresh produce and chilled prepared meals, have also developed "composite distribution" – delivery lorries with separate compartments at different temperatures – to allow food stores to be serviced by one full truck rather than several half-empty ones. This logistical breakthrough is allowing Tesco and Sainsbury to make a profitable return to the small and congested high street sites they forsook for suburban superstores a decade ago. After a slower start, continental European food retailers, some of which are coalitions of independent store owners, are now adopting such methods of supply-chain management.

Both Wal-Mart and supermarket retailers enjoy the advantage of fast and fairly stable stock-turns and predictable volumes. But clothing retailers, too, use computers to control their supply chains. The pioneer was The Limited, a fashion chain based in Columbus, Ohio, which in the early 1980s set up EDI links with clothes makers based in Hong Kong. Using computer-aided design and air freight, it has cut the lag between order and delivery to three to five weeks instead of the nine months once standard for department stores. The system allows The Limited to adjust the sizes, colours and patterns of its collections in response to actual sales, rather than relying purely on its buyers' hunches. The Limited is now squeezing costs further by getting its suppliers to take on tasks previously done in its own stockrooms, such as attaching price tags to clothes and packing them ready for display in the store.

EDI has forced a shake-out in many areas of manufacturing because it requires suppliers to make their own investment in information technology or risk losing their retail customers. Most retailers have narrowed their supplier base over the past decade, though Marks and Spencer, for example, is careful to maintain a spread of competing suppliers for its products. But the arrival of cheaper PC-based computer systems has also provided opportunities for smaller suppliers. A small local cheese producer now supplies a single Tesco supermarket in York. Five years ago that would have been uneconomic.

As the rest start to catch up with the best, retailers are finding that logistics is becoming a "core competence" – a vital skill they cannot do without. Sears, Roebuck last year hired Lieutenant-General Gus Pagonis, who had been in charge of logistics for the United States armed forces in the Gulf war, to take command of its distribution system. His job includes all aspects of relations with suppliers and importers, encroaching on territory that store buyers once considered their private property. But many retailers still have work to do on logistics. A recent study by Andersen Consulting, a management consultancy, found that in America "retailers and manufacturers are often operating a patchwork of incompatible information systems, not just between companies but sometimes within the same company."

Mining the data

Information technology is a precondition for success, not a panacea. "Competitive advantage is what we do with the system, rather than the system itself," according to Bruce Watson of The Gap, a clothing retailer based in San Francisco. For the leaders, that has thrown up two issues. The first is that they must mine more effectively the data they already have. Retailers have been slow to exploit one of the main advantages computers give them: knowledge not only about what they sell, but also to whom they are selling it. Using this information for data-based marketing is shaping up as the next battleground between manufacturers and retailers (see next article).

The second issue is how retailers should organise themselves to get the maximum benefit from information technology. Initially, computers shifted many management functions – such as buying and pricing – away from the shop and towards the centre. Some supermarkets use computers to plan the allocation of shelf-space. Store managers at Carrefour and other French food retailers used to enjoy a large degree of autonomy, doing much of their buying locally. They would be appointed a year before a hypermarket opened and, Carrefour says, be given "a blank cheque" to supervise store-building, fitting and hiring staff. But in 1993, concerned that it was losing buying power, the firm moved 80% of its buying to the centre. It does not deny that the transition has been painful.

But centralising everything risks ignoring the peculiarities of local taste that can make or break a particular store. Some retailers are now customising their computer systems, allowing each store to set its prices and adjust its assortment according to local conditions. Wal-Mart, for example, uses a computer model incorporating more than 2,500 variables (including demographic data, climate and local competition) to tailor its assortment for particular stores. On top of this, its store managers have the power to override the system.

The best way to run a retail chain, says John Brady of McKinsey, a management consultancy, is to operate every store differently, with locally-tailored ranges and prices, but he adds that this is complicated to manage. "The winner will be whoever dominates the industry intellectually", he says. Computers have not changed the old saw that "retail is detail". Instead, they are giving retail managers ever more detail to grapple with.

Computer-dating the customer

WHEN it started a century ago, marketing treated all customers as the same. By the 1960s, marketers were able to break that anonymous mass into segments. Now computer databases allow them to treat customers as individuals. They may know consumers' names and addresses, what they buy, what they have stopped buying and even how they respond to a rise in the price of dog food.

For big multinational retailers, this is the equivalent of going back to the days of the individual store owner who knew and greeted each customer personally. The benefits are potentially huge: instead of spending millions on advertising beamed at people who may be indifferent or even hostile to it, retailers can use databases to help them hang on to their existing customers and persuade them to spend more. This is important: typically, 20–35% of customers generate 70–80% of a retailer's profits. But it is not trouble-free: databases are expensive to collect and analyse, and customers may expect big discounts in return for their loyalty. Some may also see such individual marketing as an invasion of their privacy.

Retailers traditionally think of themselves as merchants, as buyers and sellers of goods. They have been slow to harness computers to manage customers as well as stock. Manufacturers have been nimbler. Firms such as Procter & Gamble, Nestlé and Kraft General Foods (a division of Philip Morris) are building databases, offering free samples to persuade customers to fill in questionnaires.

Mail-order firms have a built-in advantage because they already maintain databases, and so do department stores that issue their own credit cards. But American food and clothing retailers have started to invest in database marketing as well. Vons, a Los Angeles supermarket chain, offers customers a "Vonsclub" card that entitles them to discounts on selected items and gives presents such as a Thanksgiving turkey to big spenders. It also uses the club to promote higher-margin items and own-label products. Vonsclub's large number of known customers – more than a million use the card regularly – makes it worth manufacturers' while to dip into their national pool of promotion money to offer discounts on their products. Fred Schneider of Andersen Consulting reckons that around a quarter of American shoppers now have access to supermarkets' frequent-shopper programmes.

Talbots, a 385-store women's clothing chain based in Massachusetts, has compiled a database of 7m names that includes information about customers' sizes. This has enabled it to forecast more accurately which sizes will sell in particular stores. Talbots also runs a mail-order catalogue, which has been helpful in building up its database, and issues a store card, whose holders get access to special sales and, if they have spent enough, Christmas presents. Like Wal-Mart, Talbots asks all customers for their zip codes (though not their names) when they pay, to help it plan new store openings. The effort seems to be paying off. For the past five years the company has been opening around 50 new stores a year.

But as some airlines have found, database marketing can easily turn into an unprofitable exercise, especially in markets that are dominated by a few large firms. That is why Tesco hesitated long and hard before in February 1995 becoming the first British food retailer to launch a loyalty card.

Make it your own

THE third prong of retailer power, after bigger shops and computerised control of distribution, is own label (known as private label in America). As margins drop and competition intensifies, retailers are becoming ever more aware that selling goods under their own brand-name has two important advantages. The first is that own brands provide fatter margins. The cost of goods typically makes up 70–85% of a retailer's total costs: anything it can shave off that cost must be good business. The second benefit is that own-label goods strengthen a retailer's image with its customers. Since shops the world over increasingly look the same, exclusive products can make a helpful difference.

Own label is most developed in Britain (see chart 3) – where Marks and Spencer is unique among large international retailers in selling only own-label goods – and in food retailing. It accounts for close to 60% of sales at Sainsbury, Britain's largest supermarket chain. Own label has helped British food retailers to achieve profit margins averaging 8% of sales, egregiously high by international standards: a typical figure in France and the United States is 1–2%.

Britain's lead in own-label goods goes back a long way. Retail co-operative societies pioneered own label during the 19th century. Around the turn of the century Sainsbury began setting up its own farms and food-processing plants to ensure quality and value for its customers as well as higher profits. Weak trade-mark legislation has allowed British supermarkets to sell close copies of manufacturers' brands. In a relatively small, cohesive market food retailing soon became concentrated in a few large hands. Work by the Boston Consulting Group, a management consultancy, shows that own label's share of food sales tends to rise in line with market concentration (see chart 4).

But own label is no longer just a British phenomenon. Across Europe, its share of food retailers' sales is rising steadily. This trend has further to go: for example, Promodès, a large French food retailer, plans to boost its own-label sales from 17% to 26% of its total turnover in the next two years. And supermarkets' own-label products are now challenging some of the world's most powerful brands. Helped by Cott, an upstart Canadian soft-drinks supplier, supermarkets in America, Europe and Japan are challenging mighty Coca-Cola with own-label look-alikes.

In America, private label was long regarded as a cheap and nasty generic substitute for the real thing, rolled out by retailers during reces-

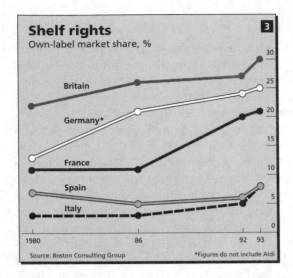

Shelf rights 3

Own-label market share, %

Britain

Germany*

France

Spain

Italy

1980   86   92   93

Source: Boston Consulting Group   *Figures do not include Aldi

sions and discarded once the economy picked up again. But no longer is that so. Private-label goods' share of total supermarket sales of packaged groceries increased to 19.7% by volume in 1993, from 15.3% in 1988, according to IRI, a market research firm. Just as importantly, the growth came from premium private label – goods that compete in quality with manufacturers' top brands; the share of cheap generics is tiny and declining.

Several American supermarket chains have decided to increase or upgrade their private-label programmes, and some of the industry's largest firms are making the fastest progress. Mark Husson, of J.P. Morgan Securities, a stockbroker, reckons that by the end of the decade private label will account for 27% of American supermarket sales. Own-label development is strongly associated with market concentration, whereas American food retailing has traditionally been fragmented. The top five firms account for only 21% of the market, compared with a median of around 65% in other rich countries, according to Mr Husson. But that is set to change. Several of the larger supermarkets are now emerging from debt piled up through leveraged buy-outs in the late 1980s. The leaders are expanding fast again. And as they reap the benefits of information technology investments, they will increasingly start to swallow up smaller, weaker firms.

Wal-Mart shakes the aisles

A second factor will speed up the shake-out: Wal-Mart's entry into food

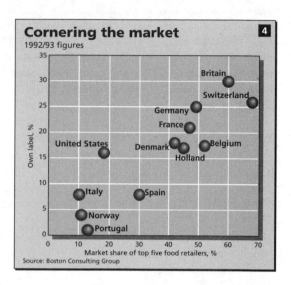

Cornering the market `4`
1992/93 figures

Own label, %

Britain
Switzerland
Germany
France
United States
Denmark
Belgium
Holland
Italy
Spain
Norway
Portugal

Market share of top five food retailers, %

Source: Boston Consulting Group

retailing, which has left many supermarkets quaking in the aisles. By the late 1980s, Wal-Mart had begun to saturate the American market with its discount stores. It started to diversify in 1983, opening its first warehouse club. In 1988, it launched into food retailing with its first "supercentre", a combination of a supermarket and a discount store. It had a struggle to adapt to fresh-food distribution at first, but is now planning to double the number of such stores to 200 this year. Supercentres aim to offer one-stop, low-price shopping. They average 150,000 square feet (14,000 square metres), around half of which is devoted to food, and typically carry about 150,000 different products, compared with the 20,000–30,000 products carried by an average supermarket of 40,000 square feet. Kmart and other discounters have followed Wal-Mart in building such supercentres.

Supermarkets, many of whose workers are members of trade unions, have found it difficult to compete on cost with Wal-Mart supercentres. For example, sales, general and administrative expenses at Kroger, America's biggest supermarket chain, in 1993 added up to 20.5% of sales, five percentage points above those at Wal-Mart's discount stores and two points above its supercentres. So supermarkets are starting to look to customer service, quality – especially in fresh produce – and own label to defend themselves against supercentres.

In America's food manufacturing business, the growth in private label has already forced a shake-out: in 1994 earnings declined, restructuring charges reached a 15-year high and four firms were swallowed up in $1 billion-plus mergers. Les Pugh of Salomon Brothers, a stockbroker, notes that whereas food company shares used to rise on news of restructuring charges, now they fall. "The restructuring benefits that in the 1980s were passed to shareholders are now being passed to the consumer," he says.

Consolidate or bust

MINNEAPOLIS, a city of frozen winters and hot, insect-infested summers in America's mid-west, has played a starring role in recent retailing history. It was there in 1956 that the Southdale Mall, the first enclosed shopping mall, was built to cosset shoppers from the rigours of the climate. And there in 1992 the $650m Mall of America, the largest shopping mall in the United States, opened its 2.5m square feet of retail space to the public. It is surpassed by only one mall in the world, in still-colder Edmonton in Canada. With four department stores, over 400 other shops, 45 restaurants, nine nightclubs, 14 cinema screens, 12,750 on-site parking spaces and a built-in roller-coaster, family theme park, Lego city and synthetic rain forest, all at a constant 70°F, the Mall of America has been hailed as a new concept in shopping, and has drawn tourists from all over the world.

Even so, it is likely to be the last of its kind – at least for a while. Mall-building in the United States has slowed sharply: only four malls bigger than 800,000 square feet opened in 1993, compared with 27 in 1989, according to the International Council of Shopping Centres (ICSC), a New York-based trade association. Mike Gregoire of Homart, the mall-development arm of Sears, Roebuck, reckons there is scope for only six to eight new "regional malls" (over 400,000 square feet) a year, compared with 20 a year in the early 1980s. Increasingly, developers are turning to smartening up existing malls rather than building new ones. In 1993 the ICSC recorded only 449 new shopping-centre projects of any kind started in the United States, compared with 2,131 in 1985, but 779 expansions or renovations of existing centres.

Sated America

The malls are being blasted by competition from "category killers" – specialist stores selling huge ranges from low-cost warehouse sites – often grouped together with discounters in new "power centres". Factory outlet centres, where manufacturers unload discontinued lines, also draw some of the malls' trade. But the slowdown in mall building reflects the growing saturation of the American retail market: total shopping-centre space in 1993 reached 18.5 square feet per head, compared with 13.1 square feet in 1980, according to Schroder Real Estate Associates, a division of an investment bank. People in the industry think that, as a rough rule of thumb, 14 square feet per head is all the American public needs.

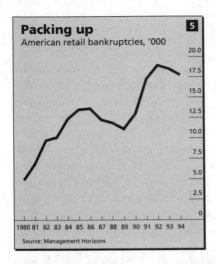

Packing up [5]
American retail bankruptcies, '000

Source: Management Horizons

In Western Europe, 40m square metres (431m sq ft) of purpose-built shopping-centre floorspace has been built in the past three decades, most of it in France, Britain and Germany, according to Jonathan Reynolds, of the Oxford Institute of Retail Management. By 1993 the number of shopping centres had risen to 2,326, from 1,372 in 1984. That figure may double over the next ten years. Some analysts detect approaching saturation in several north European countries – but different regulatory regimes, and the lack of a single European market in retail statistics, make this hard to judge. By the late 1980s the expansion of modern ways of shopping had wiped out many small, family-run shops in America and Britain. More recently, small traders in Germany, France and Japan have also lost market share.

On both sides of the Atlantic, leading retailers' investment in information technology and logistics has begun to pay handsome dividends. As consultants from McKinsey have noted, "there is a significant – and sustained – gap between the financial performance of the front-runners and the format average." The upshot is that the strong are getting bigger and the weak are going to the wall, unable to compete as margins decline. Bankruptcies in retailing in the United States have leapt in the 1990s (see chart 5). Conversely, the top 70 non-food retailers in 1993 accounted for well over half of total sales of general merchandise, clothing and furniture, a 10% leap in market share over a period of ten years, according to Goldman Sachs, an investment bank.

The leaders have increased their market share in most sectors of

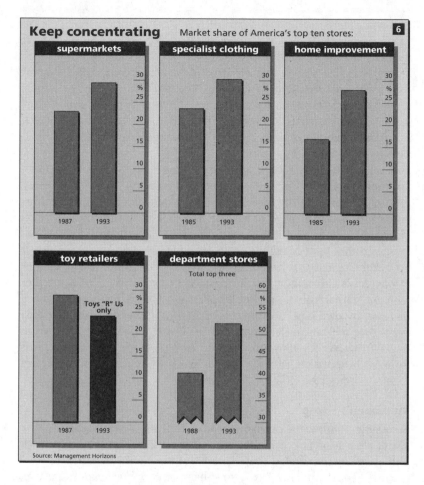

Keep concentrating Market share of America's top ten stores: **6**

supermarkets — 1987, 1993

specialist clothing — 1985, 1993

home improvement — 1985, 1993

toy retailers — Toys "R" Us only — 1987, 1993

department stores — Total top three — 1988, 1993

Source: Management Horizons

American retailing (see chart 6). In toys, to take the most dramatic example, in 1987 the top ten retailers had 28.8% of the market, trading from 1,764 stores. By 1993 Toys "R" Us alone had nearly a quarter of the market, trading from only 581 stores, according to Management Horizons, a retail consultancy. Or take warehouse clubs, one of America's newest retailing formats. In 1986, this sector was made up of 17 companies; now there are only three.

As most of the easy pickings have gone, large American retailers now find they can gain market share only at each other's expense. Competition is particularly fierce in clothing, where specialist stores have come under attack from discounters, revived department stores and mass merchandisers. A wave of department-store mergers culminated in 1994 with the union of Federated Department Stores (which includes Bloomingdales) and R.H. Macy, leaving the industry in the hands of half a dozen major firms. Most of the survivors have cut their costs and dropped their prices, focused their range more narrowly and moved towards centralised buying. For the department stores, the worst seems to be over. Their sales in 1994 crept up by 2.1% in volume after four years of flat or negative growth, according to Management Horizons.

But the biggest comeback story of the past two years has been Sears, Roebuck. Long the ailing giant of American retailing, Sears has divested itself of its non-retailing businesses, cut its sales, general and administrative costs from a peak of 33% of revenues to around 25%, and re-invented itself as a mall-based mid-market department store. It has increased the share of clothes in its product mix and plans to push it up further. Its rewards have been the highest same-store sales increases of any American retailer in the past two years. This revival, together with an earlier turnround at J.C. Penney, which featured a strong increase in own-label clothing sales, has put pressure on specialist stores such as The Limited and even The Gap. If this trend continues, it is gloomy news for the mall industry, which earns most of its rents from such specialist stores; coveted "anchor" department stores get their sites rent-free.

Rule-bound Europe

Across the Atlantic, the department-store industry is starting to stabilise again, after a long decline that has left most European countries with only two national chains. Germany's four main department-store groups merged into two last year. The survivors are revamping: London's Selfridges, for example, is spending £50m on a facelift for its elderly Oxford Street store and on new computers. French department stores have boosted sales of clothing from a quarter to half their total sales, with an eye on a faster stock-turn.

It is not just food retailers and department stores that are consolidating in Europe. Metro has built its leading slot in European retailing through quiet acquisition. Since 1992 Pinault, originally a French wood-products and trading company, has rapidly assembled a diversified retailing empire taking in the Au Printemps department-store group and FNAC, a chain of music and video stores.

But government regulation leaves European retailers with less elbow

Cross-channel differences 7

Europe's top retailers in 1992:

by pre-tax profit margin			by sales per employee		
Company	Home country	Profit margin,%	Company	Home country	Sales per employee £'000
Great Universal Stores	Britain	16.9	Kesko	Finland	389
Marks & Spencer	Britain	12.4	Pinault-Printemps	France	281
Benetton	Italy	11.3	Casino	France	214
Boots	Britain	10.2	Promodès	France	203
Argyll	Britain	8.0	Carrefour	France	202
Tesco	Britain	7.7	Galeries Lafayette	France	198
J. Sainsbury	Britain	7.6	Colruyt	Belgium	163
El Corte Inglés	Spain	7.4	Comptoirs Modernes	France	160
Wm Morrison	Britain	6.4	FNAC	France	156
Kingfisher	Britain	5.8	Kwik Save	Britain	156

Sources: Oxford Institute of Retail Management; Corporate Intelligence

room than their American colleagues. America is the world's most competitive retail market because barriers to entry are low. Venture capital, labour and land – and therefore retail space – are all cheap and abundant, and regulation, apart from the Robinson-Patman act, is light. For the past two decades shops have been allowed to open for seven days a week, 24 hours a day, and retailers face few planning restrictions. That means "you can have a new idea today and have a 100,000-square-feet store operating four months later", says David Bell of the Harvard Business School.

Compare that with many West European countries, where retailers face restrictions on opening hours and tight planning controls aimed at preserving small shops, city centres and precious countryside. In some countries high property prices form a further barrier. Different rules and customs have created great diversity in Europe's national retailing environments.

Thanks to planning deregulation in the 1980s – now being put into reverse – Britain has the most modern shops in Europe. But it also has the highest retail profit margins: a study by the Oxford Institute of Retail Management and Corporate Intelligence, a retail consultancy, showed that eight of Europe's ten most profitable retailers in 1992 were British. British retailers have more advanced supply-chain management systems and benefit from cheaper labour than many of their continental rivals. But they are not necessarily more efficient: the same study showed that

French firms had the highest sales per employee (see chart 7).

One explanation for British retailers' profit margins is the barrier to entry posed by high property costs. A recent study by Jones Lang Wootton, an estate agent, found that rents and associated outgoings such as property taxes make London's top shopping streets the most expensive in Europe. Land costs for out-of-town retail developments are also steeper than in many other countries. Richard Hyman of Verdict, a retail consultancy, points out that the British tradition of upward-only rent reviews has added to the problems of new entrants, as landlords prefer to leave high street sites empty rather than lower their rents.

Throw in a spate of mergers and acquisitions in the 1980s, and a retail sector in which most firms are publicly quoted, and it is no wonder that Britain is dominated by a dozen or so top retailers. The extraordinary uniformity of British high streets up and down the country bears witness to that. But increasingly, shopping sameness is not a British monopoly.

Wet markets and warehouse clubs

A STROLL through Kowloon, on Hong Kong's landward side, offers a potted history of shopping. The "Golden Mile" along neon-swathed Nathan Road boasts department stores and a host of modern boutiques. Round the corner on Peking Road is a small supermarket and adjoining drug store run by A.S. Watson, a division of Hutchison-Whampoa, a Hong-Kong Chinese trading company. Down the side streets are poky shophouses, selling herbal remedies or a few tired groceries, and pedlars hawking watches, compact discs and clothing, some of dubious provenance. Not far away are "wet" (produce) markets that dominate Hong Kong's perishable food trade, but also three warehouse clubs opened in 1994 by Wal-Mart in partnership with Charoen Pokphand (CP), a Thai conglomerate.

With astonishing speed, many Asian countries are embracing a retail revolution which in Europe and the United States took decades to develop. It is powered by the emergence of a middle class newly able to shop for more than bare necessities. But different places are at different stages: China, India and Indonesia are just starting, while in Taiwan and Thailand the changes are well under way and in Malaysia retailing is at take-off point. Even in Mongolia, a former professional wrestler has opened a chain of consumer electronics shops and announced plans for four supermarkets.

In Japan, an old-fashioned shopping system is being shaken up: the growth of discounters led the government in 1994 to loosen its retail laws, enacted in the 1950s to protect small shopkeepers and wholesalers. The liberalisation released a flood of plans for superstores from the country's four big food and general merchandise chains. Invaders such as Toys "R" Us are introducing Japanese consumers to the benefits of "category killers": in barely three years since entering the market, after conquering red tape and hostility from wholesalers, the firm has opened 24 stores.

Japanese retailers once looked set to dominate Asian shopping. A decade ago, their balance sheets buoyed by the bubble economy at home, Japanese department stores and chains such as Sogo, Isetan and Yaohan planted stores across South-East Asia's capitals. Now they have been outpaced by others. The 1990s in Asia, says Katherine Newman Mack of Kleinwort Benson, a merchant bank, is the decade of specialist-store chains and of European and American invaders. "Customers use department stores as a training ground in modern shopping. Then they want value", she says.

Already Hong Kong, Singapore and Bangkok are saturated with department stores. Shanghai will follow soon: Yaohan, which moved its head office to Hong Kong to target China, is building a $150m, 100,000 square metre, 21-storey department store in the city, due to open in December. It will compete with half a dozen others, including Isetan and a franchised Au Printemps store.

Lane Crawford, a Hong Kong department-store company, saw pre-tax profits for the six months to September 1994 drop to less than half their level a year earlier, despite (or because of) opening a large new store in Singapore. Robinson, a Thai department-store chain, suffered an operating loss in 1993, forcing it to restructure. Having narrowed its range and tightened logistics, it has returned to profit.

Meanwhile, local clothing chains such as Giordano and Esprit Asia are booming. So is Marks and Spencer: a rival reckons its Hong Kong business has a pre-tax profit margin of 17%. Its seventh shop in the colony, at Shatin in the New Territories, was an instant success when it opened in December 1994; sales at the others are growing by over 30% a year, says Colin Buchanan, the firm's local director.

The Makro effect

Conventional wisdom, derived from city states such as Hong Kong and Singapore, held that high property costs, traffic congestion and the dominance of wet markets would slow the spread of modern forms of food retailing in Asia. Conventional wisdom was wrong. In Taiwan in 1987, only 3% of the population bought groceries in modern shops; in 1994 over half of them did. In Malaysia, Mrs Mack reckons that a similar transformation, which began in 1994, will take only half as long. Thailand may go from one supermarket chain to at least three by the end of 1995. Bangkok already has two of the world's five biggest shopping malls.

What made the difference in Taiwan was the entry of Holland's Makro, a cash-and-carry firm, France's Carrefour, and Hong Kong's Dairy Farm, a discount supermarket company. Carrefour's Taiwanese stores are smaller than its French hypermarkets, and the firm says it buys 98% of its goods locally. The only French products are wine, water and camembert cheese. What the stores do have in common with their French cousins is their low-margin approach to retailing – previously unknown in Asia. Carrefour has already opened in Malaysia, and is targeting Thailand and China.

Makro has pioneered the discount warehouse in Asia, selling bulk cartons of groceries as well as office supplies and computers at its 23 stores in the region. It already operates in Thailand, Malaysia and Indonesia as well as Taiwan, and plans to move into China and South Korea by next year. Many of its customers are small retailers, and even local wholesalers. This is a formula that could work well in China – if its operators can handle the nightmare of setting up a supply chain.

For the moment, the putative early leader in Chinese mass-shopping is A.S. Watson. It has one of only three confirmed licences so far issued outside Guangdong province that allow retailers to sell imported as well as local goods. A.S. Watson has opened two supermarkets in working-class areas of Shanghai. Although their sales per square foot are half those of its Hong Kong stores, rents and labour cost less than half, says Ian Wade, the firm's managing director. He plans to open 40 stores a year in China for the next five years.

A.S. Watson owes its lead largely to the mainland political connections of Li Ka-shing, its parent's boss. Many of the American and European retailers who talk of going to China will lack such clout. They may also find they have over-estimated demand and under-estimated costs. But that may not deter new entrants, since retailers are becoming ever more footloose.

All the world's a shop

WOOLWORTH opened its first store outside America in Liverpool in 1909. C&A, a privately-owned Dutch clothing chain, set up shop in Germany in 1911 and in Britain in the 1920s. But until recently not many retailers tried to be international, and of those that did not many succeeded.

That has changed dramatically in the 1990s. Converging consumer tastes, saturation and planning controls in home markets, lower trade barriers and the opening up of Asian and Latin American economies have combined to send retailers scurrying to foreign parts. A handful of them are well on the way to becoming truly global businesses.

For many, the first step was to move into markets next door, often under the umbrella of regional trade blocks. American retailers looked to Canada and Mexico first. Japanese department stores spread across Asia in the 1980s. In Europe the single market, coinciding with recession in home markets and the opening up of Eastern Europe, prompted a plethora of cross-border moves: between 1990 and 1993, according to a study by Corporate Intelligence, retailers made 610 such moves in Europe – almost the same figure as for the whole of the 1980s. As well as food retailers, particularly discounters and hypermarket operators, this total included category killers selling such products as music goods, office products, computers and furniture.

The shift started in the 1970s, when the less developed retail markets of southern Europe – Spain, Italy and Portugal – were invaded from the north. Four of Spain's top five food retailers are now French-owned. France's Promodès says that because of planning restrictions and saturation it can open only one hypermarket a year at home; but it reckons Spain will have plenty of scope for new stores until 2005.

The 1990s have seen cautious movement into Eastern Europe, led by Germany's traditionally inward-looking retailers. Julius Meinl, an Austrian grocer, has returned to its pre-war markets in Hungary; several Finnish retailers have tiptoed into Russia. These neighbours have been joined by contenders from further afield: Britain's Tesco and Holland's Ahold have bought into supermarkets in Hungary and the Czech Republic respectively, as has Belgium's Delhaize in both countries.

The next step for Western Europe's powerful supermarket chains will be to create a genuine single market in food retailing. Several factors have conspired against this: the difficulty of launching hostile takeovers in Europe, differences in regulation, and variations in consumer behaviour. Since 1988 some food retailers across the continent have begun to gang up, forming eight loose alliances. As yet they have done nothing more daring than sharing information on logistics and marketing. Expect them to dabble with joint buying, and to press food manufacturers to sell at a single price throughout the European Union. Already Promodès has set up an international buying office in Geneva to negotiate volume rebates for its operating companies across Europe.

There are other signs of convergence in European food retailing. Through its purchase of Catteau, a French supermarket chain, Tesco is introducing the British model of high-margin food retailing into continental Europe. But just when that model is also catching on with American supermarkets, it is under attack in Britain itself from agile continental food discounters. These began in Germany in the 1950s, selling a small range of manufacturer brands – typically 300–500 products – in small, no-frills stores. Despite their low prices, they make a profit thanks to fast turnover, low capital and operating costs, and huge volume discounts from manufacturers. Having saturated Germany by the late 1980s, privately-owned discounters such as Aldi and Lidl & Schwarz set out to conquer the rest of Europe.

Together with Kwik Save, a homegrown discounter, such invaders had grabbed around 15% of Britain's grocery market by 1994, up from 5.5% in 1990; their share may grow by around 2% a year, reckons Corporate Intelligence. The supermarkets have fought back, cutting prices on basic items, sacrificing a point or two of their gross margins to protect volume. But their margins are still about double those of the discounters.

In Germany the discounters hold 29% of the market, according to NatWest Securities, a stockbroker. In Italy, Spain and France their share is growing fast. Food discounting will be a European battleground for the next few years. The main beneficiaries will be consumers: in Britain, food prices in 1994 rose by less than the consumer price index.

Another important trend to watch will be moves by European retailers into other continents, as well as forays by American retailers into Europe. In 1994 Corporate Intelligence counted 45 American retailers operating in Europe, up from 15 three years earlier. Conversely, the more cash-rich of the European supermarket groups may go shopping for supermarkets in America. Already, Britain's Sainsbury, Holland's Ahold and Belgium's Delhaize have a substantial presence in the eastern United States.

These three belong to a new breed of trans-continental retailers likely to provide most of the excitement in the sector for the next five or ten years. For many, the most powerful magnet is Asia, followed by Latin America. Marks and Spencer gets close to 15% of its sales from outside Britain, and is expanding fast in Asia, France and Spain. Of the 1,000-odd Toys "R" Us stores worldwide, a third are outside the United States. Carrefour, which already has stores in ten countries across Europe, Latin America and Asia, reckons that in five years' time 60% of its sales will come from outside France.

Yet transplanting a retail business to foreign soil remains a complex business, requiring investment in management time, technology, logistics and marketing, as Vanessa Cohen of Coopers & Lybrand, an accountancy firm, points out. There is also plenty of scope for sometimes fatal mistakes. Risk may take the form of macroeconomic surprises: J.C. Penney has postponed the opening of the first two of four planned stores in Mexico because of the peso collapse in December 1994. Or firms may find they have to adapt a successful retail format to local consumer tastes: to suit Americans, IKEA had to increase the size of much of its furniture.

Above all, international investments can take time to pay off. This can be a problem for American retailers in particular, many of which have gone abroad in search of continued profit growth which a saturated home market has denied them. Spending on new markets and new shopping formats caused Wal-Mart's return on investment to slip from 24.6% in 1989 to 16.5% in 1993, according to J.P. Morgan Securities. This may explain why several of the more successful international retailers, such as IKEA, Makro and Aldi, are privately owned.

Despite all the difficulties, more and more retailers will enter foreign markets over the next decade. Some guidelines on how to do it have begun to emerge:

❖ **Study the market.** Toys "R" Us says that it looks at new markets for several years before taking the plunge. It has considered Mexico for five years, and "three times we decided not to go in", says Larry Bouts, the firm's international director.

❖ **Decide on your pace.** After observing Australia for four years, Toys "R" Us has opened 17 stores in its first 18 months. A slow build-up "gives less leverage with suppliers and real-estate developers, and means less customer awareness," Mr Bouts says. But others, including Wal-Mart and Marks and Spencer, start with small pilot investments in new markets, allowing fine-tuning before any full-scale commitment.

❖ **Think about local partners.** Many international retailers use joint ventures to help them deal with local politics, regulations and suppliers. Picking the right partner can be crucial: Wal-Mart's success in Mexico owes much to its alliance with Cifra, the country's top retailer. Conversely, Carrefour blames the failure of its hypermarkets in Britain on the shortcomings of its local partner, an investment company.

❖ **Adapt to local conditions.** This may mean local sourcing, or adjusting ranges to fit local tastes and constraints. For example, in Marks and Spencer's shops in Hong Kong food accounts for only 10% of sales compared with 40% in Britain, because the company found it could not get local supplies of acceptable quality.

❖ **Stick to core skills.** Newcomers must ensure that their logistics and computer systems can be made to work in new markets, and that they can maintain their reputation for quality, low prices, or service. This means exporting single-format businesses has proved easier than, for example, department stores.

❖ **Develop local management.** This is the key to understanding new markets, and the biggest constraint on international expansion. Transferring a retailer's corporate culture across borders is perhaps the trickiest part of internationalisation.

❖ **Ignore some or all of these rules** if they clash with your corporate culture or business methods. IKEA jumps into new markets without local partners and with only cursory research. The firm says it needs to be in a market to understand it, and needs to have achieved a high volume of sales before it can profitably adapt its products to local tastes.

Despite the complexities, venturing abroad will be a main source of growth for both European and American retailers in the next few years. But even as they stride out, American retailers in particular are looking anxiously over their shoulders at a new threat in their own backyard. What if new technology allows their customers to dispense with stores altogether? What if consumers find they can do their shopping from home?

Click, clunk, shop

WILL the Willard family of Orlando, Florida, occupy an important place in retailing history? On December 14th 1994, as part of an expensive experiment by Time Warner, a media company, and US West, a telephone firm, the Willards' home became the first to be hooked up to a broadband multimedia system known as a full-service network.

The Orlando trial, which is meant to extend to 4,000 homes, uses a set-top box to convert the TV set into an interactive tool. Apart from compiling their own TV programmes, viewers can shop by pointing and clicking their way through on-screen catalogues. They can peruse products (from companies such as Warner Bros Studio Store and Spiegel, a cataloguer), order them, and have them delivered. They should soon be able to order groceries from a joint venture between Shopper Vision, a home-delivery service, and Winn Dixie, a supermarket.

The project is a year behind schedule. Sceptics doubt whether the technology will ever be cheap enough, whether consumers will be interested, whether home delivery can be cheap and reliable, and whether payment systems can be fraud-proof. All of these conditions have to be met before interactive shopping has any prospect of a mass market. As delays and doubts have mounted, electronic-retailing hype has swiftly swung to cynicism.

Yet the concept remains beguiling, and might just deliver another retail revolution: the final passing of shopping power from retailers to consumers. With a few clicks, consumers could shop whenever they want from a potentially limitless range of goods. Unlike conventional TV shopping, whose growth has been modest, the viewer would control what products were on display; and unlike CD-ROM discs, the catalogues would be in real time.

But how much more will consumers have to pay to shop at home, and how much are they willing to pay? Retailers would save by not having to keep a store – typically 20% of their total costs – but interactive technology and home delivery may add more to costs than they take away, at least at first. Provided access becomes cheaper, competition in the virtual mall could prove fierce: price comparisons would become instant and effortless.

The debate on interactive shopping has so far focused on the technology. Yet to the consumer it may make little difference whether the main interactive tool is the TV set or the computer. The more important question, as Ray Burke of Harvard Business School points out, is whether consumers are interested. We may soon have some answers: up to a dozen multimedia shopping experiments are being put together across the United States; British Telecom launched a similar trial in 1995.

A mass market could be years away yet. Consultants at McKinsey forecast a $4 billion–5 billion market for interactive home shopping in the United States by 2003; after that, they think, sales could rise steeply. What does that mean for store-bound retailers? The answer starts with the skills required to cater for home shoppers: selecting a range of goods, data-based marketing, and order fulfilment. This points to the fast-growing catalogue industry as one potential leader in interactive retailing. Another is CUC, a direct-marketing company that is taking part in several of the trials.

For manufacturers, interactive shopping offers the tempting prospect of bypassing retailers and dealing directly with consumers, through a medium which gives strong brands an advantage. But that may be wishful thinking. Someone, be it a retailer or direct marketer, will still have to select an assortment of goods for display in the virtual mall, and get them to the consumer.

Interactive retailing is likely to start with goods already sold by catalogue, such as clothing and consumer durables. But the biggest prize could be America's $400 billion food-retailing industry, and especially packaged goods. Consumers do not have to touch or smell a packet of detergent or a tin of soup before buying it. And surveys show that many see grocery shopping as a boring chore.

A handful of tiny electronic food retailers, offering home delivery of groceries ordered by modem or fax, have started up. Peapod, which operates in Chicago and San Francisco in a joint venture with a supermarket chain, American Stores, in 1994 doubled its membership to 11,000 and attracted investment from Ameritech, a telephone company.

Peapod makes up its orders at American Stores' supermarkets, charging customers for the service. Food Express, which started operating in 1995 in New Hampshire, hopes to do away with the store by setting up a warehouse where it will make up orders for collection by the customer. David Cuthbert, who at 26 is one of the founders of the venture, reckons he can match supermarkets on price. He says the warehouse can serve as many customers as a supermarket in a third of the space. Caveats aside, the idea of electronic shopping is too influential for retailers simply to ignore it.

Back to basics

EVEN if interactive retailing grabs only a small slice of retail spending, that will be enough to bankrupt hundreds, perhaps thousands, of marginal stores. But retailing history suggests it will not wipe out existing store formats altogether. Rather, it will accentuate an existing trend: already, saturation and ever-more-intensive global competition are nudging shopping power away from retailers and towards consumers.

This will force even today's powerful retail elite to take a fresh look at the way they do business. Back in 1989 Walter Salmon, professor of retailing at the Harvard Business School, argued in the *Journal of Retailing* that "excellence in execution" would in future distinguish the winners from the losers. By this he meant that retailers had to add new skills in marketing, organisation, logistics, accounting and the management of information and labour to their traditional merchandising prowess. He was right, as this survey has described. Yet six years later mastery of such skills has become a necessary condition for survival rather than a sufficient guarantee of success for retailers. In future, they will have do all this, and more.

Thanks to computers, retailers have not only seized control of their supply chain; they also have acquired more information about all aspects of their business than ever before. That should allow vast chains to manage each of their hundreds of stores as if it was unique; but it also risks swamping retail managers with complexity. In future, retailers will need to make their businesses simpler to run. In addition, they will have to revisit two of the basic disciplines of their trade: merchandising and customer service.

Never before have shoppers faced such a wide choice of shops and merchandise, yet paradoxically never before have so many of them felt that they shop in a desert of uniformity. Skilful retailers will combine greater knowledge of their customers, acquired through databases, with merchandising flair to create a narrower range of products that their shoppers want, rather than trying to cater for all tastes – or none.

Service is the other ingredient in creating uniqueness. Already, many customers find the lack of help in category killers intimidating; interactive shopping will seem unstaffed to the consumer. That provides an opportunity for store-bound retailers. Sears, Roebuck owes part of its revival to having put more people on the sales floor (and fewer in its back office). Cutting sales assistants should be the last thing a retailer does to restore profitability, though too often it has been the first, argues Walter Loeb, a New York retail consultant. It is no coincidence that the department stores in the United States and Britain with the best return on investment over much of the past decade have been Nordstrom and the John Lewis Partnership respectively. Both put customer service from a highly-motivated, well-rewarded workforce at the centre of their corporate culture.

As the bigger retailers become international businesses, they will face the trickiest hurdle of all: how to replicate, across thousands of employees, hundreds of stores and dozens of countries, the attitudes, systems and skills that make up a firm's corporate culture. For the category killer as much as the corner shop, retailing remains a people business. Its most successful practictioners must combine computing and logistical prowess with merchandising skill, customer service and staff empowerment. If they fail, their customers will go and shop elsewhere.

THIS SURVEY ON RETAILING WAS FIRST PUBLISHED IN
THE ECONOMIST ON MARCH 4TH 1995

Postscript

In the event, 1995 proved to be as tough a year for retailers as had seemed likely. Few retail chains could thrive in the face of stagnant consumer spending and intense price competition stemming from low inflation and a saturated market. But retail firms with well-established skills in technology and marketing did less badly than many of their rivals. In America, Wal-Mart reported an increase in operating profit in its core discount store division of 14% for the first nine months of the year, but its underlying growth was slowing and some of its long-term debt was placed under review by Moody's, a credit rating agency. But this was a creditable performance compared to that of many of its rivals. Kmart dumped Joseph Antonini, its chief executive and chairman, but continued to make losses. Caldor, the country's fourth largest discount chain, sought protection from creditors under Chapter 11 of America's bankruptcy laws, as did two other discounters.

In Britain, to the surprise of sceptics, supermarket loyalty cards proved to be highly successful in attracting customers. In the six months after its launch in February 1995, 6m shoppers signed up for Tesco's card. This helped the firm register an increase in underlying sales volume of 6% (after stripping out the effects of sales at new stores and inflation) in the six months to August. Its great rival,

Sainsbury, initially dismissed the loyalty scheme as a gimmick, but then launched its own card; even so, its underlying sales volume declined by 2.2% in the 28 weeks to September 23rd. These results meant that Tesco overtook Sainsbury to become Britain's largest retailer of packaged groceries, according to one market research firm. A continuing price war among the big supermarkets slowed the expansion of continental European food discounters in Britain.

China continued to attract international retailers, despite the difficulties of operating there: by December 1995, the Chinese authorities had granted licences for more than a dozen large-scale retailing ventures, many of them involving Asian firms. Marks and Spencer, Wal-Mart and Makro were all studying the Chinese market.

It looked increasingly as if the Willard family in Orlando, Florida would be no more than a footnote in retailing history: though Time Warner had hooked up 650 families to its full service network by mid-1995, and British Telecom's trial got underway, most analysts were betting that the Internet, rather than interactive television, will be the main vehicle for electronic shopping.

7

DEFENCE TECHNOLOGY

The technologies of warfare are undergoing a revolution. The most important weapon now is information.

OLIVER MORTON

The information advantage

IN THE skies above Korea two knights faced each other, as in a medieval tournament. Their horses were the first supersonic jets, their lances missiles; their technology was the highest the 1950s had to offer. That technology gave one pilot the advantage.

One fighter climbed and flew faster than its adversary, and could bank more sharply. Yet it was the other fighter that had the advantage. The Russian jets, faster and more powerful, were consistently bested by their American adversaries. The American jets had better hydraulics, so they could switch more easily from one manoeuvre to another; and they had better cockpit design, allowing unobstructed views of more of the sky. As one of the Americans, John Boyd, later put it, they got through a cycle of observation, orientation, decision and action (OODA) just that bit faster, allowing them to maintain the initiative. Good visibility and sensitive controls gave them an information advantage which more than made up for being slower.

In 1991 the world saw that same advantage writ large. "One of the most unequal conclusions ever recorded", in the words of John Keegan, a British military historian, was reached in the sands of Kuwait and Iraq. All victories have many parents; the allies had better resources, better machines, better leadership, better training and better morale. But perhaps the key was the information advantage provided by a communications network that linked satellites, observation aircraft, planners, commanders, tanks, bombers, ships and much more. It enabled the allies to get around Colonel Boyd's OODA loops at breathtaking speed in a sort of continuous temporal outflanking. A completely new air-tasking order – a list of hundreds of targets for thousands of sorties – was produced every 72 hours, and would be updated even while the aircraft were airborne. Iraq's radar eyes were poked out, its wireless nerves severed.

Technology does not win wars. But an innovative combination of new technologies and tactics can, on occasion, give an overwhelming advantage to a well-organised, ardent fighting force. In response to such changes, all others must either try to master the same tactics and technologies or to develop counters. In so doing, they revolutionise the way the world fights. Such a revolution is now under way. It turns on the ability of countries, armies, commanders, soldiers and individual weapons to gather, process and use information.

Military revolutions		
Selected innovations in warfare		
Field/name	**Innovation**	**Date**
Cavalry	stirrups	5th century
Infantry	pikes and longbows	early 14th century
Artillery	cannon	early 15th century
Naval warfare	ship-borne cannon	early 16th century
Napoleonic	mass armies	end 18th century
Land warfare	rifle/rail/telegraph	mid-end 19th century
Steamship	engines and armour	late 19th century
Interwar	tank/aircraft/radio	early-mid 20th century
Nuclear	fission/fusion/missiles	mid 20th century

Not the Russian revolution

Military revolutions have happened before, though no two historians will produce the same list. Chart 1 rounds up a few favourites. Some are innovations of a purely military kind, such as the development of the dreadnought. Others are the military articulations of greater changes, either economic and technical – say the rail-rifle-telegraph revolution of the 1860s and 1870s; or more broadly social – say the mass armies of the Napoleonic era, revolutionary in every sense.

In the late 1970s, a Russian marshal, N.V. Ogarkov, wrote about a revolution in warfare made possible by technologies then on the horizon. Extremely mobile forces making use of excellent communications would be able to carry out co-ordinated attacks throughout large theatres of operation, rather than on a linear front. As the battle was expanded in space, it would also be foreshortened in time. So it turned out to be. Whereas America's long bombing of Vietnam was operation Rolling Thunder, its first plans for attacking Iraq went by the name of Instant Thunder.

Russia had neither the resources nor the technology to realise all of Marshal Ogarkov's ideas. America has. The Americans who have taken up his ideas – most notably Andrew Marshall, the veteran head of a Pentagon think-tank – model their work on one of the more recent previous revolutions: the linked set of transformations between the two world wars. That period saw the widespread integration of the internal-combustion engine, the medium- and long-range aircraft and the radio into military equipment and doctrine. Then, as now, the technological base was far from exclusively military, and was thus widespread. What mattered was not so much what technology you had as what you did with it. The Americans and the Japanese developed modern carrier-based navies. The Germans developed *Blitzkrieg*, literally "lightning war".

Another similarity between the inter-war years and the present is a relative scarcity of resources. After the slaughter of the first world war, the great powers drastically reduced their manpower and their budgets. The innovations of the 1920s, which were incorporated in the rearmament of the 1930s, were for the most part developed on a shoestring. Carrier aviation was devised with a handful of carriers, strategic bombing with a bare minimum of strategic bombers.

NATO's military spending now, $464 billion in 1994, is hardly a pittance; but the West's armed forces are significantly smaller than they were during the cold war. America's army is moving down from 18 divisions to ten, and its allies are making similar cuts. New procurement is falling. These straitened times might seem to offer little prospect of radical innovation. In fact, they provide an excellent opportunity. While the revolution now in progress calls for some new capabilities, its basic tools – remote sensing, precision-guided weapons, stealth and above all communications – are already at hand, just as tank, radio and aircraft were available at the end of the first world war. It is a matter of making existing equipment fit together and adding a few innovations. That requires thought. Such thought is the consequence of tight budgets that rule out solving problems simply by buying large quantities of bigger, more expensive weapons.

Today's revolution is different from that of the 1920s in some important respects. Military change then was still possible on a service-by-service basis, whereas now all the services must get together to dominate large theatres of war. In the 1920s different nations could gain supremacy in different niches, whereas now the size and complexity of the many co-ordinated systems involved suggest that only one nation can take full advantage of the opportunity on offer. Smaller countries can modernise and improve their performance, undoubtedly, but only America has the resources to go all the way. Today it spends almost as much on the use of satellites – tools of intelligence and communications that are crucial to getting a whole army around an OODA loop quickly – as Britain spends on its entire military establishment.

That could engender complacency, but another difference between now and the 1920s counsels against it. This revolution is built on information technologies. Information technologies are now developing far faster than the underlying technologies of that previous revo-

The big guns							2
Top ten, 1993:							
Defence spenders		Defence spenders as % of GDP*		Armed forces		Armed forces per 1,000	
	$bn		%		'000s	population	
United States	297.6	Bosnia	48.7	China	3,031	North Korea	53.0
Russia	113.8	Angola	32.4	Russia	2,250	Israel	36.8
China	56.2	North Korea	25.2	United States	1,837	Syria	28.5
France	42.6	Iraq	15.3	India	1,265	Jordan	26.2
Japan	41.7	Oman	15.3	North Korea	1,200	Croatia	21.3
Germany	36.7	Nicaragua	13.4	Vietnam	857	Oman	21.3
Britain	34.0	Saudi Arabia	13.1	Turkey	811	Iraq	21.2
Italy	20.6	Yemen	12.5	South Korea	750	Taiwan	21.0
Saudi Arabia	20.5	Kuwait	12.1	Pakistan	580	United Arab Emirates	20.7
South Korea	11.9	Sudan	11.6	Iran	528	Greece	20.3

Sources: U.S. Arms Control and Disarmament Agency; *International Institute of Strategic Studies

lution, in ways that are obvious in everyday life. Eliot Cohen of Johns Hopkins University, the director of the US Air Force's Gulf War Air Power Survey, points to this as the real evidence for a military revolution. Information technology is revolutionising everything else – why should soldiers be exempt?

Outpaced

Inside a hollow mountain in the Colorado Rockies sits the North American Air Defence command, protected by a kilometre of solid granite. Its buildings are insulated from war's outrageous fortunes by more than a thousand shock-absorbing springs, each the size of a child, each weighing half a tonne. This is the nerve-centre of the cold-war military machine. When it was built in the early 1960s, it represented the height of technological prowess. But that was a time when the Pentagon provided most of the American market for sophisticated electronics. Now it makes up less than 1% of that market; almost any office has the sort of computer power that it was once worth hollowing out a mountain to protect. It takes more than springs to absorb that kind of shock. When the hollow mountain is fitted with new systems, they will be nothing more than customised versions of the kind of moderately priced workstation familiar to medium-sized companies everywhere. In many ways the soldiers are following the revolution, not leading it.

In that, the armed forces of the developed world resemble the large companies that supply them – companies now facing small, agile competitors. The large and previously successful are by their nature slow to adapt to change; like supertankers, they live in a world of great inertia and far horizons. Weapons systems on the drawing board today could still be in the field in 50 years' time. Such weapons and their military establishments may come to look increasingly unwieldy. In the world of business, the pace of change is lowering barriers to entry, allowing newcomers with less history and more processors to do quickly with a few what used to be done slowly with many. In some ways, the same could apply to waging war.

Mr Marshall talks of Wal-Mart war. Computers could do for the military what they have done for the supermarket, making it cheaper and more responsive than it is now. However, to match America's might would still take a lot of time and money. And without matching America's might, fighting it on a battlefield would be unwise. Potential aggressors are more likely to look at ways to wage war differently, including ways that allow the new technology its head. After all, Mars has many temples.

Beyond Clausewitz

This leads to the last great difference between the 1920s and today. The earlier period was bounded at both ends by total wars between nation states. Karl von Clausewitz, a Prussian military theorist, saw war as a function of the relations between government, military and people, the "wonderful trinity". The world wars fit this model, but the wars of today and tomorrow may well not. Martin van Creveldt, of the Hebrew University in Jerusalem, is one anti-Clausewitzian proclaiming the end of the "trinitarian" war; John Keegan is another. In Mr van Creveldt's view, the seeds of von Clausewitz's downfall were contained in the second world war: first, nuclear weapons, which made mutual destruction a possibility; and second, the wide acceptance of a role for partisans, fighters without uniform or clear governmental legitimacy.

Since 1945, nuclear weapons have largely forestalled major wars between states, while partisans and freedom fighters outside the Clausewitzian model have toppled states all over the world. This trend, argues Mr van Creveldt, looks likely to continue. The world-wide clash of communism and capitalism may no longer engender low-intensity wars, but there are other reasons to fight. Thomas Homer-Dixon, of the University of Toronto, has suggested that environmental collapses might be a serious cause of conflict. Changes in climate, or overpopulation, could easily lead to war and mass migration in the third world.

"Low-intensity conflict" and nuclear proliferation provide options which mastery of the battlefield cannot counter. These, too, will be affected by the growth of information technologies. The free flow of information makes it easier to produce weapons of mass destruction.

Computer and voice networks, among other things, will open up new ways of co-ordinating low-level conflict and disseminating information about it.

Geography, from the terrain of the battlefield to the structure of geopolitical relationships, has always dominated military and strategic thought. Now it is under attack. Environmental change disrupts the geographical basis of the state. Nuclear weapons provide a more radical challenge to geography, being as immune to distance as they are to defence. Partisan forces do not care about geography. They live off the land without front lines or logistics trains, fighting a delocalised war. In the information age, delocalisation is becoming ever easier and more radical.

The military faces this confusing future with some advantages. It has experience in the integration of complex systems, as well as strong cultures and traditions that have survived many revolutions before. And the West is not at present facing any parlous danger. That means planning can be based not only on assessments of threat but also on assessments of opportunity – the opportunity for sustained peace after a century that has encompassed terrible war.

The new dimension

BEFORE the shooting starts, the generals pore over their maps to take the measure of the field – its length and its breadth, its lows and its commanding heights. Now they have a fourth dimension to contend with: that of the electromagnetic spectrum. The wavelengths of light visible to the eye, the narrow band from red to violet, make up only a tiny part of that spectrum. Imagine yourself with inhuman eyes sensitive to all of it, and sweep your vision across tomorrow's battlefield.

To begin with, at the lowest frequencies and longest wavelengths, there is a deep featureless night. Then, out of the darkness, the radios start to appear, spread out over a huge number of frequencies. In the Gulf war, the allies used 35,000 different bands; in future they will use more. Some move, some stay still; some shine at a single frequency, others spread their messages across a wider wedge of the spectrum. Some are constant, others flicker, sending bursts of digital information. The flickers may change colour as the radio hops from frequency to frequency to avoid interception and jamming. If any jammers are switched on, their gaudy brightness hurts your eyes.

As the warriors in these radio constellations move across the land, their guiding stars shine above them at 1575.42 megahertz. At any time, at least four of the 24 satellites in the Global Positioning System should be quite high in the sky. The precise oscillations in their light carry immensely accurate time signals, some in code, that allow microprocessors all around the battlefield to know where they are. Bright communications satellites girdle the equator, beaming data down to the troops. Other communications satellites may fly by in low orbits, forwarding information from one to another.

As the wavelengths shorten, a bright star catches your eye; looking around, you see its light reflected dimly from the terrain around you; it is a radar satellite. A similar light casts oblique shadows across the land, evidence of a surveillance aircraft circling 100km away. Specks of light, pinpointing aircraft illuminated by radar, flit through the sky. Occasionally one brightens briefly as it uses it own radar for a glance at the world, ever fearful lest a homing missile fasten on to it.

The wavelengths are now shortening into the infrared; everything begins to glow softly with stored heat. At long infrared wavelengths the paths of vehicles begin to appear, tracks in the landscape. At other wavelengths, you see the tiny spots with which infrared lasers illuminate targets for smart missiles. And then the

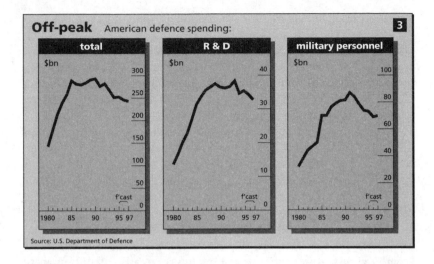

Off-peak American defence spending:

| total | R & D | military personnel |

Source: U.S. Department of Defence

hot things come to light: tanks, helicopters, people.

Above that, in the world visible to humans, there is nothing to be seen; it is a moonless night with an overcast sky.

Beyond-the-rainbow warriors

Control the electromagnetic dimension of the battlefield, goes today's wisdom, and you are most of the way to controlling it all. Admiral William Owens, vice-chairman of America's Joint Chiefs of Staff, sees the goal of the military revolution as providing dominance of the information battlespace – a volume hundreds of kilometres on each side and 10 trillion wavelengths deep. He thinks that the technical means are already at hand; everything seen in the description above, and everything needed to see it, already exists. America has dozens of sophisticated reconnaissance, communications and targeting systems – probably too many. As yet, though, they still have trouble talking to each other. If they could be opened up – opened to expansion, opened to the possibility of using data from other sources, opened to use on hardware other than that for which they were originally designed – their effectiveness could be dramatically increased. Admiral Owens aims to create such a "system of systems".

Think of it as information logistics. The earlier mechanisation revolution drove new logistical demands: an infantry division in 1914 needed 100 tonnes of supplies a day; a Panzer division in 1940 needed 300 tonnes a day; a mechanised division today needs perhaps 1,500 tonnes a day. The information revolution is spurring appetites in a similar way. Happily, information is easier stuff to shift around; it takes up next to no space and, in digital form, can be copied as often as required. That might seem to make it less daunting than getting fuel, provisions and parts into the field; but the infrastructure and planning needed to get it where it is going, and to deal with constantly changing requirements, is just as daunting.

In the Gulf war the allies suffered from various types of information shortage. The data needed to assess bomb damage were hard to gather. As tactical reconnaissance aircraft became overstretched, strike aircraft were reassigned to reconnaissance, but the data shortfall persisted. This has triggered a great deal of interest in long-duration unmanned aerial vehicles (UAVs) to deliver reconnaissance and surveillance data.

Satellite imagery, often plentiful, could be slow to reach the planning centre in Saudi Arabia, though there were ways to speed it up. David Deptula, one of the air-war planners, recalls satellite imagery arriving within four hours when General Buster Glosson, the officer in charge of the bombing, asked a friend at the Pentagon to send it direct; via official channels, it could take 48 hours.

Information about the location of friendly forces was also a problem, both in detail and in the grand plan. In detail, three-quarters of the American vehicles destroyed or damaged in the Gulf war were hit by their own side. In the broader sense, the decision to stop the ground war after 100 hours was made under the misapprehension that the Iraqi forces in the theatre were trapped, and that further fighting would be wanton slaughter. In fact the route to Basra was still open, and part of Iraq's republican guard used it to retreat.

The multiplexed division

General Gordon Sullivan, the American army's chief of staff, wants to make sure this kind of thing does not happen again. To prevent it, he is pushing the idea of the digital battlefield. He means to turn the army into a military Internet, where every component is able to shuttle data to its neighbours. Automatic systems will keep track of all friendly forces in range. Targets spotted by one system may be attacked by others better placed or less busy, the necessary data passed over automatically.

The more advanced weapons already have these sorts of abilities. Apache strike helicopters fitted with the impressive new Longbow radar, capable of tracking more than 200 moving targets, can shuttle

targeting data between each other. The Comanche, a stealthier helicopter still in development for armed reconnaissance and strike, can
pass targets to ground forces, too; it carries the number-crunching
power of a couple of supercomputers. However, the army cannot wait
for the latest advances to come in only with new equipment. So to
allow everyone to play their part in the network, computers are being
fitted to older vehicles through a programme known as Appliqué.

The advantages this brings will be measured through a series of
"war-fighting experiments". The first of these, an exercise in 1994 at the
national training centre at Fort Irwin, California, was at best a mixed
success. A battalion decked out with all manner of high technology
went up against the "opposing force" based at Fort Irwin, which thanks
to the experience it has gained enjoys a huge advantage over most of its
attackers. Compared with previous exercises, the new force suffered significantly fewer losses and inflicted many more on its enemy; but the
opposing force still won.

Next time, it may be different. The digital battalion that fought in the
1994 exercise was a pretty ad hoc affair. Now the 2nd Armoured Division – motto: Hell on Wheels – is being kitted out as an experimental
force to try and make all the different gadgetry work together, a microcosm of Admiral Owens's system of systems. In June 1996 – the "good-
idea cut-off date", or GICOD – it will stop taking on anything new and
concentrate single-mindedly on what it has got. In February 1997, one
of its digital battalions will take on the opposing force at Fort Irwin. A
year later, a digital division will go through the mill, and a year after
that a whole digital corps. By the end of the process, the army expects
to know what works and what does not, and to have a handle on the
tactical and operational doctrines that make sense when fielding such
a force – dubbed, with a touch of millenarian excitement, Force XXI.

Past GICOD

William Perry, a technophile moderniser at the Pentagon in the 1970s,
and now secretary of defence, says that this excitement is part of a
change brought on by the Gulf war. Where once technology had to be
pushed at the services, now they eagerly seek it. The air force, at its new
space warfare centre in Colorado Springs, is trying out different ways
of getting satellite information to the warriors in the field without having it delayed by intermediaries. For example, it would like to get precise details of the launch point of a Scud missile to the cockpit of a
nearby strike plane.

The navy's Co-operative Engagement Capability (CEC) is another example of new strength through networking. It uses radio links capable of passing many megabits of data a second to combine the radars of individual ships into a single system. As a result, everyone can see what anyone can see. In a task force with CEC, ships can launch self-defence missiles before their attacker is anywhere near them, relying on radars elsewhere to guide those missiles to their destination. In recent tests, a carrier group equipped with CEC reportedly shot down with ease all 20 of the drones impersonating cruise missiles that were launched at it.

All these systems simply integrate hardware already in existence. But military revolutionaries also have ideas for new sorts of armament. In the navy, for instance, a post-cold-war identity crisis has prompted calls for new types of vessel: submerged barges carrying thousands of ground attack missiles; perhaps new classes of "littoral supremacy vessels", sophisticated helicopter carriers that would carry assault craft. Some in the army and air force have similarly radical wish lists, often centred around a perceived need for speed. Some in the air force want rocket planes that go all the way to space; the army has fans of guns that fire their projectiles far faster by using electrical power instead of chemical explosives.

Thinking about such new systems is helpful. According to General George Muellner, in charge of the Joint Advanced Strike Technology (JAST) aircraft development programme, his team's computer simulations to explore JAST's potential role in 2010 have helped to make clear exactly how current systems can work together: they have been passed on to Admiral Owens's staff. Yet at the moment costly new systems with vastly increased power are simply not required; they would be only if a real possibility of a "Large Peer Conflict", as the planners put it, were on the horizon. So radical changes in the weaponry available are frankly unlikely.

The system of systems, on the other hand, could be achieved quite cheaply. It might, eventually, save a lot of money by revealing and removing redundancies among the many systems. Still, putting it together has challenges. It will cross traditional service lines and require a willingness on the part of senior staff to face up to details normally left to techno-nerds (with which the American military is well endowed). And it will mean changing the organisation of the military, and its doctrine and tactics.

Schools of history and imagination

ARMIES have always trained; Wellington's drills were bloodless battles, and his battles bloody drills. The scope of training now, though, has grown beyond belief. Tank drivers do not learn to drive in tanks; they learn in simulators. The same is true for pilots, and for most of the other people who manage complex electronics in some sort of battlewagon; and it will increasingly become so for the foot soldier of the future, beginning to rely on the head-up display mounted on his visor. As the practice of war becomes ever more synthetic, so synthetic war becomes more practical.

Simulators make training cheap and effective in an era of expensive and sometimes fragile hardware. According to Lieutenant-Colonel Bob Birmingham, of the American army's Simulation, Training and Instrumentation Command (located close to Disneyworld in Orlando, Florida), when 18 Apaches crossed the border into Iraq to fire the first American shots of the Gulf war, only three of the 36 airmen on board had fired a real Hellfire missile before. All the others had done their target practice in simulators. But they were confident they knew what to do, and they did it perfectly. The only surprises were the bright flashes of fire from the other helicopters as they launched their missiles – an effect the simulators did not incorporate. Throughout the war there were similar stories of troops that had not seen action but were well prepared for it.

But this virtual training is only part of the story. To fight imaginary battles and wars, and thus to work out how to make the best use of the abilities available, and what extra abilities are worth developing, the American military is committed to the creation of "synthetic theatres of war": multi-faceted computer networks which bring together troops in simulators on different bases around the world and troops in real exercises at places such as Fort Irwin. These real and virtual exercises are then embedded into bigger computerised war games in which commanders control their forces without knowing whether they are in real vehicles, in simulators or in the active imagination of the computers knitting it all together.

Such simulations, it is hoped, will train armies as a whole in the same way that hardware simulators now train warriors as individuals. They will also show how the capabilities available can best be used. Just as simulations allow weapons designers to trade off different qualities against each other, so they will allow the forces as a whole to re-engineer themselves. For example, they might suggest that, with highly accurate indirect fire by missiles available, forces should not be as concentrated as they now are. They might show exactly how mobile the forces can hope to become as their *Blitzkrieg* tactics evolve. They might show that the organisational structure of divisions, brigades, battalions, companies and platoons needs to be flattened out to make the best of the networking capabilities. As any financial planner bent over his spreadsheet can attest, computers make marvellously light work of showing up the complex consequences of a hypothesis. It is hypothetical wars, not real ones, that will shape doctrine in the years to come.

The art of electronic war

These simulations will give commanders their first taste of information supremacy – of knowing, or being able to know, everything about the battlespace. Wars fought with such abilities might be quite unlike today's souped-up *Blitzkriegs*. Information might do what brute force does today.

A Chinese general, Sun Tzu, who lived in the 4th century BC (making his "Art of War" the oldest as well as one of the most respected treatises on the subject), said that the greatest achievement was to destroy the enemy's strategy before it could be implemented. This had to be done in an unexpected way, with the unconventional use of "divine force", *ch'i*. The opposite of *ch'i* was the ordinary force, *cheng*. On the battlefield, *cheng* is a holding force that puts the enemy on the spot, *ch'i* a flanking manoeuvre that fatally disrupts the enemy's strategy. That is how Genghis Khan fought, and also how Norman Schwarzkopf fought.

It is now possible that information could take the place of *cheng*. Imagine two chess players, both with good memories, both blindfolded; an adjudicator tells them when their pieces are in a position to make a capture. This game, called *Kriegspiel*, was used to teach caution in Prussian war colleges. Though its rules are those of chess, its tactics are not; they are cautious and edgy. Now imagine one of the players taking off the blindfold. He can throw caution to the winds, and dispatch his adversary in instants with only a fraction of his available force. The enemy would be paralysed not by an opposing ordinary force, but by his own ignorance – frozen in the headlights that illuminate his every move.

The response is obvious: blind your opponent. The enemy's sensors and his channels of command, control and communication bear the same sort of relation to strategy as the senses and the nervous system bear to thought; they control its boundaries and its implementation. Sun Tzu would have considered the enemy's electronic nerves the perfect target; so do today's practitioners of electronic warfare.

If those channels of communication can be found in spectrum space, they can be disrupted by jamming. That is why military wireless communications, such as those which link warships in CEC, rely on spreading the message across a wide swathe of spectrum, and hopping from frequency to frequency. This may not make them invulnerable: armed forces all over the world put a lot of money into technologies that allow them to locate transmitters and to jam messages through a variety of means.

The fight takes place at every level. Aircraft can use radio or infrared to fool the missiles chasing them; high commands can use electromagnetic pulse generators delivered by cruise missile to burn out every circuit in a city. This type of conflict is peculiarly hard to model in synthetic wars, not least because the communications needed to pull the simulation together are the same as the ones that would be under attack. Live tests are also difficult, since jammers used at full power could damage equipment. Used in Fort Irwin, they could also disrupt communications 200km away in Los Angeles.

Still, testing is vital; a digital battalion that cannot communicate will be a sorry thing. So although the big digital-battalion experiment at Fort Irwin in February 1997 will abjure electronic warfare, thus implicitly favouring the wired-up newcomers against the trusty old opposing force, other much more hush-hush exercises later that year will try electronic warfare against the new force. As well as trying to disrupt communications among the troops, the electronic opposition may also try to jam the all-important navigational signals broadcast by the Global Positioning System (GPS). Many think GPS signals are relatively easy to jam. If so, then electromagnetic defences may be possible against America's next generation of precision-guided weapons, which rely largely on GPS.

Against relatively low-technology opponents, vulnerability to electronic warfare may not matter much, though a GPS jammer might be made quite easily. In the Gulf war, Iraq did not mess with even the most easily jammed of the allied frequencies. In the future, though, enemies may be quicker to go for the electronic jugular. A single nuclear weapon exploded in orbit might burn out a substantial part of America's mighty satellite systems – a sort of "scorched-spectrum" strategy.

This might in the end be a deciding factor in the style of war fought with new technologies. Some have suggested that if commanders can see everything, they will try to control everything, thus losing the advantages of local tactical autonomy. If command systems are seen to be vulnerable, the decentralisation which would offset that problem becomes even more desirable. In general, western experience with information technology points to increased decentralisation and its counterpart, a system-wide sensitivity to every particular, as widespread consequences of networking. The same may yet be true in war.

To dissolve, to disappear

A LARGE American aircraft carrier is the most impressive weapon platform ever built. In the deep oceans, it controls an area 1,000km or so across. Yet it is vulnerable. So it sails with escorts: cruisers and destroyers with the most sophisticated air-defence capabilities in the world; anti-submarine-warfare frigates; and a submarine or two of its own. The escorts are worth more than the carrier itself. And still a lucky cruise missile, or one with a nuclear tip, could put paid to the whole thing.

All concentrations of mass are increasingly vulnerable. With weapons around that can absorb and respond to a lot of data, it makes sense to keep forces as diffuse as possible. This may mean more than spreading out their current elements: those elements may be divided into their constituent parts. William Perry is one of those who suspect that some types of weapon platforms may quite soon be leaving the battlefield for some distant scrap-metal Valhalla. Some radicals suggest that all platforms have had their day.

The advantage of platforms is that they unite movement, deadliness, information-gathering and logistical requirements in a single package. The disadvantage is much the same. The need to defend platforms because they are valuable tends to make them bigger, more complex and more costly still – and thus yet more tempting as targets. And because they cost so much, they are also designed to last a long time. Tanks may last 30 years, ships 40 or 50. The new fighters currently reaching the end of development, the Eurofighter and the stealthy American F-22, could be in service well into the middle of the next century. The USS Ronald Reagan, a carrier to be commissioned in 2002, may still be in the water on the 100th anniversary of VE-day.

Meanwhile, information technology will continue to improve at a staggering rate of growth. There are limits to the number of circuits you can put on to a piece of silicon using today's technologies, and they will have been reached well before the good ship Ronnie starts to rust. But new chip-design techniques will make each circuit more effective, new software will wring ever more usefulness from a given amount of processing power, new computer design will make it easier to add the abilities of many chips together, and new packaging will make it all take up less space.

This means the weapons being pitched against the platforms will be getting smarter and smarter. Greg Canavan, a far-sighted researcher at

Los Alamos National Laboratory, suggests that on current trends the weapons of the 2030s might be roughly as bright as chickens. Chickens may not sound too fearsome. But these will be single-minded, fully net-worked hunter-killer cyberchickens – with strength in numbers. Thanks to civilian demand for smaller, quicker, better computers, they will also be relatively cheap.

The monster mesh

One possible response is to make sure that the platforms are able to take modular electronics upgrades and thus keep up; that is something Mr Perry favours. A more radical response is to keep the modules but lose the platforms: to make the battlefield into a nothing-here-but-us-chickens world of distributed smart sensors and shooters tied together by ever better communications. This is the view Martin Libicki, of America's National Defence University, takes of warfare in which pro-cessing power is in effect unconstrained. It is a world where the small and the many dominate the large and the few, in which the military network under construction today becomes far more fine-grained, with far more nodes, each far less valuable: a world in which the net becomes a mesh.

The mesh has a number of advantages. It is hard to attack, because its strength is spread widely. It is hard to damage, because there are so many communication paths. Many small sensors can provide a better picture than a few large ones. More sensors allow the information domain to conform more closely to the physical terrain. At the moment line-of-sight detection by sensors in a widespread network leaves topo-graphical blind spots – wadis, narrow valleys – in which platforms such as attack helicopters can lurk.

While nets may see through the fog of war, meshes also tackle another of the problems von Clausewitz identified: war's friction. The mesh is a war machine with almost no moving parts, save the actual warheads of the weapons. It is a solid-state device; its mechanisms have migrated far into the spectral dimension of information, leaving only a thin skeleton framework in the world of height, breadth and depth.

The amount of information in the mesh will be colossal – far too much to make sense of or seek to understand. But there will be no need to: the mesh will achieve its ends through the responses of its local elements, rather than through some top-down control. It will no more need an organising intelligence than a flock of birds does. That does not necessarily mean it will have to be totally robotic. It might well be populated by people plugged into the system, roaming the meshed landscape. A human warrior is perhaps the only platform small and intelligent enough to be viable but not hugely vulnerable in such a place.

Some pretty meshy systems are already under discussion. One example is the smart minefield, in which the mines tell each other what is going on and are able to jump up and explode above the tanks passing through. Maritime minefields and sensor-buoy networks could evolve in a similar way, though there are problems in networking under water. Perhaps the most spectacular possibility, though, is a space minefield that could ensnare intercontinental ballistic missiles.

Such mines are known as brilliant pebbles; they were thought up by Mr Canavan, Lowell Wood and Edward Teller, the latter pair at the Lawrence Livermore laboratory in California. The brilliant pebbles would be small rockets a metre or so long, with a lot of computing power and good sensors on the front end; thousands would swarm around the earth in low orbits. When their sensors picked up missile launches, the pebbles in the best position to intercept would change orbit and ram them. The responses of the individual pebbles add up to a system swinging into co-ordinated action, each segment using information from its own sensors and those of its nearby colleagues.

The advantage of this system over orbiting "battle stations" is that its strengths are widespread, not concentrated in a few costly platforms. To disable it means engaging each pebble on its own terms. Although, at present, no brilliant pebbles are being built, the idea of low-orbit swarms is gaining ground among both civilian and military satellite makers. America's next orbiting early-warning system may eventually include a little swarm of "brilliant eyes", infrared sensors that will pick up rocket launches and aircraft afterburners much more precisely than the high-orbit ones in use now. Communications satellites too are coming into low orbit as networks of smaller, cheaper satellites start to achieve what single large satellites used to. There is a lot of potential for shrinkage. Some talk of satellites 10cm across, mass-produced on silicon wafers.

Hidden glories

If such distributed systems came down from heaven to form the mesh on earth, the outlook for platforms would be dim. But there might be a way to keep them: stealth. While the mesh is almost entirely an information device, stealth tries to keep as far out of the information world as possible. Radar waves are bounced off super-smooth or faceted surfaces; structures that might focus energy are replaced by structures to diffuse it. Radar is absorbed, not reflected, and heat is spread around, removing infrared signals. Sound, too, is softened and diffused, and the whole thing is painted black.

The cumulative effect is astonishing. Before the Gulf war few were sure it would work, and some were unwilling to trust vital targets to the F-117 stealth fighters (which are actually light bombers). General Glosson, though, who was running the air-war planning, had no doubts. He had tried to track F-117s with a flight of his crack F-15 pilots at the testing range in Nevada, and had seen neither hide nor hair of them. He was pretty sure the Iraqis would not, either. One stealth pilot had any lingering doubts allayed when he noticed that dead bats were lying around his aircraft in its hangar every morning; their sonar could no more detect it than Baghdad's air defences could.

Stealth is not magic, though; it is a set of technologies that has a cumulative effect, and a few tactics that help them along. Pilots can minimise the risk of being detected through their flight path; stealth aircraft have "best angles" for stealthiness just as actresses have best angles for the camera, and make a point of showing only those angles to enemy air defences. It does not make them invisible; just a lot less likely to be seen.

At the moment, stealth looks like a good way of slipping through today's nets, if not tomorrow's meshes, and thus safeguarding the economies and synergies of platforms. A B-2 stealth bomber, for example, may be an excellent and cheap tool for carrying out some precision strikes, using weapons with brains but no real legs right on top of a target. A small number could obliterate moving tank divisions from bases halfway around the world, using bombs much cheaper than smart long-distance missiles. The expense of such stand-off weapons, each of which must have its own propulsion and guidance, keeps stockpiles low; America has still not replaced all the expensive precision-guided missiles it used in the Gulf.

Fragmentation displays

At the moment America has a huge lead in stealth, with two types of aircraft operational and one more almost developed – the F-22, a fighter so sophisticated that many see it as overkill. Also in development are the fairly stealthy Comanche helicopter, and Tier 3-minus, an unmanned reconnaissance aircraft. In the secret recesses of the budget there is probably even more. No one else has anything similar; experts in America and Europe feel that, for countries such as Britain and France, a truly stealthy aircraft would take a decade to develop and eat up almost all the procurement budget.

That is the problem. Expensive as smart long-distance missiles may be, a B-2 is 1,000 times more expensive still. The technologies needed for stealth are almost always expensive and often unique. As information processing gets generically better, stealth must get better too; but whereas the military information processor gets improvement for free from civilian markets, the stealth engineer must pay for it all out of his own budget. In the end, the information gatherer should triumph over the information hider.

Stealth is a matter of tactics as well as technology, though; even a findable stealth platform can have advantages. The quietness of a submarine means that a specially adapted torpedo can mimic one easily, thus confusing attacking torpedoes. The same would apply to stealthy aircraft confusing radars with little UAVs, or surface ships, such as France's sort-of-stealthy Lafayette and Sweden's Smyge, which could be mimicked by fairly small decoys. Decoys and electronic countermeasures will transform stealth from a way of withholding information to a way of spreading disinformation. Eventually, though, this will become self-defeating. With so many decoys around, you are half-way to building a mesh; why not arm each of them, and forget about the thing you are trying to hide?

To go

If the mesh is triumphant, the principles of warfare will change. One analogy for the change is the difference between the games of chess and go. In chess, the different pieces have different characteristics. Go has uniform pieces whose characteristics depend purely on their position. Chess pieces move; go pieces do not. Chess lends itself to a relatively simple, focused strategy; Nigel Short, a British grandmaster, sums it up with the term TDF – trap, dominate and finish off – though his locution for the F is a little more brutal. Go lends itself to a less emphatic approach. Chess is a game of plans; go is a game of patterns.

Wholesale conversion to mesh war may be unlikely, unless a pressing need appears. The military nets will, in the near future, thicken into meshes only in places and at times where it seems particularly necessary. Whether or not the mesh is built, though, it has value as a thought experiment.

Because commercial and personal decisions about technology are rarely made with eyes focused more than a decade or so ahead – not least because the pace of change reduces more distant prospects to a blur – few look as far into the future as soldiers have to. In 50 years, all sorts of systems outside the realm of the military might be as thoroughly embedded in the information world as the mesh would be; future worlds may be as different from today's as the platformless mesh is from contemporary war. These new worlds may offer whole new arenas of conflict far from any traditional battlefield. However, before discussing them, it is necessary to look at something altogether more immediate: the Bomb.

On not being the Duke of Sung

THE Duke of Sung's ministers urged him to attack the advancing Ch'u army while it was crossing the river to get to the field of battle. He refused. They pleaded with him to attack the Ch'u before they were ready, and he rebuked them. "The sage does not attack the feeble," said the duke, "nor does he give the order for attack until the enemy have formed their ranks." The duke lost.

"We are not the Duke of Sung," Mao Zedong would occasionally aphorise 2,600 years later. He and his army avoided battle, and tried never to let opportunities for initiative slip away. Mao did not play fair, but he won. In power, he looked for new ways to win without battles, and found one of the best. As he said to André Malraux: "All I need is six bombs. Then no one will touch me."

Iraq's Duke-of-Sung-like willingness to allow America and its allies time to build their supply bases, map their routes, programme their missiles and then conduct a set-piece battle is not likely to be replicated. Fighting conventional wars against America's perceived vital interests is now spectacularly dangerous. And although new technologies will largely be available to all, the skills needed to integrate them into military systems are not easily or quickly won. Innovative challenges to the West on the battlefield should not be expected soon.

Still, no one has to be the Duke of Sung. America and its allies are clearly vulnerable to attacks off the field of battle – notably terrorist and insurgent attacks on the will to fight, the most fundamental level of "softwar". They are also vulnerable to nuclear attack. Everyone is.

There are various reactions to this vulnerability. The Americans are once again talking about anti-missile defences, both for troops in the theatre and for the nation as a whole; there is European interest, too. The Nuclear Non-Proliferation Treaty (NPT) has been extended indefinitely, preserving the established nuclear order. And America has launched a "counter-proliferation initiative", recently championed by John Deutch, formerly America's deputy secretary of defence and now director of the Central Intelligence Agency.

Counter-proliferation has many forms, ranging from vigorous surveillance to military pre-emption. Its purpose is to extend the number of opportunities for intervention. It looks at all the points at which it might be possible to get involved – the launch site, the weapons-making, the acquisition of materials, the conception of a nuclear strategy – and tries to find appropriate interventions for each of them.

Gerald Yonas, once the chief scientist for the "star wars" programme and proud possessor of an SDI GUY car licence-plate, has looked at the military aspects of counter-proliferation in his present role as a director of research at Sandia National Laboratories. The aim, he says, is to make proliferation a steep slope: hard to climb up, easy to back down. Information supremacy will provide the gradient.

Take a confrontation with a newly nuclear state. As the situation worsened, something not unlike the mesh could be put in place, a network of sensors to provide "exquisite situational awareness", identifying production facilities, storage sites and the actual missiles on their mobile transporters. The proliferator, aware that this much was known about him – and it would be made clear – would find it ever harder to go on. If he continued, then, in Mr Yonas's scenario, he would be subjected to a surgical "counterforce" strike of highly precise, extremely fast missiles, launched from a distance. The weapons of mass destruction and, if it was thought appropriate, those who might have used them would be destroyed, but very little other damage would be done. Going back would still be easy; going forward all but unthinkable.

Playing the percentages

All this is a long way from today's capabilities. Mr Canavan at Los Alamos recalls that people first began to consider long-range precision strikes on moving targets 20 years ago, and suggests that in 20 years' time such strikes may actually be possible. At present they are not. The 1,000 missions flown against mobile Scud launchers in western Iraq appear to have yielded no kills. Even targeting fixed nuclear installations was difficult in the Gulf. Of the eight nuclear facilities identified when the war started, two were major targets; a third, discovered during the war, was also badly damaged. After the war the UN inspectors in Iraq found 26 nuclear sites, 16 of which were considered "main facilities". "Humint" – the wonderfully depersonalising word for spies – might have found them, but the systems actually used did not.

This record can be improved, but not perfected. The same applies to missile defence. The Patriots launched against Iraq's Scuds provided patchy cover at best. Better American systems are now on the way, and America is co-operating with Europe and Israel on other defences. If plugged into a network that provided very accurate knowledge of the incoming missiles' trajectories, such systems and their successors might try to protect countries. At the moment, they are intended to defend armies in the theatre, and carrier battle-groups.

But trying to hit warheads as they come down will always be difficult. The warheads may be small, and surrounded by decoys. They can manoeuvre. They are moving at 5km a second. Even if they are hit and damaged, they will still fall on the defender. By contrast, a rising missile is a relatively appealing target. It is all in one piece, it gives off a nice bright infrared signature, and it is still picking up speed. It is also still over the enemy's territory, which means the warhead never goes near the defender. But how do you get at it?

The best bases for boost-phase intercepts will be air- or space-borne. Possibilities include a fast missile launched from a circling F-14 or F-15 or from a long-range UAV. More futuristically, you might use an airborne laser. Since today's most powerful lasers are big and rough, they need big platforms; if America's air force goes ahead with a prototype, it will put it on a jumbo jet, creating an extremely big and valuable target with no hope of stealth and a need for an escorting fleet of fighters and strike aircraft. If such flying dreadnoughts are not expensive enough, add a swarm of brilliant pebbles, too. It will still not be a perfect defence. No military system currently hits 100% of its targets; very likely none ever will. And, for nuclear deterrence to work, you really need only a small risk that one warhead will get through.

Virtual nuclear pluralism

To be a nuclear state, you need fissile materials – plutonium or enriched uranium. You also need a reliable design for a weapon and probably an arsenal, though that can be quite small. By these criteria, the world at present has five official nuclear-weapons states – America, Russia, Britain, France and China – plus three unofficially acknowledged ones – Israel, Pakistan and India – and four states that have recently become, or are about to become, ex-nuclear – South Africa, Ukraine, Belarus and Kazakhstan. Around the world, people worry about the list lengthening.

Martin van Creveldt, in his book "Nuclear Proliferation and the Future of Conflict" (Free Press, 1993), suggests that such worries may be misplaced. His argument is that nuclear weapons make people cautious and careful, whether or not they are superpowers. He points out that, in each region where they have been introduced, they have in effect abolished large-scale interstate conflict. This influence might now be expected to extend to all of the Asian "Rimlands", the sites of most big conflicts since the end of the second world war (see chart 4).

This does not mean an end to all war. Nuclear states occasionally

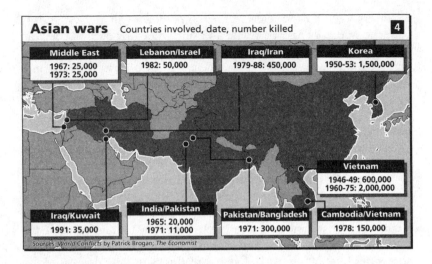

Asian wars Countries involved, date, number killed   4

Middle East	Lebanon/Israel	Iraq/Iran	Korea
1967: 25,000 1973: 25,000	1982: 50,000	1979-88: 450,000	1950-53: 1,500,000

			Vietnam
			1946-49: 600,000 1960-75: 2,000,000

Iraq/Kuwait	India/Pakistan	Pakistan/Bangladesh	Cambodia/Vietnam
1991: 35,000	1965: 20,000 1971: 11,000	1971: 300,000	1978: 150,000

Sources: *World Conflicts* by Patrick Brogan; *The Economist*

attack non-nuclear ones, as Panama and Lebanon know. Non-nuclear states sometimes feel able to attack nuclear ones, too, if they calculate that their target will accept a moderate loss. Thus in 1973 Syria and Egypt attempted to relieve Israel of the Sinai and the Golan, and in 1982 Argentina tried to grab the Falklands. Non-states, which are immune to the nuclear threat, will fight anyone: the mujaheddin against the Soviet Union, the Vietcong against America. But the spread of nuclear peace does seem to mean that the "softwar" of deterrence has proliferated in step with the "hardwar" of nuclear weaponry. Some strategists dismiss fears that "rogue regimes" such as Iraq's will ignore the logic of deterrence as thinly disguised racism.

Nuclear proliferation may not necessarily put a complete stop to large wars between states. If the Americans were able to ignore Russian nuclear weapons in planning a conventional defence of Europe, then similar acts of denial would surely be possible elsewhere. And deterrence may not always work. Its chances of working may be improved if nuclear weapons, too, retreat from the physical world into a virtual world, losing some immediacy but little power. The Indian and Pakistani deterrents are already more notional than numerical. Britain and France might move the same way, and in America there is talk of "virtual abolition", in which the know-how is treated as the arsenal.

An opposite process of "virtual proliferation" is already going on. States such as Canada, Belgium and Japan are technically able to proliferate with ease. They could, if they wished to, just pull out of the NPT and use their plutonium, computing power and aerospace industries to go nuclear. It would take less than a year if they wanted to do it. By 2030, technically advanced countries might be permanently perched days from a bomb, even though they had never tried to proliferate.

Unless plutonium is removed from the international economy – and even that might not work – a world of virtual nuclear pluralism is unavoidable. It would not, however, need to be a world with any real nuclear weapons, or any intention by governments of using them. The more intractable problem may be the non-states. In rich societies the means of proliferation are in private hands. Big construction companies with experience in nuclear power could already build their own nuclear weapons. In time these abilities will trickle down. And the logic of deterrence does not apply to organisations without a centre open to attack – organisations linked together by bonds of belief, not necessity; by networks, not nationality. These may be the enemies the world has most cause to fear.

The ties that bind

ONCE upon a time, revolutionaries would promise you heaven on earth. These days, all they are willing to commit themselves to is a new paradigm. Pressed on what that paradigm might be, the military revolutionaries will, at some time, offer the phrase "information warfare".

Information warfare has as many meanings as it has proponents, detractors and observers. Most of what has been discussed in this survey is information warfare to someone. Air-power theorists see it on the wings of Desert Storm; tank commanders see it in the American army's Force XXI; simulator designers see it in their virtual experiences; computer visionaries see it in the mesh; and strategic-war planners see it as a way to lay waste to whole societies. Information-war studies are proliferating within the American armed forces almost as quickly as the networks that carry them from desktop to desktop.

The confusing panoply stems from the fact that the information revolution, whether it is in uniform or in mufti, relies on the latest technologies to do the oldest things. Thus it is always a peculiar mixture of the familiar and the shockingly new. In that war is about strategies, command and morale, it has always been about information. All war is information war, and so every aspect of fighting wars in the information age can be called "information warfare" by someone.

If information warfare means something new, it is the use of information as a substitute for traditional ways of fighting, rather than as an adjunct to them. This survey ends by looking at three ways in which that might be achieved: by the high-technology equivalent of brute force; by subversion; and by a new form of deterrence.

Shoot not to kill

In the past few years, non-lethal weaponry has become voguish in America. Among the motley array of would-be and some-day weapons the term refers to – guns that shoot rags and foam, blinding lights and sickening sounds – information weapons have pride of place. Subtler than electronic warfare, this form of information warfare seeks to get inside the enemy's collective head and wreak havoc, quickly and bloodlessly, through the application of intelligence (in all its senses) and disinformation.

In the past such things were possible; but in this respect, information technology has made the present and the foreseeable future fundamentally unlike the past. Encoding messages is tedious and time-consuming, but relatively simple, and so computers do it with ease. Breaking codes is far, far harder. The result is that, today, a modest piece of circuitry can be used to encode a digital message in ways that no supercomputer can fathom. Nor are the codebreakers likely to catch up; the codemaker's advantage is endlessly renewable. Every time the code is made a little more complex, the resources needed to break it increase enormously. Unless there is a fundamental mathematical, or possibly physical, breakthrough in computing, uncrackable codes are here to stay.

Many countries are looking at making unbreakable codes illegal. However, it is a fair bet that prohibitions will not apply to those countries' security forces. Despite the efforts of the American government to restrict their export, good encryption technologies are already widely available, and better ones – easier to implement, yet harder to crack – are not too hard to come up with. So anyone with moderate means and a serious need for secrecy can now get what is required. That is good for armies trying to keep their information secure, and bad for those who want to tap into it; it is good for insurgents, terrorists and criminals, as well as for all law-abiding people who want to make sure that their privacy is kept sacred; it is bad for snooping governments, be they on the side of the angels or the devil.

If you cannot subvert the enemy's information flow, you can perhaps destroy it. This is another suggested mode of information war; destroying information systems with weapons of pure information, such as computer viruses. Such weapons might attack stock exchanges, or utility grids, or telephone networks, or all of the above, as well as purely military targets. Again, information warfare seems to provide impressive powers, allowing victory without a shot fired in anger. Again, things are not so simple.

Viruses and logic bombs can doubtless do great damage under some circumstances. Destruction, though, is not enough. Predicting the effects of a hacker attack on a complex set of computer systems would be next to impossible; so would assessing exactly what damage had been done. A weapon with unknown effects and unknown collateral damage would not be acceptable in an arsenal which, in all other respects, is being made ever more precise. And even a hugely successful first strike by hackers – one with severe economic consequences – would be unlikely to destroy the victim's ability for military reprisal.

Hacker war is not a particularly good offensive strategy for America and the West, and certainly not an alternative to the allies' conventional (or for that matter nuclear) military capability. It might, though, according to some, be a powerful weapon against them – wielded by enemies of all shapes and sizes, from within and without. America, Europe and Japan provide "target-rich environments" for such attacks. And the drawbacks to hacker war would matter less if a non-state, rather than a state, were waging it. If the aim is relatively modest – and terrorists tend to keep the size of their actions limited, so as not to provoke too strong a response – imprecision may not matter so much. Hacker attacks are appealingly frugal, since they need little more than a highly gifted programmer and a good computer. There is no evidence that an army of hackers is much better than the single best hacker, given enough time. And time is not a problem. Low-intensity conflicts are normally low-frequency conflicts too.

Martin Libicki, of the National Defence University, plays down such worries. Defences against such attacks are not too difficult to arrange in well-run networks; and the people who run those networks are capable of putting up those defences without any special impetus from governments. They already do, and as more of them experience the damage computer criminals can inflict, more of them will tighten their security appropriately. Governments are simply not fully sovereign in the world of information; their powers within it are strangely limited. In the end the protection that is put up privately against criminals will in all likelihood also be a protection against terrorists and enemy powers, which would have little advantage over criminals in such situations.

This weakness of government control within computer nets – a product of strongly protected privacy, a lack of frontiers and confusions of jurisdiction – make them natural places for subversion. Any insurrectionist or terrorist who is not working out how to turn modern communications to his aims is not doing his job. Any Leninist worth his salt would have given up half the cadres in his cumbersome cells for the communication systems now readily available.

A continuation of antipolitics by other means

This does not necessarily translate into military advantage. Although a guerrilla force with good communications is undoubtedly better off than one without, the growing capabilities of organised armies may well offset such advantages, if governments are willing and able to employ them. Though encrypted digital communications cannot be tapped, if they are wireless they can be traced. And the high-flying observation systems that can help on the battlefield can help in most other places, too, though cities pose problems for them. The information advantage conferred by a set of observation systems should be enough to keep an irregular enemy dispersed, since to gather is to provide a target. And a dispersed but visible enemy can be tackled bit by bit.

But it is not necessarily a purely military advantage that guerrillas, freedom fighters and other sorts of non-state warriors need. They have always fought information wars, wars of the heart and mind as well as of the eye and arm. And network-building offers them new ways to do that. David Ronfeldt of RAND, a Los Angeles think-tank, and his colleague Michael Arquilla, now at the Naval Postgraduate School in Monterey, have distinguished between battlefield information warfare of the sort that might be used against insurgents by a high-technology opponent – which they call cyberwar – and the sort of information strategies that such insurgents might themselves employ. These they call netwar; but what they mean by that hardly looks like war at all.

As an example, Mr Ronfeldt points to the Zapatists, Mexico's southern rebels. Their leader, Subcomandante Marcos, his pipe poking through his bandana, his laptop plugged into the cigarette lighter of his jeep, talks a lot more than he fights. His messages go to specific sympathisers, to local newspapers, to bulletin boards on all sorts of computer networks. This may not be as dramatic as taking territory, but it provides some clout.

Mr Ronfeldt says that when the Mexican government launched a counter-insurgency campaign against the rebels, the networked Zapatists quickly marshalled international support from non-governmental organisations. Observers were sent and fusses made. The government campaign staggered to a halt. Networked co-ordination turned a wide range of interest groups – development consultants, environmental activists, workers'-rights advocates, women's groups – into a powerful force. Patching such lobbies together provided the rebels with the strength of their own "system of systems". It was not necessary to get a vast army to share an ideology; all that was needed was to share an idea, promptly, that mattered to a lot of people.

C'est ni magnifique, ni la guerre; but it is an attempt to change politics, and by other means. In fact, it fits neatly into the notion of "antipolitics" developed by George Konrad, a Hungarian writer, in his book of the same name (translated by R. Allen, Quartet, 1984) and influential throughout Eastern Europe in the 1980s:

> *What I have in mind is not some kind of anarchic, romantic rising; the time for that is long past ... The most effective way to influence policy is by changing a society's customary thinking patterns and tacit compacts.*

It is by bringing together different interests quickly, and offering them opportunities to change those thinking patterns, that information technology may make its greatest contribution to struggles against the status quo.

The condition of liberty

Against well-connected, internationalised antipolitics, it is the legitimacy and effectiveness of government that matters, not any information advantage that its armed forces may enjoy. There are other areas of military powerlessness, too. The limits on counter-terrorism tend to be more political and social than technological; new information technologies will marginally favour the terrorist. Another limit is not knowing what, if anything, you can do – an obvious point, but one that is still worth stressing. The reason why Bosnia has been a low-technology war is that no one with high-technology weapons has made a serious attempt at winning it. That is because nobody with such weapons has any clear idea of what desirable result their military action might achieve. No information technology will solve that.

It is when wars have not yet begun, or just ended, that information systems can come into their own. At Sandia National Laboratories, there is a small but promising experiment that hopes to show the way. The co-operative monitoring centre there seeks to make available in today's trouble-spots monitoring technologies and procedures acquired in the cold war. It hopes to see potential adversaries build up monitoring networks – procedures, people and remote instruments – that allay the fears which might otherwise pit them against each other. Already, the centre has brought Israelis and Arabs together to play simulated monitoring "peace games" on their computer screens.

The ideal would be to set up such systems before disputes first turn into wars, rather than after a long series of them. Reducing the possibility of the surprise attack would make a lot of wars more difficult to start. This could be done locally or regionally, by establishing monitoring zones; but it could also be done globally. "Spacecast 2020", a far-sighted (and in parts far-fetched) American report into the future of military space, produced in 1994, presented as a primary goal the creation around the earth of an "infosphere": a system of satellite sensors that provides real-time monitoring on many wavelengths. The infosphere would build on today's photo-reconnaissance capabilities, infrared missile-launch detectors, proposed radar satellites and so on to give the American military a god's-eye view of the world in real time.

That view could be shared. At first, perhaps, it would be done surreptitiously, on a case-by-case basis, to allies in need of an information edge – rather as America's satellites helped Britain in the Falklands war. Before too long, though, much of the infosphere will come to be a widely shared resource, rather as the Global Positioning System already is. It will, after all, be largely civilian – weather satellites, medium-resolution imaging systems, world-wide air-traffic-control networks; and the communications to link them all will not be primarily military. In a world with an infosphere that allows threats to be remarked upon, not just by soldiers and diplomats, but also by companies, by the media, by non-governmental organisations of all sorts, even by antipoliticians and netwarriors, one can imagine a certain sort of stability becoming the endlessly renegotiated norm.

To know all is not to deter all, any more than it is to forgive all. But it is to be better prepared, and to have at least the rudiments of wisdom at your disposal. It is perhaps the oddest aspect of the information revolution that, if circumstances are arranged correctly, information can be shared without being devalued. Indeed, sharing can be the only way to know what others know. Controlling information matters a lot, almost as much as knowing how to use it, which is the key to everything. But control is not simply denial. The military revolution turns on information; but so does peace.

THIS SURVEY ON DEFENCE TECHNOLOGY WAS FIRST PUBLISHED IN
THE ECONOMIST ON JUNE 10TH 1995

8

THE FUTURE OF MEDICINE

The business of medical care is under attack from all sides.
Luckily, new technologies are set to transform medicine,
eradicate most disease and hugely improve people's health

ALEXANDRA WYKE

New anatomy lesson, please

THE medical world is in a sorry state. Doctors and hospitals complain that they cannot satisfy what has become an unlimited demand for medical care. Medical breakthroughs are quickly taken for granted; eager patients soon want more. Even with the best available therapy, many sufferers are provided with only partial solutions. Some are left permanently disabled, unable to cope with everyday life. Meanwhile, such ordinary illnesses as the common cold remain virtually untreatable. And everywhere cash shortages are biting; patients grumble because they have to wait for treatment or because they get no treatment at all. The world is crying out for more, and better, medicine.

Since the discovery in the late 1930s of drugs that could kill bacteria, modern medicine has burgeoned into a multi-trillion-dollar business. With a few exceptions, doctors had been mostly powerless before antibiotics. They may have been adept at diagnosis, spotting a disease among a hotch-potch of complaints; or at prognosis, guessing what might happen to patients as a result of illness; but they could offer little in the way of treatment. Antibiotics changed all that. And explosive technological development after 1940 gave the medical profession enormous new powers to fight disease and sickness. Patients duly put their health care into the hands of these omnipotent doctors who, encouraged by medical manufacturers, prescribed liberally.

Yet there is, surprisingly, little or no evidence that modern doctors, pills or surgery have improved people's overall state of health. The increase in Americans' average life expectancy from 63 years in 1940 to 76 today (see chart 1) has been ascribed more to increased wealth, better sanitation, nutrition and housing, and the widespread introduction of the refrigerator than to modern medicine.

In 1992 the World Health Organisation (WHO) concluded that the world's population is not getting any healthier. The WHO study showed that people are reporting more frequent and longer-lasting episodes of serious and acute illness than they did 60 years ago. The world is still plagued by a string of nasty diseases, many of which afflict the growing elderly populations of richer countries. As for antibiotics, even they have become an overworked remedy. They may have saved millions of lives since they first appeared 50 years ago; but today some infectious diseases that were once curable no longer respond to treatment. Tuberculosis is reappearing in America and Europe because doctors have

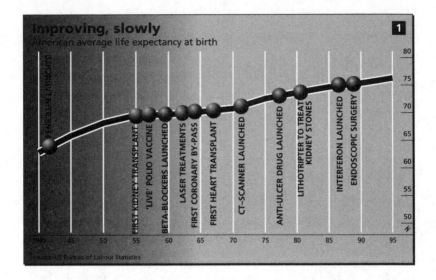

improving, slowly
American average life expectancy at birth

Labels (left to right): PENICILLIN LAUNCHED · FIRST KIDNEY TRANSPLANT · 'LIVE' POLIO VACCINE · BETA-BLOCKERS LAUNCHED · LASER TREATMENTS · FIRST CORONARY BY-PASS · FIRST HEART TRANSPLANT · CT-SCANNER LAUNCHED · ANTI-ULCER DRUG LAUNCHED · LITHOTRIPTER TO TREAT KIDNEY STONES · INTERFERON LAUNCHED · ENDOSCOPIC SURGERY

Y-axis: 50 · 55 · 60 · 65 · 70 · 75 · 80
X-axis: 1940 · 45 · 50 · 55 · 60 · 65 · 70 · 75 · 80 · 85 · 90 · 95

Source: US Bureau of Labour Statistics

dished out antibiotics too carelessly, giving bacteria an opportunity to evolve drug-resistant strains.

The problem is not confined to rich countries. The burden of sickness is growing in poor countries, too, as populations explode, new diseases like AIDS take their toll, and heart disease and cancers strike those who manage to survive beyond middle age. After childhood disease, heart disease and cancer are the biggest killers in poor countries. Not surprisingly, the WHO thinks there is still considerable scope for the discovery of new drugs and medical techniques.

Mindful of their previous shortcomings, scientists have taken up the challenge: to discover effective medical products. The financial rewards, they know, could be huge; health care is one of the world's biggest industries. Luckily, too, they have new technological tools at their disposal. Biotechnology, faster and smarter computers, telecommunications and robotics are coming together to transform health care. New products are rolling out of laboratories at breathtaking speed. Here is some idea of what may be to come.

There will be drugs for hitherto untreatable diseases. There will be easy-to-use medical tests that predict a person's prospective state of health throughout his lifetime so steps can be taken to prevent diseases. There will be surgical robots operating with a precision that puts their human counterparts to shame. Doctors, nurses, hospitals and manufacturers will all be linked through a network of computers, telephones, optical fibres and satellite link-ups that a patient can plug into. The entire health-care business will be automated and closely monitored for cost and efficiency.

There will be more careful assessment of the benefits of medical treatment. Such benefits are obvious for procedures like mending broken bones, removing eye cataracts, or treating ulcers or bacterial infections. But the value of many other present-day treatments remains obscure; indeed, in many cases, no proper study of their effects on health has ever been done. And even when treatments can offer temporary help – such as removing a blood clot from a heart-attack victim – there is little change in a patient's underlying complaint, so that he stands a good chance of falling sick from the same disease again. In the meantime the surgery or pills that he has been given may have had harmful and not always well-monitored side-effects.

The new generation of medical products will change this by making it easier to measure health outcomes. Surgery will be less intrusive, less painful and safer. In some cases it will be performed without the knife. Patients will recover more quickly and need less hospital care. As for drugs, biotechnology will re-engineer them from mere palliatives into full-scale cures that tackle not just the ills of rich countries but those of poorer countries too.

These innovations have come at a good time for health-care businesses. In the past decade governments, insurers and employers in all rich countries have realised that they can no longer pay health-care bills that were growing enormously as populations became older and more demanding (see chart 2). In 20 years' time the proportion of most rich countries' populations aged 65 and over will have doubled to around 20–25%. Old people today consume a third of total health spending; the way things are going, by 2000 they will be consuming half.

Those who finance health care – ie, governments and insurance companies – are responding by demanding more information about the cost, effectiveness and quality of the services they are buying. They increasingly want health care to be "managed" – that is, delivered for a prepaid fee. They hope that this will get rid of medical tests and operations that are unnecessary; and persuade doctors to prescribe only the most cost-effective drugs or surgical procedures. New technologies may help. Computerisation will provide more information with which to manage costs. Even on the medical level, though many new technologies will be expensive, they will yield offsetting savings by reducing the

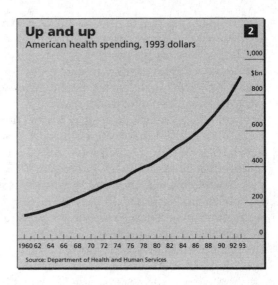

Up and up
American health spending, 1993 dollars

Source: Department of Health and Human Services

need for hospitals, doctors and nurses.

The movement of most health-care systems towards managed care is clear, especially in America, where well over half the privately insured are now enrolled in managed-care plans. The Clinton administration's plan to reform America's health-care system through the creation of large health alliances that choose mainly among competing managed-care plans will be a further boost – if Congress adopts it, or something like it. Those who have made a fat living from America's bloated health-care system are certainly resigned to change. (See Postscript on page 263.)

The "Hillary factor", as some American circles have dubbed the change of mood in the health-care market, has already prompted insurers, hospitals, doctors and medical suppliers to regroup into health-care networks offering one-stop shopping for patients. According to David Vandewater, chief operating officer of Columbia Healthcare, a hospital chain based in Louisville, Kentucky: "The strategy at Columbia is to establish a provider network, where we can offer anything the patient needs, be it diagnoses or skilled nursing facilities, not just hospitals." Sir Richard Sykes, chief executive of Glaxo, a British drug firm, agrees: "Ultimately Glaxo will have to manoeuvre itself from drug firm to health-care concern, from Glaxo to Glaxocare."

Throughout America competitive medical networks, whose success will be determined by their performance, efficiency and cost, are springing up. Every business in the health-care market is entering part-

237

nerships by acquisition or through alliances to deliver a comprehensive health service. Columbia Healthcare merged with Galen Health Care and HCA, increasing the number of hospitals under its umbrella from 21 to 192. Columbia is also forging new associations with nursing homes and health maintenance organisations (HMOs), the flagships of managed care, which offer health services in return for a flat fee. Merck, the world's biggest drug company at the time, paid $6 billion for Medco, a drug distributor. Merck made the acquisition after it concluded that the days of traditional pill manufacturers flogging their wares to gullible doctors were numbered.

In Europe too, managed care is arriving. Holland is shaking up its social-insurance system to introduce it. Germany is trying to inject more competition into the 1,000-plus sickness funds that insure most of its population. In Britain the government has created an "internal market" under which providers compete for business from purchasers. It is now pushing most general practitioners towards "fund-holding", which would give them set budgets out of which to pay for most hospital services and drugs for patients on their lists. Fund-holders are already proving effective at shopping around for the best and cheapest care. That is forcing hospitals to vie for doctors' business; many have appointed special sales representatives to plead their case on the basis of high-quality service or bargain deals.

Thanks to these changes, drug firms and other health-care suppliers, all of them under fire for making excessive profits on useless products, will become more dependent on R&D to produce new products. Doctors will have to demonstrate, with the help of computers, that their work is cost-efficient. Hospitals will be encouraged to treat more people as out-patients or even at home to curb health-care costs. In 1993 one in three hospital beds in America were empty each day.

Robotics and other new technologies are now poised to accelerate change – rapidly enough to come as a shock to many patients, let alone to the producers who will have to alter their ways. This survey offers a tour through some of the world's industrial and academic laboratories in order to spotlight the huge changes that technology is about to impose on health care – and their consequences.

Automating health care

SHINY machines may clutter doctors' surgeries and hospital wards, but when it comes to exploiting the information revolution health care is still in the Dark Ages. In the medical world communication means doctors writing (often illegibly) on scraps of paper that are stored in filing cabinets to be forgotten or lost. Consultants, junior doctors, nurses, pharmacists and even managers crowd around hospital beds, but their association with each other stops outside the ward. Family doctors practising outside hospitals rarely meet their peers inside. One result is unnecessary duplication. Today's health budgets are too tight to support such haphazard and wasteful practice.

Health-care systems are creaking under the growing mounds of documents, facts and figures they need to store and process. The mounds are becoming mountains as insurers and governments clamour for evidence that doctors do any good. Meanwhile doctors are finding it hard to absorb ever more information. An average American doctor spends nine hours a week educating himself. And for most doctors, integrating data generated in each hospital on each patient and applying the knowledge gained from reading journals has become an art as much as a science. The information can often be conflicting and few doctors have any idea how to resolve such conflicts.

Enter, belatedly, the computer. By becoming doctors' helpmates they can manage medical data, combine information sources and advise on trade-offs using something more than enlightened guesswork. Plummeting computer prices combined with rapid increases in computer power are allowing the development of information systems that can satisfy most doctors' needs at affordable prices. Paul Clayton, who is introducing an information system at Columbia Presbyterian Medical Centre, in New York city, reckons that within a decade all the data generated about the 50,000 in-patients admitted each year to his hospital and its 800,000 out-patient visits will be storable on magnetic disks for $63,000 – or on optical disks for as little as $4,500. Already it is cheaper to store information on optical disks than on paper.

As computers become more mobile and smaller – with desktop workstations miniaturised into mobile clip-boards or dictating-machines – the risk of their physically intruding on a doctor's dealings with patients will decrease. According to Ifay Chang at IBM's Thomas J. Watson Research Centre, in Yorktown Heights, New York city, computers already deliver information in the integrated form that doctors require. Systems allowing people at different sites to collaborate via computers have already been designed. Computers should soon allow a surgeon sitting in Minneapolis to operate by proxy on a patient thousands of miles away.

Modern methods of compressing huge amounts of data will permit complex pieces of information, such as x-rays or even moving pictures of a surgical operation, to be sent across long distances via satellites or fibre-optic cable. High-definition television can provide imagery good enough for diagnoses that require subtle differences of colour or tone. The multimedia revolution will let medics and patients write to, talk to and see each other simultaneously.

Hospitals have already largely automated the prescription of drugs. A start has been made on a global medical database. The electronic Internet has helped patients to make contact with, and perhaps learn from, fellow sufferers. Several small firms now sell do-it-yourself diagnosis software that can run on most consumers' personal computers. Bigger changes loom ahead: notably the electronic storage of all medical records with systems that facilitate access, retrieval and information-sharing. That should provide enough information for computerised clinical decision-making to become the norm. Managed-care information systems will generate (and update) the value-for-money appraisals that insurers and governments now demand. They will also help doctors to take the right decisions.

Some doctors may not like the notion of machines monitoring their performance. But patients and those paying health-care bills will benefit hugely. Information technology should speed up delivery so that surgical waiting lists or hanging about in out-patient departments become things of the past. On the clinical side, even if information technology does no more than identify useless and unnecessary treatment, it could save lots of money.

A poor medical record

The writing and collection of patient records has changed little in response to the computer age, as doctors have been reluctant to abandon paper for electronics. The first generation of electronic medical-record systems required some computer know-how. InterPractice Systems, a joint venture between EDS (a subsidiary of General Motors created by Ross Perot) and Harvard Community Health Plan, a health-maintenance organisation, installed a mini computer in 1988 at a health centre in Burlington, Massachusetts. The system stores all the information on the centre's 8,000 patients, from the minute they walk into reception. The centre's 15 doctors each need a powerful Apple computer, however; terminals have also been installed in the examination room.

Computerised record-keeping systems will become simpler. Stanford University's Medical Computer Science Laboratory, among others, has compressed data collection down to a portable pen-based computer for roaming doctors that can store a complete set of patient records. When the computer "reads" what seem to be illegible scribblings, it flashes up on the screen its guesses of what was written. The system has graphics and a palette of 256 different colours, so doctors can draw the anatomy of the abdomen, say, and show where a pain is being felt. Most important, the electronic pad can communicate with a central computer, which is continuously updated with information entered by doctors wherever they are.

As patient records become digitised they also become easier to process. Clinical information systems (the most elementary form of data-processing designed to give patient data to those who need it) are spreading fast through hospitals and doctors' surgeries. IBM and Kaiser Permanente, America's largest HMO, are testing one such system in Colorado. Digitised patient records are shared through an information network among all of Kaiser's 400 doctors, employed in 17 health clinics. Eventually the electronic network will be linked to local chemists' shops, to laboratories and to hospitals, all of which will feed data into the system. Hewlett-Packard, DEC and AT&T are among other companies working on similar networks.

Multimedia can do more than computerise records. Linda Tetzlaff of IBM's Thomas J. Watson Research Centre is developing a system for parents who look after young children with leukaemia. A computer set up at home answers such questions as how to give drugs; what to do if the child has a seizure; or simply what a seizure is. The answers are given in writing, orally or on screen. There is an interactive link with a doctor in the clinic, who is kept up to date whenever a parent logs on with trickier queries that the computer cannot answer.

This kind of computer doctor can be "intelligent". The Imperial Cancer Research Fund in London is developing a system that signals whenever patients are allergic to particular drugs; and another that keeps track of recent reports on medical practice or changes in clinical guidelines. Stephen Pauker of Tufts University in Massachusetts is working on a system that looks at awkward clinical choices, such as whether somebody who has just had a heart attack should be operated on, whether to carry out a coronary by-pass operation on a patient who has cancer or the risks to a fetus if a pregnant woman with cancer is given radiation therapy.

Lots of gadgets are being developed to improve the quality of patient records and the information that can be extracted from them. Some feed directly into the health-care electronic network. Biocircuits of Sunnyvale, California, is testing a desktop analyser that measures hormone concentration or the presence of viruses in a pinprick sample of blood. Usually such tests have to be done in pathology laboratories, which take days to deliver the results; the Biocircuits device can be used in a few minutes.

Patients too will soon have products they can use to examine themselves. They can then feed their own reports into a home computer health diary. Separately, BioControl, an American firm based in Pennsylvania, and Omron, a Japanese firm based in Kyoto, have developed gadgets that can read the broad chemical content of blood when it is placed on the skin – without so much as a drop of blood actually being shed. According to Koichi Takizawa, a research director at Omron, it should be possible to miniaturise any hospital medical equipment, even body scanners. The difficulty, he says, is to adapt the information generated by such machines so that it is intelligible to patients. Next on Omron's list for miniaturisation is electro-cardiography, which measures the electrical action of heart muscle and gives information on the pumping action of the heart.

Aprex, a firm based in Fremont, California, has SmartCaps, which incorporate the simple electronics of a digital watch into a pill bottle-cap to record the time and date when the bottle is opened. This helps doctors monitor whether their patients are taking prescribed medicines. Aprex hopes to adapt SmartCaps so they can "talk" to doctors' information systems. Such a discourse could ensure that action is taken immediately if medication is being skipped.

For the future, Ted Shortliffe of Stanford University suggests that computers will be used to disseminate medical literature; to offer access to individual patient records, which is useful for tracking people when they move; to handle billing and general accounts; to bring specialists via interactive TV to inner cities, rural areas or poor countries where they are scarce; to give individuals, sick or healthy, their medical bulletins plus a personal health database; to create databases on how well populations and patients do on particular medical regimes, which are also primed to give doctors advice; and to prepare clinical reports for drug regulators that have to approve the use of experimental medical products. All this will have huge implications for patient privacy, a point to which this survey will return.

Saving money too

From Silicon Valley in California to NTT in Tokyo, computer and telecoms firms are piling into the health-care market because they see a chance to make big profits. Patients will usually welcome anything that improves their care; payers of health-care bills will also be keen if it helps to contain costs. And some recent studies have shown just how big the savings might be. In 1993 the Regenstrief Institute at the University of Indiana published the results of a trial that produced savings of over $800 per hospital in-patient when doctors used computers to order tests or to receive reminders. The figures suggested that the hospital concerned could save over $3m a year. The savings across the whole country could approach billions of dollars – for just one computerised procedure.

Until recently, little state- or federal-government support for such projects has been forthcoming. But President Clinton's plan for health-care reform refers explicitly to the cost savings that can be made by using information technology. The so-called "Gore-2" bill to promote an information superhighway (initiated by then-Senator Al Gore before he became vice-president) could speed up the wiring of America's health-care system. The government is encouraging the private sector to build the superhighway with promises of further deregulation. In return, however, the telecoms industry will be expected to provide free links from the highway to every American hospital and health clinic by the end of the decade.

The remaining obstacles to a super-efficient electronic-communication network for medicine are mostly practical. The cottage-industry approach of most doctors has been the cause of enormous inefficiencies in health care. It has also created an excess of medical languages. Consider the six teaching hospitals in Boston. Each has a different technique for creating medical records. Their doctors describe symptoms and remedies differently. In 1991 the Institute of Medicine, part of the National Academy of Sciences in Washington, DC, published a report on computer-based patient records that argued strongly for the creation of a single medical language. It triggered a huge global effort. Europe is perhaps more advanced than America, through the Advanced Informatics in Medicine (AIM) programme based in Ghent, Belgium.

Even the most conservative believe that by 2010 computers will enable health-care workers to work more efficiently. But the computers' contribution will not end there. Their enormous processing power and the new channels of communication they have created are about to trigger an even more profound revolution – in the hospital operating theatre.

A trip to the theatre

FROM their origins as barbers, surgeons have accepted illness or even death as an unfortunate side-effect of their craft. Surgeons have rarely been criticised even though much surgery seems primitive. Surgeons cut big holes in bodies in order to repair them. To do good, they plead, they have to do harm. Yet how much better it would be if surgery were less violent. Patients would suffer less and recover more quickly. And for those worried about costs, less violent surgical treatment ought also to be less expensive. As John Wickham of the department of minimally-invasive therapy at Guy's Hospital in London puts it: "Open surgery with its hands-in approach will appear quite gross when viewed by the standards that will be set in the next 20 years."

Two technological advances, image-guided therapy and robotics, are behind the forthcoming revamp of the operating theatre. By hooking up conventional medical tools to computers, image-guided therapy offers surgeons the ability to see into and through patients' bodies. Surgeons should then do less damage to their patients. Of the several research groups round the world working on these technologies, including the University of Grenoble and the National Cancer Centre Research Institute in Tokyo, the largest is led by Ferenc Jolesz of Brigham and Women's Hospital and Harvard Medical School in Boston, Massachusetts. Dr Jolesz's sponsors are General Electric, which is funding most of the project, IBM, Sun Microsystems, Kodak, Zeiss and Thinking Machines Corporation. Dr Jolesz says that image-guided therapy "enhances reality" by improving upon the naked eye; and unlike virtual reality, it depicts a real patient.

Since the discovery of x-rays at the end of the 19th century, doctors have used medical images to peer inside bodies. Pregnant women are delighted when ultrasound gives them a glimpse of their fetuses, even though the images are usually fuzzy. More distinct pictures come from x-ray computerised tomography (CT) and from magnetic resonance imaging (MRI), which provide two-dimensional slices of a patient's body. Although MRI cannot "see" bone in the way that CT can, it picks up everything else including skin, blood vessels and even cartilage with a resolution of 0.5–1mm, the dimensions in which surgeons usually work. MRI can also differentiate the heart from the kidney or cancers from healthy tissue.

Seeing like Superman

Medical imaging is typically used by doctors to make a diagnosis: the existence of a brain tumour, say, or a fractured bone. With powerful computers, according to Dr Jolesz, it can be put to even better use by giving the surgeon in the operating theatre supernatural sight. But several technological leaps have to be made to get this far. By putting sliced CT/MRI images of the body on top of one another, a computer can construct a see-through three-dimensional model of a patient, exposing his flesh and bones. Like Superman, the computer can choose just how far it wants its CT/MRI eyes to penetrate below the surface of the skin.

The next trick is to bring computerised images into the operating theatre. The problem here is "registering", matching life to image. A real patient will not stay in exactly the same position as when a CT/MRI scan was taken. Tiny errors in registering can have devastating results. A displacement of a millimetre can make the difference between hitting and missing a blood vessel. Using fancy computer footwork, several research groups have worked out ways of improving registration. One, developed by Ron Kikinis, of Brigham and Women's Hospital, is to relay a video of the patient to the computer, which then blends the CT/MRI image with a video image of the live patient. The video camera is fixed to certain visual features of the patient. If the patient moves, the CT/MRI image moves in concert with the video image as the camera repositions itself.

To many surgeons this sounds like gobbledygook. In practice, says Eric Grimson, of Massachusetts Institute of Technology, a surgeon will be able simultaneously to see a live patient and an overlaid detailed image of his internal anatomy. Mr Grimson is developing, with the help of a firm called TASC, a transparent panel rather like a teleprompter that will be placed above the patient during the operation. A three-dimensional image of the patient will be projected on to the panel. The surgeon can be wired into the system too. As he moves his head the image will reflect the new angle from which he is viewing the patient. If scalpels are loaded with light-emitting devices they can be registered too, so that the computer follows the surgeon's movements and projects them on to the panel. The surgeon can dig with greater precision and safety because he can follow where the scalpel is in parts of the body he could not normally see.

Even open-body surgery offers a limited view. A surgeon can see only the surfaces of the parts of the body that he has laid bare; he has little idea of what lies below. Dr Jolesz gives an example of a child with a brain tumour that was close to the part of the brain that controls movement. Normally the surgeon, after consulting a few MRI slices, would have cut the quickest route through to the tumour to remove it. But this time the surgeon asked for a computerised registration. Knowing the exact position of the tumour and the other parts of the brain's anatomy, the computer showed the safest way to the tumour. Without the computer, the surgeon would have had to open up a large part of the brain.

Image-guided therapy has also proved effective in surgical planning. Court Cutting, a plastic surgeon at New York University's Medical Centre, has, with Russell Taylor at IBM, used CT images of the deformed skull of a girl and, helped by a computer, determined the best breaks and alignments needed to match her skull to a computerised model of an average skull. Without a computer masterplan, surgeons have to cut and paste the skull together in the operating room. Because the face swells under surgery the outcome is not always clear. Not surprisingly, several operations are usually necessary before surgeon and patient are happy. In computer-assisted surgery fewer are needed.

Image-guided therapy promises more even than this. The recent introduction of keyhole surgery has made many operations less harrowing. Endoscopes (thin, flexible rods) are inserted through a small incision in the body to give an inside view – literally. Long, thin appliances carrying miniature surgical tools, working through other manmade portholes, then carry out the operation.

Endoscopy still involves some violation of the body. The ideal operation would be done with what is called "trackless" surgery, in which operations are conducted without touching the body at all. Ultrasound waves can be focused on diseased tissue, for example – leaving the rest of the body unscathed. But first surgeons would need to see inside people to know where to point their deadly beams. Working blind they could, as with present-day invasive surgery, end up damaging healthy parts of the body as well.

Dr Jolesz's group is now putting the final touches to a grand plan: to remove a breast tumour without making a single cut. Image-guided therapy marks out the breast tumour, which can then be destroyed by zapping it with ultrasound. However, says Dr Jolesz, trackless surgery should be immensely powerful in getting rid of brain and other cancers too. In fact image-guided trackless surgery should be so simple that it can be performed by a doctor thousands of miles away from the treated patient. Because everything is computerised, there is no need for direct patient contact and the operation can be executed through a network of satellites. (As such it has earned the soubriquet "Nintendo medicine.")

First, though, several important adaptations must be made. The MRI and CT images are, like photographs, just a historical record. During surgery much can change – there can be unexpected bleeding or organs can be accidentally knocked and moved into the knife's position. What is needed to cope with this is real-time imagery. General Electric has now built an MRI machine that scans a patient while an operation is going on. The first one has just been installed in the basement of Brigham and Women's Hospital. Dr Jolesz and his team are adapting the computer so it can generate real-time, three-dimensional, moving MRI images from the data produced by the new machine. The group will carry out its first trackless operation this year (1994).

The cost of all this technology is, of course, high. The GE machine plus all its extras comes to a cool $40m–50m. But, says Dr Jolesz, if it improves the chances of survival, decreases pain, or does away with the need for anaesthetics or hospitalisation, the investment should be worth making. Trackless surgery still has its limitations. It can be used only in "ablative" procedures, in which the surgeon's job is to destroy a body's rotten fabric. For stitching or mending, new trackless tools must be invented; they seem some way off. But another scientific field, robotics, is also producing new challenges to old surgical habits.

Robodoc takes charge

Some years ago William Bargar, an orthopaedic surgeon, and Howard Paul, a veterinary surgeon, both from the University of California, Davis, approached IBM with a problem. To complete a hip-replacement surgeons must hollow out a specially shaped cavity in the thigh-bone designed to take the prosthesis. The tighter the fit, the better the chances of success. But the hammer and broach that surgeons now use to make the cavity are primitive – and operations can sometimes disappoint. Surely, they thought, IBM could design a robot to do a better job? IBM's answer was Robodoc, which is now being developed by Integrated Surgical Systems in Sacramento, California.

The skills demanded of a surgical robot are different to those needed on a factory floor. In the factory efficiency and speed are the priorities. In the operating theatre it is precision and safety. In the case of Robodoc, it must mill out a cavity matching the desired prosthetic shape to within a few thousandths of a centimetre and place the cavity within 0.05 centimetres of the desired position in the thigh-bone, which could otherwise fracture. This fine placement can be done using image-guided therapy: CT scans of the thigh-bone are registered to the live patient.

The robot, which is linked to the main computer, positions itself using information obtained from CT and then mills the cavity in the thigh-bone, which is held immobile in a clamp. A separate computer attached to the robot monitors its movements, checking with the CT model that the robotic drill is in the right place. This makes Robodoc 20 times more accurate than a human doctor. As a bonus the computer can, with the help of CT data, plan the ideal-shaped prosthesis to fit into the thigh-bone. Before, this was done mostly by pot luck.

Clinical trials of Robodoc will be concluded by 1995. Preliminary results show that patients treated by Robodoc recover faster than those operated on by humans. Though designed for use by surgeons, Robodoc is so simple to use that eventually technicians might do most hip-replacements. According to Bela Musits, who left IBM to run Integrated Surgical Systems, the Robodoc will be priced to be equivalent to the cost of normal hip-replacements. But there should still be significant cost savings because patients should recover more quickly.

The three-dimensional accuracy and easy reproducibility of automated procedures, says Mr Wickham of Guy's, have still to be fully exploited. Mr Wickham was partly responsible for the development of the first surgical robot in 1989. It removes a diseased prostate (a male gland that helps make semen) via the urethra (the tube connecting the bladder to the exterior). The task is delicate because the gland has to be sliced off a little at a time. Thanks to its precision, the robot can perform the task in 20 minutes, a third of the time it takes a human. It too is being tested in clinical trials.

Mini-robots are another possibility. Electric motors less than a millimetre in size, made by etching tiny gears and mechanisms on a silicon crystal, power tiny surgical devices or tractors bearing cameras. Such a miniature battalion can be swallowed and, when instructed by remote control, perform delicate operations in the gut, eliminating the need for invasive surgery.

Perhaps most exciting of all is the prospect of "tele-presence surgery", where surgeons can operate at a distance from patients using robots guided by remote control. So far only a few researchers have got anywhere near setting up a remote surgical system. The Technical University of Karlsruhe, in Germany, is one; another is the American Defence Department. The Pentagon is taking a keen interest because of the chances of improving the treatment of wounded soldiers on the front line (in past wars, up to 90% of deaths of those injured at the front line happened because the wounded did not reach a hospital in time). Electronic advances in health care could bring a remote doctor to a casualty's side.

Sponsored by the Defence Department, Philip Green of Telesurgical in Redwood City, California, has developed robotic precision instruments that can give to remote controls the same feelings of contact and cutting as if a surgeon were using the scalpel himself. Colonel Richard Satava, of the Advanced Research Projects Agency, dreams that "with medical informatics and networking, and mechanically driven doctoring, the physician can see, feel and interact at a remote site from the patient. Surgeons will be able to operate in dangerous and inaccessible areas, from war zones to third-world countries, without the expense and time of travelling there."

So far remote surgical operations have been conducted only on animals. But in June 1993, at Fort Gordon, Georgia, the United States Army Medical Department conducted a field training exercise of a medical battlefield that might exist at the end of the decade – including remote surgery.

Once the paramedic has reached a wounded soldier at the front line, he can have a tele-consultation with experts around the battlefield to agree on a decision to operate. To bring the expertise of the surgeon, who could be anywhere, to the wounded soldier, a tele-operation system, which is installed in an ambulance and acts as a mobile operating room, can go immediately to the soldier. The surgeon, watching on a three-dimensional monitor, performs the operation using a central master controller that manipulates remote robot forceps, scalpels and needles while tele-consulting with a paramedic in the ambulance who has prepared the patient for surgery. "There is very little difference", adds Colonel Satava, "between a wounded soldier and a patient, so all these technologies have a civilian use as well."

Engineering health

COMPUTERS, telecommunications and robots may make doctors and hospitals more efficient and safer. Biology will take medicine to places that are not even dreamed of – yet. In the past two decades scientific discoveries have turned biology from being a discipline dedicated to the passive study of life into one that can alter it at will. Biologists today believe that by tinkering with people's genes, the units of heredity, they will eventually be able to eliminate most of the diseases that now plague the world. Tomorrow, such extraordinary ambitions may seem modest, as scientists start to work on improving a person's genetic lot in life.

It all started in the early 1970s, when scientists first learnt how to clone and engineer genes. In cloning, a single gene is isolated from millions of others. Before this, scientists were confronted with the genetic equivalent of noise. Now they were free to study the structure and function of gene entities in isolation. By the end of the decade, Genentech, in San Francisco, had launched the first-ever genetically-engineered drug, human insulin. What Genentech had done was to take the cloned gene coding for human insulin and transfer it to bacteria. Genentech had synthesised a new life-form, a bug capable of making a protein foreign to itself. For centuries selective breeding has produced novel crops or cattle, but always with unpredictable results. With genetic engineering, scientists can be surer of outcomes: that a particular bacterium will produce insulin, say.

Scientists now have a rag-bag of new tricks to help them probe nature. Mike McCune of SyStemix in Palo Alto, California, an experienced geneticist, points to four other bits of cleverness crucial to the progress of biotechnology, as the new field of biology became known. On the McCune list are the cloning of pure antibodies, polymerase chain reaction, differential hybridisation and multiparameter flow cytometry. Without going into the details of what this jargon means, all four aim broadly at the same goal: to provide a better understanding of what makes nature tick. This knowledge is now being put to good effect, with the discovery of powerful new medicines.

Biotechnology has made big promises before, without delivering on its early hype. But as Glaxo's Sir Richard Sykes pointed out in 1994:

Just the past year has seen a paradigm shift in modern biology, because it is revealing so much information about the basic mechanisms of disease for which drugs can be developed. In the past, pharmaceutical firms relied on serendipity to find new drugs. In future that is not the way to go if the idea is to produce medicines of value.

The rest of the drug industry feels the same way. According to Steve Burrill, a biotechnology buff, in the year to June 1993 drug firms formed around 100 strategic alliances with small biotech firms to tap into their know-how – twice as many as in the previous year. Research successes have fuelled a huge expansion of the biotechnology industry. In 1993 Mr Burrill counted 1,300 biotech firms in America, 200 in Britain, and 400 elsewhere in Europe. Mr Burrill reckons that by 2010 biotechnology firms' sales will have grown ten-fold compared with 1993, to some $100 billion. Because of the long lead-times involved, products began to trickle out of biotech R&D laboratories only about five years ago. Two drugs already have sales in excess of $1 billion a year, because they are so good at what they do: Amgen's EPO, which prevents anaemia during kidney dialysis, and its Neupogen, which decreases the incidence of infection in cancer patients undergoing chemotherapy. But these two seem dull compared with what the next generation of biotech products will bring.

Views differ about where biotechnology's biggest contribution will be made. But for a 2010-plus outlook the overwhelming vote goes to human genetic engineering.

The gene genie

On September 14th 1990, after years of foot-dragging, America became the first country to allow new genes to be introduced into people. On that day French Anderson, Michael Blaese and Ken Culver, all at the National Institutes of Health (NIH), used a gene drug to treat a four-year-old girl with severe combined immunodeficiency (SCID), a rare and dreadful disease, whose sufferers once had to live inside a sanitised plastic bubble. Those with SCID lack a gene that controls the production of an enzyme known as adenosine deaminase (ADA), which plays an important role in the body's immune defences. Dr Anderson put copies of the ADA gene into the girl's white blood cells. In early 1991 a nine-year-old girl with ADA deficiency was also treated under the gene therapy programme. In May 1993 the two young girls appeared at a press conference looking happy and healthy. The striking results achieved in these two cases have spurred on the use of "gene drugs".

ADA deficiency is one of 4,000 known disorders that result from a single genetic flaw. Most are as rare as SCID; a few, such as cystic fibrosis, are quite common. "But the grand strategy of gene therapy", says an NIH booklet, "also envisages a much broader use of the new techniques to include assaults on heart disease, diabetes and other major health problems that are influenced by the functioning genes." The development of such diseases depends on how a person reacts to environmental factors, such as pollution or smoking. However, the body's susceptibility to them is imprinted in a mix of bad genes inherited from parents. Gene therapy tries to correct these genetic faults to abolish or at least reduce the spread of disease. Dr Anderson, now at the University of Southern California School of Medicine in Los Angeles, says that "it can be used to treat disease, but its primary value will be in prevention." Genetic screening at birth can tell what diseases a person is susceptible to – so genetic protection can be given to prevent the diseases appearing in later life.

In 1993 a lot of progress towards this goal was made. The Centre d'Etude du Polymorphisme Humain (CEPH), in Paris, published the first genetic map of a human genome, the totality of human DNA. Before then, only 2% of the genome had been mapped. What the French did was to establish landmarks (marker genes) among the 100,000 genes that stretch along the human genome. This helps to track down genes that cause most inheritable diseases; patients suffering from such diseases often also inherit distinctive marker genes that are absent in healthy people. With the new map researchers can quickly isolate genes closely associated with the markers to determine which ones cause a disease. The map will also help to obtain a more detailed account of the human genome itself. Thanks to the global efforts of the Human Genome Project, it is hoped that by 2010 the structure and function of almost all human genes will be understood.

Even without the map, in 1993 the genetic causes of several diseases were found. A gene that leads to Huntington's disease, a form of dementia, was found after years of searching. Scientists are close to tracking down genes that cause breast cancer. Tests to screen several diseases were also invented in 1993. Oncor, a tiny biotechnology outfit in Gaithersburg, Maryland, launched a genetic testing service for breast cancer that uses computers to interview patients about family cancer history. It also screens for gene markers associated with breast cancer. As soon as genes that cause breast cancer are found, these too will be screened for to predict a person's chances of contracting the disease.

Those with bad test results could opt to take the radical step of having their breasts removed. In time, however, they may get gene drugs that prevent the disease from occurring altogether.

In 1994 some 250 patients were being treated with 12 different gene drugs in 74 approved trials around the world: the majority were for cancer, the rest for single-fault genetic diseases, which include haemophilia. The results of several trials are trickling in. Patients with abnormally high levels of cholesterol have, after receiving gene drugs, seen their cholesterol levels fall. Three out of eight patients with terminal brain cancers have experienced a reduction in the size of their tumours. Nobody has reacted adversely to any of the drugs, except for one cystic-fibrosis patient who had breathing difficulties for a few hours. That may have been because the drug was administered through the trachea.

Such technical problems of delivery, which is currently laborious and painful, are slowly being sorted out. There is still some worry about the safety of the delivery system, because viruses, even though inactive, are involved. The virus is a vehicle that carries gene drugs to cells in patients' bodies. Apart from the treatment of cystic fibrosis, the therapy has been administered by extracting bone-marrow cells from the patient, treating them with a virally-packaged form of the gene drug in the laboratory, and then returning them to the body. In 1993 Vical, a biotechnology firm in San Diego, found that by combining fat with DNA, it could bypass this procedure and inject genes direct into the bloodstream, much like any conventional drug. Dr Anderson is also working on injectable gene drugs. Researchers are trying to refine delivery systems so that they are longer-lasting and require only a single shot in a lifetime. It is still early days to be sure of the results, but most of the signs emerging from the research are encouraging.

So encouraging, indeed, that Daniel Cohen of CEPH reckons that by 2010 gene doctors will have found a way of dealing with most diseases caused by single gene defects. Over the next 50 years most common serious diseases will also succumb to gene therapy. And 50 years, he adds, is almost no time at all in the history of medicine (penicillin is now 50 years old). These are inspiring goals.

More controversially, gene doctors also want to shape human destiny. So far they have confined themselves to delivering genes to the somatic cells that make up most of the body. Germ cells in the testes and ovaries are not affected; the new genes are not passed on to the next generation, which remains as vulnerable as its parents to disease.

But germ-line gene therapy would correct a genetic defect in the reproductive cells of a patient; offspring would also be corrected and disease
could be eradicated.

Human genetic engineering could also enhance or improve "good"
traits – for instance an extra copy of the human-growth-hormone gene
could be added to increase height. On December 31st 1993 a scientific
journal, *Nature Genetics*, published an article by CEPH that examined
two genes in a group of 338 French people over 100 years old. They
found that the centenarians had different levels of genes compared
with younger people. A person carrying the right gene variants had
twice the chance of reaching old age. This was the first time that genes
had been linked to longevity. It follows that gene therapy might extend
life-expectancy. And though scientists still do not understand enough
about the genetic processes that make humans intelligent or beautiful,
it might eventually be possible to tailor people to taste.

Some scientists believe that nature will act as a brake on genetic tinkering, because the human genome might be able to accommodate
only a limited number of extra genes. It would also be hard to deal
with multi-gene traits. As with the genie in Aladdin's lamp, people may
be offered a fixed number of wishes: a cure for cancer, a height-inducer
or whatever. Once their wishes are used up their genetic make-up will
be unalterable – at least by their own hand. Yet no matter how they are
dressed up, such uses of gene therapy will have moved medicine from
the business of curing or caring into the more ethically dubious areas
of life-enhancement and eugenics: two issues to which this survey will
return later.

In 2010

THIS whirlwind tour of the progress being made in medical science in the laboratory scarcely does justice to the scale of today's changes. It has not touched upon the headway made in transplanting body-parts, *in vitro* fertilisation (conception in a test-tube) or the synthesis of biotechnology-based drugs to treat disease before the introduction of full gene therapy. Even so, the trend is clear: technological change is on the verge of creating a new world of health care.

This is true on several levels. Information networks, computer-assisted therapy, robotics and new drugs will increase efficiency and precision. Patients will be less damaged by the treatments they receive, which in turn should be more potent than their predecessors. Some robots and gene drugs will provide treatments where there was none before. The workload of doctors and surgeons should be significantly lighter as computers and robots take over many of their jobs and people become healthier.

Picture the new-age health-care consumer in 2010. In the 1990s an average person would visit a doctor four or five times a year. By 2010, or probably well before that, doctors will be on call via home personal computers, through electronic mail or teleconferencing. The consumer will anyway do a lot more of his own doctoring. By wearing a "health-watch", he will keep a continuous medical check on his physical and mental state. The data will be fed direct to the computer. Individuals' medical records will be stored in two ways: in a database accessible to anybody with the right password, and on a smart card that is held by the individual.

The computer/doctor will diagnose whatever is wrong with the patient and determine the best treatment. By matching a personal medical profile to databases and services that are available globally, the computer/doctor will be able to tailor advice to patients' needs. If drugs are prescribed, these will be ordered electronically and mailed to the home; or by using a smart card they will be obtained from an automatic dispensing machine rather like bank cash machines. At home, on-line pharmacists or drug manufacturers will be able to advise about therapies.

If surgery is needed a patient will not need to go to hospital and stay there. The rapidity with which patients will recover from new surgical procedures will mean that most operations can be performed in a day. And if an overnight stay is necessary, a local "health-motel" will provide nursing and transport. A fleet of ambulances will also tour areas deprived of surgical facilities, doubling as mobile operating theatres. Instead of a patient travelling miles to the nearest hospital, the operating room will come to him. Many operations will be performed by robots assisted by nurses, although specialist surgeons will be called upon (via telemedicine) in emergencies or for tasks that robots can still not tackle alone.

What will happen to today's health-care infrastructure? Hospitals look likely to empty as traditional surgical wards become largely redundant. Many will close; others will tend only emergency patients or the chronically ill. Doctors' clinics will also be far less busy. The consumer will take far more responsibility for his own care. In return the availability and quality of medical help will improve, as those delivering health care will have a greater interest in ensuring that their treatments are successful.

As the health-care system switches to computers, and information begins to flow freely among doctors, nurses, drug makers and patients, the health-care market will become more transparent. The latest bulletins on the prices and the performance of health-care deliverers will be available on information networks for anybody to read, just as investors keep in touch with stockmarket prices. This will encourage more competitive buying not just by insurers and governments but also by patients themselves, making doctors and other health-care providers more accountable than ever before. Every patient will shop around for the health clinic that best suits his medical needs at fees that he can afford. Clinics will be linked to the health information network but will also belong to a larger managed-care conglomerate – call it Health Care Concern – that provides all medical services. Health Care Concern will keep a close track of all medical services, buying in only the most cost-effective in order to attract customers by offering them the best deal.

As for overall health-care costs, new investment in high technology may be largely offset by savings from hospital closures and fewer health-care staff – which currently account for the bulk of health-care spending. The balancing act between costs and savings may become harder, however, as demand for better medicine increases. When surgery is no more painful than visiting one's mother-in-law, many more will want quick treatment. However, if the net effect is to reduce the sickness in the population, governments and other health-care payers should end up profiting.

Such savings have often been promised before – for instance, with the introduction of health insurance in America, the establishment of Britain's National Health Service and almost every campaign for healthy living. Yet savings have rarely accrued. Indeed policy-makers have usually discovered that as life expectancy increases, new diseases or old-age complaints emerge that place huge extra demands on health-care systems. Hence the inexorable rise in spending in the past 50 years.

This time, though, things could be different. Most of humanity's serious diseases involve renegade genes – and so are curable through the right gene therapy. If new gene mutations or undiscovered infectious agents were to appear, as they certainly will, these too can be picked up by genetic screening and corrected by gene therapy. One worrisome exception is a group of diseases known as spongiform encephalopathies, which includes "mad cow" disease and its human equivalent, Creutzfeld-Jacob syndrome. Nobody knows what causes encephalopathies, but it does not seem to be genetic. There may be a risk that, with all other diseases cured, encephalopathies will run rampant. Even so, the elimination of other diseases should massively reduce health-care spending – as well as improving people's lives.

What's up doc?

The social consequences of the changes in health-care delivery will be equally significant. The implicit contract between doctor and patient will have to be rewritten. Patients, not doctors, will drive the system. Doctors will be relegated to mere members of a wider health-care team, which will include clever robots. For centuries doctors have claimed a monopoly on medical authority, based on their wide knowledge, training and experience – to which consumers had no access. According to Stephen Pauker, professor of medicine at Tufts University, medical information will now be out there for everybody. The difference between the skilled and the novice will lie less in the knowledge they already have than in knowing where to look for information. Nor will doctors be defined by their manipulative skills, as surgeons become those that control robots.

Computers will not dehumanise medicine any more than did the introduction of the stethoscope. There will still be a whole range of treatments that require flexible, human skills that cannot be replicated by computers. And doctors will anyway continue to have contact with patients through information networks. There is also something else that computers cannot replace: the placebo factor. Among patients with a migraine, the mere act of "seeing" a doctor induces recovery in nearly a third of cases.

Some of the medical practice for 2010 outlined above could be happening today – were it not for the dogged resistance of the medical profession, reluctant to take on board any new technology that threatens its position. However the introduction of managed-care systems first into America and then into Europe will give more power to those who pay for health care, forcing doctors to be more accountable to managers and patients. That will also provide more incentives for the spread of new technologies. Future arguments may indeed be more about their costs than about whether they usurp the role of doctors or hospitals.

And beyond 2010?

These new technologies, as this survey has stressed, are not just products in the vivid imaginations of a group of unhinged scientists. Many have already moved out of the laboratory to actual testing. The speed at which they will now come to the marketplace will depend on several things. The most important will be their performance in tests. According to Dr Anderson, if gene drugs prove to be as effective as antibiotics were in the 1940s in curing disease, the public demand to get them quickly will be too great for governments to resist. Antibiotics literally raised people from their death-beds. Similarly, the application of painless surgical procedures will be demanded by patients as they learn of the chances of cure by machines without bodily trauma.

Much will also depend on the speed of telecommunications advances – and especially how soon certain technological hiccups can be cured. For example, Masaaki Terada, director of the National Cancer Centre Research Institute in Tokyo, believes that image-guided therapy is still too insensitive to track cancers that have metastasized – the point when cancer cells spread from a primary tumour to other parts of the body. Such cells cannot be picked up by body scanners, but in 20 years, he believes, the electronic imagery should be good enough. But as a substitute for the surgical removal of solid tumours (which have not metastasized) image-guided therapy will still be used a lot more than invasive surgery. Only solid tumours are anyway operated on today.

All of this is about the immediate future: ie, the next decade or so. Look further ahead, say to 2050, and there is a distinct possibility that

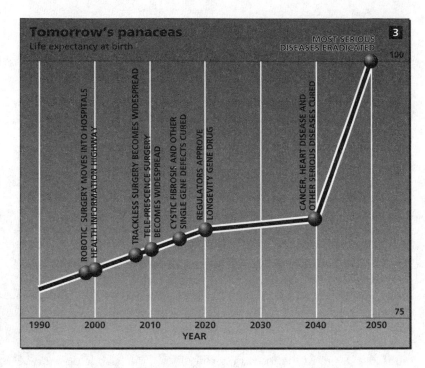

Tomorrow's panaceas
Life expectancy at birth

3

MOST SERIOUS DISEASES ERADICATED

100

ROBOTIC SURGERY MOVES INTO HOSPITALS

HEALTH INFORMATION HIGHWAY

TRACKLESS SURGERY BECOMES WIDESPREAD

TELE-PRESCENCE SURGERY BECOMES WIDESPREAD

CYSTIC FIBROSIS AND OTHER SINGLE GENE DEFECTS CURED

REGULATORS APPROVE LONGEVITY GENE DRUG

CANCER, HEART DISEASE AND OTHER SERIOUS DISEASES CURED

75

| 1990 | 2000 | 2010 | 2020 | 2030 | 2040 | 2050 |

YEAR

gene drugs will have dealt with most major serious diseases. By the middle of the next century, in other words, man could live a life free of illness, barring the odd accident – and he could be living a lot longer than he is now. Chart 3 offers a rough guide to what might happen when. There will be upheavals along the way; there may be resistance from medics or others with an interest in stopping change. But the concomitant health gains will be so great that such obstacles are bound to be overcome.

So is the future entirely rosy? Not to be disingenuous, there are several caveats, most of them ethical, to bear in mind before we can jump to that reassuringly comfortable conclusion.

Hippocrates's dilemma

"I WILL prescribe regimen for the good of my patients according to my ability and my judgment and never do harm to anyone." So wrote Hippocrates, a Greek physician on Cos; hence doctors' Hippocratic oath. Though medicine is advancing towards potent therapies that produce better cures and less physical harm, talk of computer doctors and gene drugs will still frighten many into believing that we are heading towards Aldous Huxley's nightmare in "Brave New World". Most of these fears are baseless; but there are legitimate reasons for concern. That is the nature of medical innovation, which challenges traditional precepts. Even Hippocrates had to fight off critics of his day who argued that his empirical methods were worthless. "Desperate diseases require desperate remedies," he said.

The wholesale overhaul of health-care systems will produce an information network that puts more responsibility on consumers' shoulders. If doctors no longer act in patients' best interests and as general guardians of health, who will defend consumers against commercial interests? Or against prying governments? In tomorrow's medical world, highly personal information will swill around health information networks, from details about blood pressure to hidden genes predicting prospective states of health. This could be used by the unscrupulous. In December 1993 China, which plans genetic screening of its population by 2000, announced that women carrying defective genes would be sterilised or prohibited from marrying. This sort of interference has prompted some opponents to argue that the information should not be collected in the first place.

But if health-care systems are to be made more efficient there must be some way of measuring their input (sick patients) and output (cured ones). To garner this sort of information a patient's welfare has to be tracked from medical records, data must be pooled and processed and the outcome of any treatments must be monitored. The more data there are, the greater the knowledge about what works and what does not. And there are ways to protect patients' privacy. Lawrence Fagan of Stanford University reckons that the level of security provided by electronics is now ten times better than that offered by hospital manual records today. The flow of medical data could be regulated. There may, for instance, be a case for restricting access to the results of genetic screening to the patient concerned, just as is now done for AIDS tests – unless and until treatments are found.

Human genetic engineering also has some opponents who believe that it is wrong in principle to interfere so blatantly with nature. Most people might think that the administration of genes to a sick person to cure a serious disease is welcome. But they might be less sure about extending gene therapy so that it changes people's offspring. After all, by genetically engineering individuals alone, many serious illnesses could be wiped off the face of the earth. But populations might then build up latent pools of "bad genes". Dr Anderson suggests that people could become fortgetful and not take gene drugs. Disease could then suddenly return to surprise all – as whooping cough has done today.

That is why Dr Anderson believes in genetically engineering germ cells (reproductive cells) to correct all "bad genes" in future generations and so eradicate disease once and for all. The only legitimate objection to this, he thinks, is the possibility of a genetic mishap causing apparently irrevocable damage to the unborn. But knowledge is progressing so fast that any conceivable mishap can easily be reversed by correcting the gene mix later.

What about life-enhancing, as opposed to disease-eliminating, gene therapy? Why should people not use gene therapy to improve their lot in life? Taking a growth gene might be compared to having a face-lift or other cosmetic surgery. Criticism of life-enhancing genes might be stilled if therapy were restricted to the individual. The newly-acquired traits would then not be passed on to children, who would be free to choose for themselves what characteristics they might like.

Not all life-enhancing traits should be considered in the same light, however. Widespread adoption of a longevity gene might cause social havoc as the proportion of the population aged 70 or more soars within a single generation. Isolation of behavioural genes – those associated with aggressiveness or athleticism, say – might raise concerns if everyone tried to choose the same types. At the moment, drugs have to demonstrate only safety and effectiveness to be approved. It is time for regulators to consider the social and ethical consequences of medicines, on a case-by-case basis.

A big remaining question will be who will pay for all this life enhancement. This is not just a matter of how much gene therapy itself might cost. It is more a question of broader costs if people start to live to 100-plus. Pension and other welfare arrangements will need to be changed. On the other hand, if a longer-lived population is also a healthier one, it could be economically a more productive one; assumptions about retirement ages must change.

Putting concerns about privacy and the ethics of human genetic engineering aside, the biggest worry may be "humanity's inescapable triumphalism". This, says John Maddox, editor of *Nature*, is what accompanies a rush of discoveries that leave the impression that scientists know much more than they really do. New technologies are adopted with wild enthusiasm, even when they need a lot of further work. This time, though, science is being cautious. New regulatory bodies have been set up to oversee genetic engineering. New medical products cannot come to market without undergoing rigorous testing – though there may be a case for broadening the tests' criteria.

What would Hippocrates have done? He would soon have found that, although many new technologies raise tricky medical, ethical and social problems, they can be managed with legislation and with the right regulatory constraints – just as society now decides how to deal with such controversial issues as *in vitro* fertilisation. Given this, it is hard to see why anyone should reject the opportunities that new medical technologies are likely to offer. The reward, after all, could be a guaranteed hale and hearty future for all.

THIS SURVEY ON THE FUTURE OF MEDICINE WAS FIRST PUBLISHED IN
THE ECONOMIST ON MARCH 19TH 1994

Postscript

The speed at which technological change would be introduced into the world of medicine has been even faster than the survey anticipated. America and Europe introduced measures to digitise medical records. The first surgical robots have been approved for use. The US defence department helped sponsor a huge new project, "The operating room of the future", at the Massachusetts Institute of Technology, which is to construct the sort of environment where surgical operations will be conducted in the next few decades.

On the other hand, progress in genetics has been slower than anticipated. But most agree that the hitches can be resolved – and gene therapy still holds out just as much promise as when the survey was written.

Although the Clinton administration's health-care reform plan did not make it into law, businesses pre-empted politicians by forming huge alliances. In 1994 and 1995 mergers and acquisitions reached record levels in the health-care industry. In 1995 Columbia/HCA became the world's biggest health-care firm; and Glaxo merged with another British pharmaceutical firm, Wellcome, replacing Merck as the world's biggest drug firm.

9

THE FRONTIERS OF FINANCE

The idea that a financial market can be predicted is no longer
confined to cranks.

MATT RIDLEY

On the edge

A FEW years ago, James Hall was using his recently acquired PhD from the University of Illinois to help his employer, John Deere, design an automatic combine harvester that could cut corn without a driver. He gave a routine talk about his work to senior executives in the firm, with fateful results. The manager of Deere's pension fund persuaded him to try his engineering skills on the stockmarket as well. Now he runs a computer program that buys and sells shares in a $100m portfolio, about 10% of the firm's pension fund. He will not say how well he is doing, but confesses that he would have been back on combine harvesters if the first six months had not been promising.

Is this the capital market of the future? Are brokers, fund managers and speculators doomed to be sacrificed on the altar of automation as so many assembly-line workers have been before them? Can computers buy and sell futures, pick portfolios, forecast indices and exploit arbitrage opportunities as well as people do? Will the next system of fixed exchange rates be undone not by George Soros and his friends but by George Software and its cousins?

Financial markets are being automated in the same way as every other industry. Huge sums are being spent (and wasted) on computer networks on Wall Street and in the City of London. But that kind of automation is not what this survey is mostly about. It is about "intelligent" computer software, which can ostensibly predict the movement of markets. It is about replacing not clerks and secretaries but highly paid star traders.

Such software is already at work. Recent years have seen more prediction programs "go live" in the world's financial markets than in all previous years put together. One observer thinks that up to a dozen firms are now managing more than $100m each on the basis of advice generated by computers. A handful of companies, among them Midland Global Markets and the Prediction Company of Santa Fe, will admit to having taken the plunge with large funds. Others will say so off the record, and still others will pointedly say nothing.

Clever computers are no use without clever people. Physicists, you may have noticed, have gone rather quiet recently. There has hardly been a squeak about new particles or superstrings, or edges to the universe. A mischievous thought occurs. Perhaps they are all working as consultants to banks, teaching them "non-linear statistics", the hot topic of the moment. Certainly Wall Street is crawling with physicists, mathematicians, neuroscientists – even chemists.

The finance industry has been hiring people with PhDs and ballpens in their shirt pockets for many years, but never on this scale. The clash of cultures is palpable. Most of the scientists are a bit embarrassed to be caught rubbing shoulders with Mammon. They do not think much of their new colleagues. "Don't say I said so, but most traders and investors are not very bright," says one, adding: "I am involved in a not inconsiderable way with such an enterprise."

The suspicion is reciprocated. Financiers are caught between not wanting to get left behind by the bandwagon, and not wanting to be seen falling for a fad. So they keep a few tame scientists – in the basement, lest they frighten the secretaries – periodically ask them how they are getting on, and disparage them mildly in board meetings.

The crossing of economic and mathematical theory has yielded a bumper harvest of jargon. Does the stockmarket show generalised auto-regressive conditional heteroskedasticity? Can time-delayed embedding explain and profit from the leptokurtosis of stock trades, or will the limit set by the Lyapunov exponent forever make it impossible? Does the back-propagation of errors lead inevitably to overfitting?

Do not be alarmed. This survey begins with the presumption that jargon is used to disguise as much as to describe, and will cut through it to find the surprisingly simple arguments that rage behind. Its purpose is to discover whether a combination of computer horsepower and mathematical brainpower has made it possible to find new sources of profit in the forecasting of financial markets. Its answer, to cut to the chase, is that it has.

This answer is based on four developments. First, there is for the first time empirical proof that persistent predictability exists in financial markets. Second, there is growing evidence that a set of new mathematical techniques, developed in the 1980s, can discover this predictability, given sufficient data to work from. Third, computers have suddenly become powerful enough, and their memories large enough, to make this a practical proposition. And fourth, there is a way to explain how the trick can keep working, even when everybody knows the secret.

Efficiency and after

SOON after the attempted coup in Russia in 1991, a retired hairdresser in Moscow realised that inflation was eating away her pension and her savings. She had noticed that clothes were always cheaper at one street market than at another one she visited near her daughter's home the other side of Moscow. As a good socialist she had always railed against profiteering middlemen, but she had an idea. She took 2,000 roubles from her savings, went to the cheap market and bought a pile of clothes; then she took the metro across the city and sold the clothes for 3,000 roubles at the other market. She had discovered arbitrage.

Arbitrage means buying something cheaply and immediately selling it more dearly elsewhere. It is simple in both conception and execution, but opportunities are few. Far too many people are abroad in too many markets looking for moments when, say, dollars are trading for more pounds in London than in New York, and rapidly extinguishing those opportunities by exploiting them.

The hairdresser's opportunity arose because of different prices in different places. There is no accepted name for an arbitrage in time rather than place, but the concept is essentially the same: buying something cheaply now that you know for certain can be sold more dearly later. It is far harder to do because it requires prophetic powers, and yet (in theory) far more opportunities exist for it, because so few people have prophetic powers. It is what most people who trade in financial markets are trying to do, not just those who buy futures contracts. So how do you arbitrage the future?

One way, as every Rothschild knew, is to get information faster than anybody else. If you know a day in advance that American interest rates will rise, you can buy dollars and make a profit. But not only is that illegal in most markets, it is also governed by the law of diminishing returns. One firm recently spent $35m on a supercomputer to gain a two-second advantage in arbitraging stock futures in Tokyo. As the speed with which information is assimilated increases, the opportunities for time-arbitraging information decline. A stock price is usually suspended pending a big announcement, allowing the market to react instantaneously.

Classic economic theory suggests there is no other way to beat the market than by getting information faster. In recent years, market theory has been dominated by versions of the "efficient-market theory" developed in the 1960s. The weak form of the theory says that in a market that assimilates information efficiently it is impossible to predict the future price of a security on the basis of its past price. The "semi-strong" form says that it is impossible to predict on the basis of publicly available "fundamental" information either. And the strong form says that it is impossible to predict from any information at all. Therefore, both "technical analysts", who study charts hoping to spot the predictable madness of crowds stampeding into or out of a new fashion, and "fundamental analysts", who study economic facts such as the performance of a company in the hope of shedding light on its future share price, are to be ignored. For if one analyst discovers that the share price always rises on Friday, then he can buy it on Thursday in anticipation. But as his habit spreads, so the price will rise on Thursday instead of Friday and there will be no profit in the tactic.

Current prices, therefore, already reflect all information about the security. Only unpredictable news can cause a change in prices; old news is already discounted. And since unpredictable news is unpredictable, so price changes are unpredictable. It is a "random walk" in which each price change is unaffected by its predecessor and the system has no memory.

In the 1960s and 1970s, test after test seemed to confirm the efficient-market theory: again and again, the rules employed by traders proved no better than a buy-and-hold strategy. Indeed, because of the transaction costs, they were worse. If your stockbroker told you to buy a share because of the strength of corporate management, he was no more or less reliable than one who told you to buy the share because Venus was in opposition to Jupiter, or because a double-top had been followed by a head-and-shoulders on the charts of the index. If he was proved right, it was merely because, by the law of averages, somebody is always beating the market some of the time.

Belief in the efficient-market theory had two practical effects. First, index funds and other forms of passive management grew more popular. About half a trillion dollars of pension-fund money are now in index funds in the United States. That is, the future pensioners' money is tied simply to the average performance of the stockmarket. This represents a triumph for scepticism about the skill of investment experts.

Second, the theory had a more practical sister, the "capital-asset pricing model", which has come to underlie the strategies of many investment managers. This essentially says that prices include discounts for certain sorts of risk, which alone explains consistently higher returns by some investors. The more volatile a portfolio of securities, the lower its price for a given expected return. Therefore, the only way to get higher returns on a portfolio in the long run is to accept higher risks.

The fate of a theory

Yet if you mention the efficient-market theory to most computer nerds in the bowels of a big bank nowadays, you will be greeted by a smirk and a roll of the eyes. The efficient-marketeers went too far and a reaction was inevitable. The current generation of economists always wants to tear down or rebuild the temples of its predecessors and the theory has been the first to get the treatment.

There are two fashionable ways to criticise the theory. The first is to say it is roughly true, but that no market is perfectly efficient in its handling of information, and there are therefore many loopholes of inefficiency to exploit. The second approach – the focus of this survey – is to say that there are other ways to beat the market, because time-arbitrage opportunities can also come not from information advantages but from something else.

Analysts of the first school emerge with a seemingly endless supply of suggestions for investment strategies. The "fundamentalists" among them say: buy small firms' stocks, because they are generally undervalued, or stocks with low p/e ratios, or low price-to-book values, or high initial dividend yields. The "technicians" among them say: buy in early January, or on Monday afternoon and sell on Friday afternoon, or at the turn of the month. If these rules work, then they seem to represent unexploited time-arbitrage opportunities and market inefficiencies.

Many can be explained away. When transaction costs are taken into account, the fact that stock prices tend to over-react to news, falling back the day after good news and bouncing up the day after bad news, proves unexploitable: price reversals are always well within the bid-ask spread. Others, such as the small-firm effect, work for a few years and then fail for a few years. Others prove to be merely proxies for the reward for risk taking. Many have disappeared since (and because) attention has been drawn to them. One example is the partial disappearance of the illogical discount on closed-end funds in America (known in Britain as investment trusts), since Princeton University's Burton Malkiel drew attention to it in his book "A Random Walk Down Wall Street". The activities of traders exploiting an inefficiency cause it to disappear.

Mr Malkiel compares such holes in the efficient-market theory to proverbial $10 bills lying in the gutter. True economists say that you do not find $10 bills in gutters because someone else will already have picked them up. But sometimes you are the someone; you find the opportunity first. And although markets get steadily more efficient in terms of the speed and detail with which information reaches all traders, new inefficiencies continually appear in the form of new financial instruments. Learning how to price new instruments takes time and provides opportunities for fast learners to beat slow ones. Just as Salomon Brothers made money on mortgage bonds in the early 1980s, so others are now making money on car-leasing receivables, student-loan receivables and all sorts of new swaps and options. New markets are inefficient markets.

One variation on this theme, which is consistent with the efficient-market theory, is to posit the existence of traders who are contrarian or wrong, either because they are stupid, or because they have some deliberate reason for not wanting to maximise their expected return. These are called "noise traders". A central bank, for example, may buy a lot of its currency to support its price, not to make a profit.

The rise of diversity

What the new mathematicians are mining for is not inefficiencies in the flow of information but something entirely different. They have found new meat in the familiar fact that traders are a diverse bunch, by unearthing some of its previously unrecognised effects. Why are the new mathematicians searching just here? As the next article explores, there is some unexpected predictability in markets which cries out for explanation. And the most popular idea for explaining it has to do with the heterogeneity of traders – in particular, the fact that people reason differently about the information they receive, that they have different time horizons (some are interested in the short-term, others in the longer term) and that they have different attitudes to risk.

Among those who are using new-fangled mathematics in an attempt to exploit these opportunities are Michel Dacorogna and Richard Olsen, of Olsen and Associates, a small financial-forecasting firm in Zurich. They compare the markets to a camel going through the eye of a needle, the camel being the diversity of time horizons of traders, the eye of the needle being the present moment and its clearing price. For example, a fall in French interest rates means lower returns from franc investments for some, but better chances of economic recovery in France for others, depending on their time horizons.

Another devotee of such market heterogeneity is Mordecai Kurz of Stanford University, who stresses the difference between information and what is done with it. Two people can receive the same information at the same instant and still come to opposite conclusions about its likely impact on prices. Neither investor is irrational, although one might be proven wrong. Therefore, a market may well misprice assets, but the mispricing is not because of inefficiency in distributing information, but because of different ways of reacting to it. The Dow Jones index was overpriced in 1966 because investors rationally but wrongly expected growth in the United States to continue to average 4%. It was undervalued in 1980 because most investors rationally but wrongly expected inflation and interest rates to be held high by high oil prices.

Woody Brock, president of Strategic Economic Decisions of Menlo Park, California, who has championed Dr Kurz's ideas, concludes emphatically that it is possible, at least for a while, to outperform markets that are perfectly efficient in their distribution of information. (Whether beating the market can continue indefinitely without driving itself out of business is a question addressed later.) The efficient-market theory is therefore right that efficiency will delete time-arbitrage opportunities based on who has and who does not have information, but wrong to conclude that therefore the market cannot be beaten.

So how can it be beaten?

A dose of empirical evidence

WOULD you rather have $85,000, or an 85% chance of $100,000? Most people would take the money. Would you rather lose $85,000, or run an 85% risk of losing $100,000? Most people would take the chance.

When Amos Tversky of Stanford University posed people these dilemmas he was interested in their understanding of, and attitude to, probability, time and risk. His work has implications for the study of how a financial market works. It demonstrates that people are "non-linear". They are risk-averse when expecting a gain and risk-seeking when facing a loss.

Non-linearity simply means that effect is not proportional to cause. A straw that breaks a camel's back is non-linear. Financial markets are non-linear. The same-sized cause can have different-sized effects, depending on the circumstances. A one-point rise in interest rates will have a different effect on financial markets depending on how the markets interpret the authorities' objectives. This makes the mathematics of cause and effect complicated in the extreme.

The ability to forecast markets depends on the success of non-linear statistics. It is a new science, developed largely since 1980, and it is still in its infancy. Paul Ormerod of the Henley Centre for Forecasting in London, who is trying to find non-linear ways to predict unemployment, says that only if relationships are slightly non-linear will they be any good to forecasters. Highly non-linear relationships are still beyond them. So predicting financial markets depends on finding slight non-linearities.

Non-linear statistics is practical science: that is, it uses techniques that seem to work, and has little curiosity about how they work. It is truly a child of the computer. This irritates many economists and statisticians, who see it as merely a form of "data mining", which can mislead you badly. If you search (or "mine") the data for economic growth vis-à-vis the position of the planets, you will eventually find some pair of indices that correlate, but you have proved nothing but coincidence.

Fischer Black of Goldman Sachs explains the anomalies in the efficient-market theory by this means: "Most so-called anomalies don't seem anomalous to me at all. They seem like nuggets from a gold mine, found by one of the thousands of miners all over the world." However, non-linearists are not after anomalies but predictabilities.

Their essential tool is something called time-delayed embedding, a way of analysing data that can pick out the significant patterns in apparent chaos.

Remember that one of the strongest pieces of evidence for the efficient-market theory was that returns are not correlated with previous returns: today's price cannot predict tomorrow's. But in the 1980s, time-delayed embedding uncovered a peculiar exception to this rule. If you square the returns (ie, multiply them by themselves), they do show correlation over time. Squaring the returns removes all minus signs, so what had, in effect, been discovered, in the market studied, was that a big profit or a big loss one day was more likely to be followed by a big profit or a big loss the next, but it was not possible to say which. It was not return but volatility that runs in trends.

This is known as GARCH theory, standing for a fine example of jargon: Generalised Auto-Regressive Conditional Heteroskedacity. All it means is that volatility is clustered. Prices tend to be volatile when they have just been volatile and not when they have not. GARCH theories suggest that the way to make money is to do so by "straddling" a security by buying both a call (ie, buy) option and a put (ie, sell) option. That is in effect a bet that the price will move; it loses only if the stock does not move.

But GARCH theories are already out of fashion, because time-delayed embedding has already revealed that the relationship between price and volatility is a subtler one than GARCH theories imply. On average, there is no relationship. Volatility is clustered but prices follow a random walk. However, if you divide the market into periods of high volatility and low volatility, a pattern emerges. When volatility is low, the market tends to follow trends: it persists in rising for longer than random, or falling for longer than random. When volatility is high, the market is contrarian: trends persist for shorter than expected periods, meaning that the market keeps reversing itself. In both cases, it means that the market is partly predictable.

For example, in a recent paper, Zhuanxin Ding and his colleagues at the University of California in San Diego showed that the correlation of past and future returns on the S&P 500 between 1928 and 1991 is greater when the returns are not squared, but simply all made positive. This implies that stock indices act as if they have a relatively long memory of past events.

So markets seem to have some predictability in them. Have traders discovered it? Taking advantage of new computer power and a greater density of data than was ever available before, Blake LeBaron and William Brock at the University of Wisconsin set out to test some of the most popular chartist techniques on 90 years of data from the Dow Jones index: 20 versions of the moving-average rule (when a short-term moving average rises above a long-term one, buy) and six versions of a trading-range break rule (buy when the index goes above its last peak, sell when it goes below its last trough). Contrary to previous tests, they found that both types of rule work quite well. Buy signals were followed by an average 12% return at an annual rate and sell signals were followed by a 7% loss at an annual rate. The predictions of both random-walk and GARCH theories were plainly disproved in detail. The previous conclusion that technical analysis is useless was, in the words of Dr Brock and Dr LeBaron, "premature".

This was a shock for economists. Might chartists, that disreputable band of mystics, hoodwinking innocent fund managers with their entrail-gazing techniques and their obfuscatory waffle about double-tops and channel break-outs, be right more often than by chance? How could it be?

Chartists – who prefer to be called technical analysts – justify their techniques with quite reasonable arguments about the behaviour of investors. They do not claim to predict the behaviour of the index so much as the behaviour of the people who trade in the market. When an index breaks through a previous resistance area and therefore heads for new heights, it is quite easy to imagine what is going on. Investors think of profit-taking when a stock reaches a previous high, which produces a resistance area. "The more people share a belief, the more the belief is likely to be true," as Suran Goonatilake of University College, London, puts it.

This is a respectable tradition. There is no other way to explain the tulip mania of 17th century Holland, the South-Sea Bubble, the biotech-stocks boom of the 1980s or the boom and crash of stockmarkets in 1987, except by reference to the behaviour of crowds of people second-guessing each other's predilections and so producing a self-fulfilling prophecy. Keynes used the analogy of 1930s newspaper beauty contests in which the trick to winning the prize was not to say which contestant was most beautiful, but to guess which contestant most other readers would think was most beautiful. It is easy to see how such a process can lead a market to show consistent trends: a rising price is a band-wagon.

The easiest way to pick this up, as chartists have long maintained, is with the use of moving averages. Chartists are basking in their new respectability. Robin Griffiths, chief technical analyst at James Capel, believes with increasing confidence that a stock's price will rise as its current price rises above progressively longer-term moving averages of its past price. By the time a stock is above its 70-day moving average, he reckons, the probability that it will rise further is very high.

If chartists are sometimes right, then computers come into their own. For it is relatively hard to computerise fundamental analysis; computers cannot quiz the chief executive of a firm over lunch, or gain much from one set of quarterly growth figures. The stuff of technical analysis, on the other hand, is much more quantitative and therefore tractable by computer. It is not, however, as simple as throwing a computer at the charts and telling it to learn the answer. People do not learn languages from dictionaries alone. So the empirical study of financial data needs an injection of theory if computers are to achieve anything.

To economists this is dangerously backwards. Their golden rule is that theories must start from how people behave and predict the effects, not begin with possibly spurious patterns in the data and induce their causes. Scientists used to think like that, too. But they are gradually learning that computers have changed such golden rules. Sometimes, data must come first and theories after.

A tale of fat tails

THE year is 1907, and the place is Cairo. A British hydrologist is sitting up late into the night playing cards with himself again and again, writing down the results of each game. His thoughts are on dams and floods, not stockmarkets. But he is discovering something vital to modern econometric theory: the fat-tailed curve.

If you plan to dam the Nile, which was H.E. Hurst's concern, you do not care about normal times; you care about floods and droughts. What Hurst had discovered was that two successive floods and two successive droughts on the Nile came slightly more often than they should, given the frequency of single floods or single droughts. This puzzled him, for it seemed to suggest that the Nile had a memory of the past.

There is in statistical theory a bell-shaped graph known as the Gaussian distribution that is characteristic of many random variations, such as those found in dice, cards and human heights. It does not matter how the graph was generated, it is always the same shape: a curved bell falling away to two tails on either side, representing the rare extremes such as three dice showing sixes at once, a hand of all court cards or a seven-foot man. But because the big floods and severe droughts are more common than expected, the tails of the graph are fatter for the Nile than for a pack of cards. The graph is "leptokurtotic" (from the Greek).

After long nights playing with rigged packs of cards, Hurst eventually came up with a way to measure the deviation of such graphs from the Gaussian, random shape. His discovery is a number now called the Hurst exponent, which is simply the probability that one event will be followed by a similar event. If it is 0.5, the graph is Gaussian and was produced by a random process. If it is more than 0.5, the graph is leptokurtotic and was produced by a process that tends to go in runs: like a coin that is more likely to produce heads again immediately after producing heads and tails after tails (even though in the long run the coin is fair). If it is less than 0.5, it is contrarian: heads is likely to be followed by tails.

Enter a New York fund manager with a mathematical background. Edgar Peters of PanAgora Asset Management has plotted all the five-day returns of the s&p 500 index price changes between 1928 and 1989. They are highly leptokurtotic (see chart 1). For periods greater than 20 days and less than 110 days, returns on the s&p 500 have shown a consistent Hurst exponent of about 0.8 since 1928. Therefore, reasons Mr Peters, the

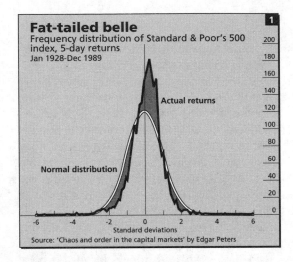

Fat-tailed belle
Frequency distribution of Standard & Poor's 500
index, 5-day returns
Jan 1928-Dec 1989

Actual returns

Normal distribution

Standard deviations

Source: 'Chaos and order in the capital markets' by Edgar Peters

stockmarket is not a random walk. It tends to trend in one direction for too long at each time. When chartists say that the market is "trending" upwards, they may not be wrong. Bull markets and bear markets do exist.

Wealth follows a fat-tailed distribution, meaning that there are disproportionately more very rich people than there are, say, very tall people. It is not hard to see why. Wealth is self-reinforcing; the more you have of it, the more you can acquire. The fat tails of markets may imply a similar thing: the more they trend in one direction, the more the trend persists. It is certainly true of weather systems: an anticyclone is more likely to persist if it has already persisted for some time.

This has three immediate implications. First, it undermines the basis of at least the stronger versions of the efficient-market theory, because information is not immediately reflected in prices and each move does depend on what happened before (weaker versions of the theory say that only some sorts of information get immediately incorporated into prices). Mr Peters believes that the reason for the fat tails is that many investors wait until they see a price trending upwards to confirm their instinct to buy that asset. They therefore tend to reinforce trends. Second, it rocks the capital-asset pricing model, because that model depends on something called a standard deviation as a measure of risk. The more leptokurtotic a curve is, the more misleading the notion of a standard deviation is, because its calculation is skewed by the largest price changes. Third, it reveals that something is causing the stockmarket to be predictable, to have memory.

Mr Peters is the first to stress that this is not a discovery, but a rediscovery of work by Benoit Mandelbrot, one of the fathers of chaos theory, who believed in the early 1960s that financial markets would prove to be "fractal". Only the arrival of computers that could handle massive quantities of data vindicated some of his claims. It is worth a small diversion into this trendiest area of mathematics, because chaos theory is held by some to be the source of all wisdom about markets, and is – therefore – treated as the source of all nonsense by most practical investment professionals.

The science of squiggles

A fractal object is one that occupies more than a certain number of dimensions but does not fill the next number. Thus, according to fractal geometry, a crumpled piece of paper is no longer two-dimensional, but it is not quite three-dimensional either. The silhouette of a mountain range is not one-dimensional, because it is not an ordinary line, but nor is it quite two-dimensional. It is therefore said to have fractional, or fractal dimensions. For example, the coastline of Britain has 1.3 dimensions; the squigglier coast of Norway is in 1.5 dimensions.

Two things are characteristic of fractal objects. First, they are similarly shaped however closely you examine them (at least until you get down to elementary particles). The closer you look, the more indentations you see (they are, in the jargon, self-similar). And second, each point in a fractal object is correlated with its neighbours. Thus a mountain silhouette is not a random squiggle, because each point on a slope is linked with the point next door.

It is the same with the behaviour of a capital market. Each day's price depends to some extent on the previous day's, and the system is therefore not a random walk. And the market shows self-similarity at different scales (see chart 2). For example, an astonishingly simple law holds true about foreign-exchange markets: the difference between price movements over one day and two days is, on average, the same as the difference between price movements over one year and two years.

Fractal theory is, in a sense, chaos theory in reverse. It describes how a random process can reveal a pattern if you know how to look at it. Chaos theory describes the discovery that simple systems in which there are few causes can still show noisy, apparently random behaviour. The point of both insights is that order and randomness can coexist.

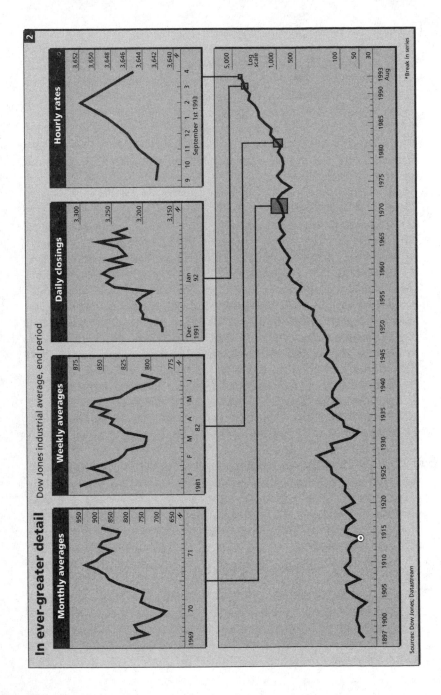

In ever-greater detail
Dow Jones industrial average, end period

Monthly averages

950
900
850
800
750
700
650

1969   70   71

Weekly averages

875
850
825
800
775

1981   J   F   M   A   M   J
82

Daily closings

3,300
3,250
3,200
3,150

Dec   Jan
1991   92

Hourly rates

3,652
3,650
3,648
3,646
3,644
3,642
3,640

9   10   11   12   1   2   3   4
September 1st 1993

5,000
Log
scale
1,000
500

100
50
30

1897 1900   1905   1910   1915   1920   1925   1930   1935   1940   1945   1950   1955   1960   1965   1970   1975   1980   1985   1990   1993
Aug

*Break in series

Sources: Dow Jones; Datastream

280

Robert May, one of the parents of chaos theory and now the British government's chief science adviser, summarises the central insight of chaos theory thus: some complicated, noisy patterns that appear random can be predicted with genuine, but declining accuracy once you know what is causing them. There is, for example, an equation known as the one-dimensional quadratic map, which is so apparently random that early computers used it to generate random numbers when mathematicians needed them. Its output looks like pure noise. Yet, using chaos theory, Dr May can take that data and predict the next step in the series without even knowing that it is a quadratic map.

Dr May's reaction to the use of chaos theory in finance was at first one of scepticism. He found it hard to believe that financial markets could exhibit the right sort of chaos, because that would imply that they were influenced by only a few ultimate causes, whereas everybody knows that the markets are driven by an infinite variety of whims and wishes. But he is now convinced that, for significant periods of time, financial data do behave in the right way for chaos theory to yield predictions. The reason, he suspects, is that people are herd animals who tend to follow relatively few fads and fashions in investing technique. So the traders themselves are the sources of the predictable chaos.

But it must be the right sort of chaos. The crucial question that will decide how predictable financial markets are is the number of fractal dimensions they possess. (More about them in a moment.) If you are dealing with a five- or six-dimensional system, forget prediction: the behaviour of the system will be impossible to discern. If it is a three-dimensional system, it might just be done. Early work using chaos theory, by two economists, Jose Scheinkman and Blake LeBaron, came to the conclusion that there are up to six dimensions involved. But by adjusting for inflation, Mr Peters thinks the S&P 500 index has 2.33 fractal dimensions, which implies that you need only three variables in an equation to start mimicking the pattern of the index.

There is nothing magical about being able to make forecasts. After all, you can forecast all sorts of things: you will grow old, the sun will rise tomorrow, a glass will break if you drop it, a golf ball that has been putted in the right direction with the right force will go into the hole. The difference between things you can forecast and those you cannot is the number of "degrees of freedom" they possess. A roulette wheel has many degrees of freedom: its own momentum, the ball's trajectory, friction, the complicated effects of rebounds. But a golf ball hit true has just two principal degrees of freedom: how hard and straight it was hit.

In terms of chaos and fractals, the number of degrees of freedom involved corresponds to the number of fractal dimensions.

To prophesy is harder than to predict

If the chaos theorists are right, then financial markets, because of the relatively predictable ways in which people react to news, have relatively few degrees of freedom and are somewhat predictable, though not as predictable as golfballs. Much the most revealing comparison is with weather forecasting, because the weather is an archetypally chaotic system: it is sensitively dependent on its initial conditions and retains a fading memory of what happened yesterday. If you could bet on the weather as regularly as you can bet on the dollar, would weather forecasters make money?

The answer is yes. Dave Dusik, a weatherman at WDAF, a television station in Kansas City, was so persuaded by his own forecasts of heavy rain in the mid-west in July 1993 that he bought some soyabean futures at the Chicago Board of Trade, in effect betting that the price would rise. A month later he had made a 250% return. The weather is said by some commodity traders to be the cause of up to 70% of price fluctuations in agricultural commodities between planting and harvest; it is therefore the principal degree of freedom.

But there is one vital difference between weather and finance. The causes of weather are the same now as they were yesterday and a century ago: pressure differentials, humidity, sea-surface temperatures and so on. Depressions produce rain and always have done. But the causes of movement in the financial markets change all the time. This problem, known as non-stationarity, bedevils all attempts to forecast markets. Oil prices were a powerful influence on the bond market during the Gulf war but are not now; low interest rates hurt the dollar more a few years ago than they do now; and so on. The world is in a state of perpetual change.

Tomaso Poggio and Jim Hutchinson, who approached the problem from the artificial-intelligence laboratory at the Massachusetts Institute of Technology, think the market can be beaten, but that it will prove difficult because of a sort of Murphy's Law: the rules of the game change as fast as you learn them. However rapidly your model updates itself with new information about what moves markets, it is always learning from outdated examples. Such non-stationarity makes the task hard, though not impossible.

For similar reasons, Jose Scheinkman of the University of Chicago is bearish about making the jump from proving chaos theory right to making predictions. He believes that the rules employed by traders change too fast. Doyne Farmer of the Prediction Company in New Mexico says that although chaos and fractals clearly have something to say about financial markets, it is still difficult if not impossible to use them. Stephen Taylor of Lancaster University suspects chaos theory may prove to be a "dead end" as far as financial markets are concerned. Even Mr Peters partly agrees. Although he says he uses some of his ideas in managing $5 billion for PanAgora, he admits that chaos is more useful for describing markets than predicting them.

Others are more optimistic, because of the evidence that each market tends to stay in what Mr Farmer calls a pocket of predictability for some time before moving on. In other words, the influences on the system change suddenly, not gradually, and so long as you avoid trying to predict the market during its sudden changes you will be all right. Nick Idelson of Midland Global Markets puts this simply: "Are you encountering market conditions you never encountered during testing? If so, hit the off-switch."

Dr May is also bullish. He believes it may be possible to dismantle a market to discover the few causes that drove the chaotic outcome. His confidence is based on the success he has had, with George Sugihara of the Scripps Institution in California, in predicting the next moves of a range of chaotic series from chickenpox epidemics to blooms of marine algae. The method, a variation of a technique invented by Mr Farmer and John Sidorowich, relies on building up a library of past patterns in several dimensions, on the assumption that when the present resembles some particular episode of the past in detail then the future will resemble what happened after that episode. Gradually, of course, that resemblance will fade as the system loses its memory, and there comes a moment, defined by a number called the Lyapunov time horizon, when the memory is lost altogether.

The trick is to find a region of the series in which the Lyapunov time horizon is high and positive, and therefore a prediction will be valid for slightly longer than usual, then make allowances for transaction costs, and so predict the price a short time hence. Dr May believes it might be done.

Others are already doing it.

The proof of the pudding

FOR every genuine thinker, groping his way towards an understanding of non-linear forecasting, there are probably 20 charlatans on the loose. How do you spot them? One sure sign is exaggerated claims. If somebody claims to predict a market index correctly for more than 60% of the time, his computer is probably infected with hindsight. Another sign is excessive use of jargon. People who really know what they are talking about rarely obfuscate. Any mention of astrology, numerology, Elliott waves or Fibonacci numbers suggests flakiness. If consciousness, the immune system and evolution are also mentioned as ripe fruit for plucking in between sessions of beating the index, shut the door fast: every problem is different. And you can always ask a pertinent question, such as: "if you are so clever, why are you telling me about it rather than getting rich?"

Actually, some people have already grown rich by risking money on the advice of computers' guesses about what markets will do next. Tod Loofbourrow, president of Foundation Technologies, a small Massachusetts firm that trains people in new technologies, believes there are about a dozen firms already managing more than $100m of assets with highly developed automatic-trading systems; and perhaps 20 software firms supplying off-the-shelf programs that just about work to allow people to trade on markets automatically.

Some of the successful groups are in-house teams employed by investment banks; others are wholly owned subsidiaries; a few are stand-alone new companies. Their experience is remarkably consistent. They all say that it is easy to lose money when a market suddenly reverses itself; they all stress that they do not claim to outperform the best human speculators; they all measure performance not by how much money their models make or how often they are right, but how consistently they are right; and they are all dismissive of too close an adherence to any one theory.

Pick your pattern

Although in a sense they are all doing the same thing (looking for patterns that recur), each has a favourite insight. This is vital, for already it is apparent that computers are going to be just as heterogeneous as human traders, probably more so. On that diversity depends the very existence of the market. Here are six examples:

❖ D. E. Shaw is a secretive New York firm founded by two computer scientists in 1988 with capital from a group of wealthy New York families. It uses its own system of high-powered computers and 100 gigabytes of data to trade in its own right in several markets, and has just begun marketing its services to other clients as well. It will not reveal either turnover or profits, but employing 20 science PhDs and opening a London office (as it did in 1993) do not come cheap. Nor will it say which techniques it uses. Lou Salkind, the president, says the firm is about to make markets in various Japanese derivative products.

❖ Midland Global Markets employs a team headed by Nick Idelson and Nick Hallam. They have a 16-gigabyte database of every tick in the s&p 500 and some other markets back to 1983, and a portfolio of computer models for predicting some market indices, principally the price of futures of the s&p 500 index. They beat the index threefold over two years, but can only be sure of being up over six months. They are especially proud of how well their computer coped with the Gulf war.

❖ Adam, Harding and Lueck is a British firm majority-owned by E.D. & F. Man, a big commodity trader. This boutique specialises in the commodity markets and advises on the management of a £250m ($375m) fund. Its database includes every trade in the main futures markets over the past ten years. It aims to produce client returns of about 10% at a tolerable level of risk, after costs.

❖ The Prediction Company is an employee-owned firm started by a pair of physicists from Los Alamos and the University of Illinois who used to try to beat the bank at roulette in Nevada casinos using computers inside their shoes. The company has an exclusive contract with O'Connor and Associates, a subsidiary of Swiss Bank Corporation, to trade a fund of its money on the foreign-exchange markets and take a cut of the profits. Their models make heavy use of "bootstrapping", a fashionable area of statistical theory. They started trading live in 1993.

❖ Prophecy Systems is a London start-up employing three people and investment capital of less than £100,000, but in partnership with a big multinational company. Its engineer, Andy Edmonds, has put several years of work into a model that specialises in a particular form of time-delay embedding perfected by a Dutch mathematician named Floris Takens. Its system went into action in 1993 on the currency markets.

❖ Olsen and Associates, a closely held Zurich company, has a continually updated string of models for predicting the parities of 53 currency pairs. It has achieved more than 10% annual return unleveraged, after transaction costs, to its clients: ie, 10% on top of interest rates.

The most unusual thing about Richard Olsen, a lawyer-economist turned entrepreneur, is his openness. He is prepared to talk about his work and discuss in immense detail the way his computers and his ideas work. (His customers, convinced that only secrecy will preserve their competitive advantage, are much more coy.) So your correspondent picked Olsen and Associates for a more detailed examination of what such a firm actually does.

The first thing you notice as you enter Olsen's offices is a large dog lying on the floor. The company is more like a research lab than a firm; jeans, dogs and late nights hacking away at computer keyboards are the order of the day. There is virtually no hierarchy. The culture is Silicon Valley, not Manhattan.

Ticks and bytes

Above the dog is a computer that suddenly springs to life with a loud beep. It has been watching the markets in 53 pairs of currencies and has just identified conditions favourable for shorting the D-mark against the dollar (ie, selling D-marks in the hope of the currency depreciating relative to dollars, and then buying back D-marks following the depreciation). Three hours later, it beeps again, this time recommending that the trader goes long (the reverse). It was right both times, and your correspondent made $11,000, after transaction costs, by trusting it – on paper, of course. He had risked $1m of assets to do so, a return of 1% a day. Not bad.

Dr Olsen founded his firm in 1985 with his own capital and won his first customer in 1989. It now breaks even on a turnover of SFr5m ($3.5m), ploughing back much of its earnings into research, and supplies 50 customers (mostly in Germany, Switzerland and London) with second-by-second advice on how to beat the foreign exchange markets, at a cost of about SFr100,000 a year each. (As a research consultancy, the firm does not trade on its own account.)

The secret is that there is no secret. No single magic wand will solve the problem of telling you what the market will do tomorrow: not chaos theory, not neural networks, nor anything else. What counts is applying many techniques to vast quantities of high-frequency data. The techniques are meaningless without the data. Olsen and Associates has been collecting tick-by-tick price movements on currencies every second since 1986. The firm takes 50 megabytes of data a month from

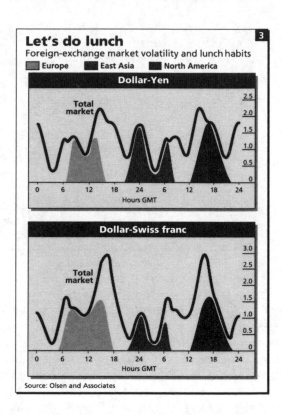

Let's do lunch 3
Foreign-exchange market volatility and lunch habits
■ Europe ■ East Asia ■ North America

Dollar-Yen

Dollar-Swiss franc

Source: Olsen and Associates

Reuters alone, and almost as much from Knight Ridder and Telerate.

To these data the firm then adds value by writing vast volumes of software to implement its own and other people's theoretical ideas. It has two essential concepts. The first we have already met: that markets consist of heterogeneous actors. The second, which is unique to Olsen and Associates, is the idea of intrinsic time. Quite simply, the software compresses time when little happens and expands time when much happens: seconds are shorter during the Asian lunch break than during the American lunch break, for example, because American traders eat lunch at their desks while continuing to trade (see chart 3).

Having redefined time in this way, the computer then draws a series of graphs incorporating assumptions about how the different traders in the market will react to a price change in intrinsic time. Each graph is the same overall shape, but with different slopes according to each trader's time horizon or risk profile. Each trader is assumed to react in a non-linear way: little at first to a price rising above its moving aver-

287

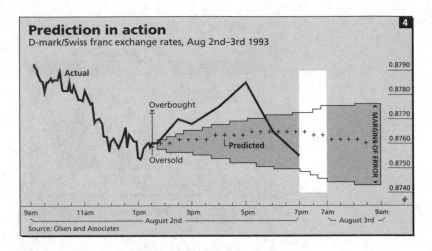

Prediction in action
D-mark/Swiss franc exchange rates, Aug 2nd–3rd 1993

age, then with increasing interest and finally to slacken off as he thinks he has invested enough. The computer merely adds up these models and arrives at an estimate of how the whole market will react to an event. It does not work with normal time, but works quite passably in intrinsic time.

Of course, the customer knows none of this. All he sees is a screen that shows the history of one exchange rate over the past day or hour, the computer's forecast for where it will go in the days or hours ahead, with a grey band of increasing width to illustrate a growing margin of error, and a little bar representing the present moment (see chart 4). When the line goes below the bar, the computer alerts him to an "overbought" opportunity – go short – and when it goes above, to an "oversold" opportunity: go long. The customer receives this information, continually updated, on his screen from the company's computers.

Compared with the indigestible porridge of figures visible on the screen of the average trader, the system is therefore extremely easy to use, which is vital to its acceptance by customers: it draws attention to salient facts, rather than just presenting all the data. Nonetheless, says Robert Ward, Olsen's software wizard, it takes a customer up to a year to learn the full possibilities of the system.

Ripple effects

What exactly is the model forecasting? "It is like a rock thrown into a lake," says Dr Olsen, gesturing towards the Zurichersee. "We cannot forecast the rock, but we can forecast the ripples once the rock has fallen in." The rock is the unexpected event: a coup in Moscow or a bomb at the World Trade Centre. Because everybody reacts differently to the news, according to his time horizons, there must be secondary reactions: reactions to the reactions. And if there are secondary reactions, a news event cannot be absorbed by the markets instantaneously. And if news cannot be absorbed instantaneously, prediction is possible for as long as it takes the market to absorb the event and its secondary effects.

Others make the point in different ways. What Dr May speaks of as the Lyapunov time horizon is the moment when the ripples from the rock become indistinguishable among the waves on the lake. Michel Dacorogna of Olsen and Associates makes an analogy with the nuclear-magnetic resonance scanners used in hospitals. The reason they produce an image is because different tissues relax at different rates after a magnetic shock, just as different traders, ranging from instantaneous market makers to long-term hedgers, react at different points in the sequence of events that follows the arrival of the rock.

Step back a short way and recall what is going on. All that any computer is doing is finding moments when markets are doing something similar to what they once did before and from that deducing what they will do next. If that sounds a fatuous way to proceed, remember it is shared by every stockbroker and weather forecaster. He tells you a stock will rise in price, or it will rain, because in the past the current pattern has proved a reliable guide to such an eventuality. So long as you can be convinced that the past is a better guide to the future than it is on roulette tables, there is really no need for the reader, or the customer, to understand more than that.

So the recipe for beating the markets is now clear. First, you need to know that the ground has not shifted under your feet in such a way that the past is no guide to the future. Second, you need a computer program that incorporates some ideas from non-linear statistical theory to compare the geometry of the data with a library of past patterns. Third, you need vast amounts of high-frequency data showing every trade on your chosen market for several years. Fourth, you need a pattern-recognising device that compares your data with your theory to find the coincidences.

This is where the "neural network" comes into its own.

Neural networking

A NEURAL network is a computer program that recognises patterns. It is emphatically not a computer that imitates real brains, nor a computer that learns, although such slogans certainly helped relaunch the technology in the 1980s, and to this day such neurobabble occasionally impresses a managing director. Neural nets are now almost as standard and boring as spreadsheets and to some extent they are already passé. They are as early-1990s as roller blades.

And, like roller blades, they still get you where you want to go. Considered as tools for comparing past patterns to the present in the hope of finding a coincidence, they work. But they are still tools, like spreadsheets or even fax machines, and they are only as good as the people who program and use them.

A neural network is designed to take a pattern of data and generalise from it. Thus, if the data are daily temperatures in New York city over two years, the neural network should emerge with a simple undulating curve that describes the way temperature rises in summer and falls in winter. It does this in effect by a sophisticated form of trial and error, or, in the jargon, varying the strengths of connections between individual processors until the input yields the right output.

The two essential features of this technology are that it improves its performance on a particular task by trial and error (neural networkers prefer to say that "it learns") and that it can be a "black box". That is, you do not need to know what mathematical equation describes its output, although you could find out if you wanted to. All you know is the output of the network. An oracle is likewise a black box – that is to say, you do not know the reasoning behind its advice – but neural networks are better than oracles.

This can be a drawback. People about to risk large sums of money on your advice generally like to know your reasoning. But Guido Deboeck, who directs research on neural networks for the World Bank, points out that most traders hardly know themselves why they decide to buy or sell. How do you ride a bicycle? You don't know; you just do it. Keith Bagnall, future-technologies manager of the TSB Bank in Manchester, who has introduced neural networks to his bank to help forecast long-term gilt prices, says investment managers could not care less how they work, so long as they get results.

For that, you need good data. According to John Loofbourrow, father of Tod Loofbourrow and chairman of Neural Trading Systems, based in

New York, if you use a neural network properly, you will spend 80% of your time cleaning and understanding your data: removing errors, pre-processing and reclassifying prices. But even with perfect data, your problems are not over. The Achilles heel of a neural network (or any computer trading model) is that it tends to "overfit" the data. What this means is that it finds any pattern, however spurious and coincidental. Suppose that in the two years of temperature data you give it, the coldest four days were all Thursdays. A person would immediately spot that this was meaningless chance. A naive neural network might think it significant and begin to predict that tomorrow will be colder than today, merely because it is a Thursday.

One solution to overfitting is to apply "fuzzy logic", which is the technical term for instructing computers to use concepts like "somewhat" and "sort of", rather than being just as emphatic when their conclusion is tentative as when it is firm. Neural networks tend to be "brittle", meaning that their conclusions lack subtlety. A bad neural net resembles a man who says it is safe to drive down a road through a minefield, but forgets to add: so long as you keep off the verges. It does not distinguish between a buy recommendation based on a pattern that fits well only in one narrow set of circumstances and one that fits well generally.

Another solution is to use a "genetic algorithm" to design your neural network. Genetic algorithms also employ trial and error, this time in a direct analogy with how evolution works by mutation and natural selection. For example, you might pick a neural network and try to improve it by "breeding" from it with some random changes thrown into some of the offspring. Each offspring network is then tried on the data and if it proves better than the others, it gets to be the parent of the next randomly mutated generation. And so on, until a particular sort of neural network emerges that cannot be improved upon. In the engineering age it was hardly feasible to build thousands of Brooklyn bridges and see which one lasted longest. But in the age of software and simulation, such genetic algorithms are an increasingly sensible way to go about designing tools.

You can buy a neural-network program for as little as $100 and run it on your personal computer. Most decent systems cost rather more, and at least 20 designed for use on financial markets are now on offer. In the United States, the most commercially successful has been Neural Ware's Professional II+ . In Britain, Richard Hoptroff, who runs Right Information Systems, has sold his Forethought program to 60 customers in the first year at £5,000 apiece. He is the first to admit that he is not selling anything "intelligent", just a useful and well-crafted tool.

So what are such tools being used for? Many are being applied to tasks other than forecasting, such as spotting fraud and evaluating loans. The neural net chugs away through the data looking for patterns and emerges triumphantly with the news that people who frequently use their credit cards for cash are poor risks for lending money to, or some such generalisation. Mr Bagnall cites the TSB Bank's success in forecasting insurance claims on loan-protection policies based on unemployment figures.

Slightly closer to market forecasting is the work that Fujitsu, Japan's biggest computer firm, has been doing with Morio Yoda of Nikko Securities on rating corporate bonds. Kazuo Asakawa of Fujitsu took care to design his neural net to incorporate some knowledge from human experts: making strong connections between profit and bond rating, but weaker ones between equity capital and bond rating, for example. This net was 40 times faster than a normal one at reaching a solution to the problem of how to rate an unknown bond and got the right answer 24 times out of 25 compared with 20 for the normal network.

The Fujitsu team went on to try and predict the Tokyo stockmarket index based on such figures as interest rates, turnover, the level of the Dow Jones and a few other obvious factors. The Fujitsu net beat the index during a 33-month bull market (1987–89) by about a third. Then, during a bear market between 1989 and 1992, it did twice as well as the index, ending with a small profit instead of a large loss (see chart 5).

Fidelity, a Boston-based fund manager, now has seven funds that use neural networks to help pick stocks and thus manage $2.6 billion of assets. The networks examine 2,000 stocks for growth potential and narrow them down to 200, from which human analysts pick 50 to invest in. One of the funds has beaten the S&P 500 by 2–7% a quarter over more than three years. That reflects well on either the computers or the human analysts or both.

Back to the Nile

However, these encouraging results sometimes conceal more than they reveal. Analysts keep quiet about funds that perform badly. And many claims of success are highly misleading. Although the Fidelity results are real ones, many boasters about neural nets have only hypothetical, "hindsight" success to boast about. There is a huge difference between success at making money on last year's data and success in the future.

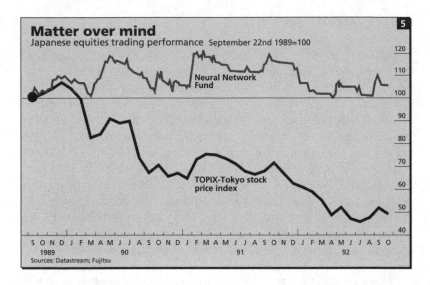

Matter over mind
Japanese equities trading performance September 22nd 1989=100

Neural Network
Fund

TOPIX-Tokyo stock
price index

S O N D J F M A M J J A S O N D J F M A M J J A S O N D J F M A M J J A S O
1989   90   91   92
Sources: Datastream; Fujitsu

Moreover, almost everybody who has used a neural network or other automatic-trading technique points out that, left to its own devices and followed blindly, it would usually get the right answer more than half the time, but would tend to lose more when it is wrong than it gains when it is right. The reason goes all the way back to Hurst and the River Nile. A market is persistent, meaning that it tends to follow a trend for longer than chance, and then suddenly reverses itself. Neural networks must be used with care.

The true measure of a system's success is not the proportion of its trades that were profitable, but the amount of money it made without taking too many risks. Dr Olsen calls this the effective return on a low-risk investment strategy. Others measure something called the Sharpe ratio – a record of how volatile the trading performance was. Others put a ceiling on draw-downs, so that a trading system will be judged to have succeeded only if it makes money without dipping into its investors' pockets too deeply in bad times. Consistency is the grail.

Neural networks are no panacea. To imagine that a neural network will do your thinking for you is an expensive mistake. "Only people who could make money without a neural network can make money with one," says Nick Idelson of Midland Global Markets. The hope is that careful use of the new technology will help them to do it better.

Cash machines?

WOULD "Middlemarch" have been a better book if George Eliot had used a word processor? Probably not. Would Hitler's U-boats have been more successful if the output of the Enigma machine had not been decoded? Probably. The question that faces the world of finance is whether intelligent computer programs are like the first technology or like the second. Will they enable people to do what they do anyway but more productively; or will they alter the course of history?

Computers have been most useful when employed to do what people are bad at, not when competing for their jobs. They are better at rapid calculation and faultless memorisation than at translating into Russian or doing your shopping. The mid-1980s hyperbole about the promise of "expert systems" – computers that mimic human experts at, say, medical diagnosis or legal reasoning – has largely evaporated, leaving little behind.

"There are things that machines are good at, but trading does not seem to be one of them," says Fischer Black of Goldman Sachs. "There's too much judgment involved; the list of factors that matter is changing all the time." Yet there are things human traders are not good at, such as recognising a four-dimensional pattern that reliably appears in the Dow Jones index eight minutes before it rises, or using non-linear dynamic theory to predict how the dollar will reverberate after yesterday's news. There do seem to be patterns in markets that prove to be reliable guides to the future, and extremely high-horsepower computers do uncover them where people do not, if they have been intelligently programmed and intelligently used.

Yet Mr Black's scepticism is widely shared by financiers, if not by computer experts. Few of those who work in this field envisage computers trading in their own right; most expect them to be used as advisers, prompting a trader with the news that an opportunity exists to make money from the dollar's strength, but letting him ignore it if he knows something the computer does not, such as that nuclear war has broken out. Dr Olsen compares his computer models to high-speed cars: replace a Deux-Chevaux with a Ferrari and you have more chance of winning the race, but you still need a driver.

Others disagree. Guido Deboeck of the World Bank argues that if you allow a trader's gut to overrule your neural network's advice, you compound the errors due to chance. James Hall of John Deere says that adding people to neural networks increases the degrees of freedom to infinity; moreover, automated traders have lower transaction costs than people; and Deere's stock-picking computer churns 60% of its portfolio a month. Human intervention would remove that advantage.

The attitude of traders to automated systems is usually one of curiosity rather than contempt. It is from managers that the contempt comes: they have met too many snake-oil salesmen bursting with buzz-phrases and extravagant claims. Again and again, it is management that vetoes an experiment with these techniques.

A cheap and furtive lunch

There is an irony here. For if you truly believe in the efficient market you should follow a buy-and-hold strategy, not employ expensive traders. Ask not what is to be gained by automating investment advice; ask rather what is to be lost. But the inherent conservatism of the big financial firms towards new-fangled technology is handing great new opportunities to small entrepreneurial ones that are inventing systems from scratch. It was always thus. It was Apple, not IBM, that had faith in the personal computer. It was Genentech, not the drugs companies, that pioneered genetic engineering. In every industry, large companies promote safe, predictable bureaucrats.

"Of course, there is no free lunch. But there is a good dinner and it is very cheap," says one believer. He adds that the fewer who come in on the feast, the more there is for others to eat. It is almost an article of faith among the new financial wizards that secrecy is the path to success. Many prominent non-linear experts will not even discuss their work for financial firms. "The smart players are not talking, and the talkers are not smart players," warns one anonymous, and presumably smart, player.

The secrecy is based largely on the idea that the predictability in the markets, like the opportunities in arbitrage, will evaporate once discovered by too many people. If computers are trading on the assumption that the market will rise tomorrow, then it will rise today, and the opportunity will be gone. Many people are concerned that a single computer model will come to dominate the market and every trader will act in concert.

There is a paradox here. It is possible to predict a market only if that market is dominated by a limited number of ways in which it reacts to news – that is, if it has few degrees of freedom. But the more it is so monopolised, the more profitable is the contrarian strategy of reacting to the reaction. This resembles the "Grossman-Stiglitz paradox": if the return from fundamental analysis were zero, nobody would do it; if nobody did it, the return from doing it would be high. So the market is protected against monopoly, because the monopolist presents a splendid opportunity for his opponents.

For this reason, some firms such as Olsen and Associates are gambling on openness, not secrecy. Olsen is determined one day to let anybody who wants it to have its software free, so that it can make money selling new models to run on the software, not selling the software itself. It is betting, in other words, that the financial-computer industry will soon be like the computer business, not the drugs business: patents will be irrelevant, and technological lead will be everything.

This raises an intriguing question. Will the computerisation of market trading fragment markets or centralise them? The optimists, such as Dr Olsen and Mr Deboeck, envisage a world of millions of amateur traders all buying home-brew systems that trade less frequently than most mutual funds do. One employee of Bear Stearns already uses a home computer to gamble with his personal pension fund. Like laser printers, quality that would have stunned Gutenberg will be in reach of everyman.

And yet laser-quality is already meaningless simply because everybody can do it. Financial markets are arms races: how well you do depends on how well others are doing. If the race will go to the swiftest in technological innovation, then Muggins, sitting at home ordering his latest model from Oracles and Miracles Inc, is hardly likely to be at the cutting edge. The specialist firms (not the big banks) will crush him and they will gradually affect the markets, making them steadily harder to predict, which will make the little man less and less able to play.

The script of this Nightmare on Wall Street continues. The big players will play for ever higher stakes and will not stop at predicting the markets. They will want to control them. Hubristic computers will eventually want not to short the dollar but to ramp it, not to go long on silver but to corner the whole market. If you are a big enough player in a market for your own moves to influence the market, then you have the ultimate predictive weapon, for you can predict your own next move.

The trouble with this nightmare is that it applies with equal force to human traders, and the success of human traders in cornering markets is increasingly sparse. Since the Hunt brothers failed to corner the silver market in 1979 and a rogue trader at Bankers Trust failed to ramp the New Zealand dollar in 1987, such manipulation has been an increasingly faint threat. Computers will not change that. Once again they will inevitably create such diversity of trading strategies that no single program will long hold sway.

Predictability will bring more traders to the market, which will increase the market's liquidity. Increasing liquidity will reduce the market's friction – its transaction costs – which will in turn increase the market's ability to generate wealth. In just the same way that cutting the cost of cars increases the demand for them and so increases the wealth to be made from building them, so the automation of speculation will prove to be an engine of economic growth. Already on the foreign exchanges between $750 billion and $1 trillion is traded every day, over 95% of which is pure Anglo-Saxon speculation, as the French call it. And yet currency trading is largely in the era of the horse and cart. Automation has barely begun.

THIS SURVEY ON THE FRONTIERS OF FINANCE WAS FIRST PUBLISHED IN
THE ECONOMIST ON OCTOBER 9TH 1993

10

ARTIFICIAL INTELLIGENCE

*Contrary to countless science-fiction plots, machines are far too
stupid to take over the world. But more intelligent computers are
already changing it by making people cleverer*

JOHN BROWNING

Cogito, ergo something

FOR over 35 years researchers have been struggling to build a computer in man's image. They are not even close to doing so. Although scientists have succeeded in giving machines all sorts of human skills, the goal of creating a machine as clever as a person seems to recede all the time. Ironically, this failure may eventually change the way in which people work and live more comprehensively than if scientists had succeeded in getting a computer to sit up and say "Mother!"

The skills with which researchers have so far endowed their machines are both intellectually impressive and practically useful. Computers called Deep Thought and M-Chess can beat all but grandmasters at chess. In Merced, a Californian county, computers work alongside clerks to administer welfare benefits. Researchers at Carnegie Mellon University in Pittsburgh have built a lorry that can drive itself. Often and painfully, researchers have learnt the lesson that being able to perform the same job as a person, even an intelligent one, is different from being truly intelligent. As Anatol Holt, a researcher in the field of artificial intelligence, once noted:

> A brilliant chess move while the room is filling with smoke because the house is burning down does not show intelligence. If the capacity for brilliant chess moves without regard to life circumstances deserves a name, I would naturally call it "artificial intelligence".

The more that computers do tasks hitherto reserved for people, the more they demonstrate an ability to be brilliant in some ways while remaining moronic in others. Herbert Simon of Carnegie Mellon University, one of the pioneers of artificial-intelligence (AI) research, has said that the biggest surprise of his decades spent trying to recreate human intelligence was "how easy the 'hard' things were to do, and how hard the 'easy' things". His first AI program, completed in 1955, enabled a computer to work out simple logical theorems (ie, principles of valid reasoning). Since then the logical skills of computers have increased by leaps and bounds. But nobody has built a machine that can navigate across a crowded room or understand a children's story. This curious combination of brilliance and stupidity leaves their creators on the horns of a dilemma.

Friend or fool

Computers are too clever to ignore but too stupid to be trusted entirely. "Expert systems", computer programs designed to capture human expertise, provide a case in point. MYCIN, one of the first expert systems, was created nearly two decades ago by Edward Shortliffe at Stanford University. Given the symptoms of a bacterial infection, MYCIN can recommend a treatment as well as most of Stanford's top specialists can. In tests MYCIN does better than many of the newly qualified doctors who are prescribing drugs for real people. Unfortunately, it cannot distinguish between a patient who needs treatment for a bacterial infection and one who needs a midwife. It tries to interpret every ache, pain and bump in terms of bacteria.

Each in its own way, all of today's intelligent computers can be just as idiotic as MYCIN. But thousands of expert systems and other artificially intelligent programs are being put to work nonetheless, because their users have found ways to overcome the machines' inadequacies. The trick typically lies in having the computer work closely with people, in order to take advantage of the strengths of each – the person's common sense and the machine's memory and logical skills.

Thus clerks at Britain's Trustee Savings Bank ask an expert system to help find which pension funds and other investments would be best for their clients, combining their own sales skills with the machine's knowledge of finance and financial products. The New York Stock Exchange uses an expert system to sort through mountains of trading statistics in search of clues to crime. Rather than replace people – as many early proponents of expert systems predicted – intelligent computers have typically been put to use making clever people cleverer.

Finding more such opportunities for teamwork between man and machine is one of the great technological challenges of the next few decades. The potential rewards are huge. More intelligent machines have already demonstrated their ability to help people work more intelligently, even if they cannot be truly intelligent themselves. They can help businesses to capture and make use of the deluge of information that computers release. And they can bring previously inaccessible knowledge and skills to people's fingertips.

Manners maketh mind

Needless to say, harvesting these rewards will not be easy. Given the nature of the tasks at hand, the technology is still relatively primitive. And nobody knows whether or not there are fundamental limits to the ability of machines to think like people – or to people's ability to share work productively with a machine.

Yet the seeds of profound change can be seen even today. To the extent that computers can mimic human decision-making, they are gradually transforming the abilities which are valued and rewarded in people. Many of the skills that make tax accountants highly paid professionals – to pick a job more or less at random – may tomorrow be available shrink-wrapped on the shelves of the local software emporium.

The process of deciding which jobs will be reserved for people and which handed over to machines is already under way. A decade or so ago a traveller facing a stormy night's flight might console himself with the thought that his aircraft was no doubt being flown by an experienced pilot; today the same traveller might well find the idea of a sophisticated autopilot equally consoling. The process of accommodation to cleverer machines is a fitful and uneven one. It depends on factors ranging from technology to manners. The technological challenge is to clear an intellectual common ground between man and machine: that is, enabling machines at least to act as if they understood words, reasoning and perception. More prosaic social challenges include giving the machines enough conversational savvy to make them worth talking to. To see the progress of machines into the world of thought, start by reviewing the successes and failures of the first generation of artificially intelligent machines.

In its creators' image

ONE of the hardest topics of debate in artificial intelligence is what sort of subject it is. Some researchers reckon that AI is a science, whose goal is to work alongside psychology and neurobiology to explain the workings of mind and brain. Others believe AI to be part of engineering, whose *raison d'être* is to make tools. In practice most researchers proceed as if the answer lay somewhere in between: AI aims to make useful tools whose design is inspired by the mind.

Though researchers have had, at best, mixed success in getting machines to mimic human thought, they have time and again demonstrated two points about humans. First, people want to believe in thinking machines – out of fear or fascination or both. Second, they are notoriously poor at defining what it means to think. Perhaps because people have encountered thinking machines only in people-shaped packages, they tend to assume that if a machine can do one intelligent-looking thing it can – like a person – do them all.

The consequence is that even people who should know better are easily fooled by AI programs, and are deeply disappointed when they are fooled. In the late 1960s a program called ELIZA was popularly acclaimed as the world's first automated psychiatrist, even though its creator, Joseph Weizenbaum, denied that it was anything of the sort. In the mid-1970s SHAKEY, an experimental robot built at the Stanford Research Institute, was touted as the progenitor of a race of mechanical men – much to the horror of the researchers who built it. They tried to explain that SHAKEY could in fact barely navigate an empty corridor, let alone an obstacle-strewn factory floor.

Great expectations

One irony of the high expectations that AI seems irresistibly to engender is that it has made successes look like failures. As a mechanical man, SHAKEY was a flop. But techniques used by SHAKEY to plan its actions were instrumental in creating programs that help people to plan everything from factory production schedules to troop movements. One such program – originally developed by Ascent Technology, a small firm based in Cambridge, Massachusetts, to help Delta Airlines allocate landing gates at busy airports – was used to help plan the deployment of men and materials in the Gulf war. America's Defence Department, which has supported most of that country's AI research, claimed that this one application paid back much of the investment it has so far made in AI.

303

Repeated cycles of enthusiasm and disappointment have also changed researchers' expectations of what an intelligent program should do. In the early days they hoped to find a general theory of intelligence; in 1956 Herbert Simon dubbed his second AI program, created with Allen Newell, also of Carnegie Mellon, the "General Problem Solver". Today most AI researchers have given up the dream of finding a general theory of intelligence. Instead they are filling a toolbox of problem-solving techniques, each one suited to different jobs.

This shift has highlighted differences of interest and approach within AI. Computer vision, for example, has evolved into a more or less separate discipline, which draws as much from theories of signal processing that would be familiar to a television engineer as it does from more abstract techniques for computer reasoning. And the traditional core of AI, computer reasoning, comprises three different (though not always distinct) main camps.

❖ One group – call them the humanists – takes its inspiration from psychology. It wants to discover how people think and then simulate those processes on a computer. So Messrs Newell and Simon based the design of the General Problem Solver on psychological experiments in which they got students to talk aloud about their efforts to solve logic problems. Although psychology and introspection have fuelled many advances in AI, it can sometimes be hard to predict when programs based on these techniques will break down and when they will work perfectly.

❖ Partly in order to achieve greater predictability, another group of researchers prefers to base AI programs on formal logic (a mathematical sort of science which attempts to codify the principles of valid reasoning). One achievement of the logicists has been to create new forms of "non-monotonic" logic. Chains of reasoning based on traditional logic fall apart if an assumption on which they depend turns out to be wrong, whereas non-monotonic systems of logic can recover and cope with the necessary readjustments.

❖ A third group reckons that both the logicists and the humanists are jumping the gun. This group – call them the structuralists – believes that the best way to simulate the workings of the mind is to recreate the information-processing capabilities of the brain. So the largest faction within this group, known as the connectionists, are building interconnected networks of artificial "neurons" on silicon, just like those found in real brains. Such "neural networks" turn out to have intriguing abilities.

These tools are being used to build AI systems that are very different to those commonly envisioned even a few years ago. Instead of big systems dispensing wisdom like some sage of old, the vast majority of today's artificial intelligences are small and barely noticeable. With a few exceptions, they do modest tasks, and are so deeply embedded within computer networks that their users often do not even know that they are there, working quietly to process motor-warranty claims, approve executive expense accounts or simply to help route telephone calls.

Steve Cross of America's Defence Advanced Research Projects Agency, one of the administrators of the $35m or so which his agency provides for AI research each year, expects AI to blossom in the role of assistant, helping people rather than replacing them. In the wake of the cold war, he argues, the armed forces will have to become more flexible and quicker to respond to the unexpected. Yet they will have to do so with fewer people, particularly in logistics and support. AI, he believes, can help.

Many computer companies share this view. Nathan Myrhvold – head of research at Microsoft, the world's biggest supplier of personal-computer software – is keen on teaching computers to cope with commands in more-or-less English. IBM is bullish about computers that can understand simple spoken commands. Aldus, which makes desktop-publishing software, is said to be trying to incorporate a small expert system into its best-selling Pagemaker software, to help advise people on how to make better-looking documents. Thus, although jaded by the over-enthusiasm of AI researchers, businessmen are giving the technology a second look.

Managing the machines

BUSINESSMEN have good reason to be sceptical of computers. In the 1960s computer salesmen told them that the mainframe computer would boost their productivity by helping to centralise decision-making. It didn't. In the 1970s and early 1980s computer salesmen said that mini- and micro-computers would boost productivity by helping to decentralise decision-making. They didn't. Then, by the mid-1980s, the salesmen were saying that AI would boost productivity by eliminating human decision-making altogether. And pigs will fly.

But despite – or, in some cases, because of – a healthy scepticism, AI has been making quiet progress in business. In Japan it has inspired new products. In western countries it has mostly been put to work in the office, helping people to cope with the floods of information that computers have released. In both places the stage has been set for AI to shine over the next decade or so.

One prerequisite for the increased use of AI is simply computer muscle: AI techniques require plenty of processing power and computer memory. They work far better when they can get their data over a network rather than having it laboriously typed in.

With today's power, all sorts of tricks become possible. Matsushita, for example, has made a video camera that cuts out the jitter caused by shaky hands. It uses a technique to detect motion that was developed by computer-vision researchers at the Massachusetts Institute of Technology (MIT) on a multi-million-dollar supercomputer called a Connection Machine. With today's circuit-packed semiconductors, Matsushita has been able to adapt a version of this technique (albeit much simplified) on to a thumbnail-sized chip.

As processing power increases, so too will the practical uses of AI. But the driving force behind the use of more intelligent computers is not more capable technology: it is more intelligent managers and computer users.

Faster, harder, smarter

Businessmen are discovering that information technology is frustratingly different from other forms of automation. The classic approach to automation is to break tasks down into smaller pieces. Frederick Taylor, a turn-of-the-century management theorist who created the modern production line, invented a discipline called "scientific management" that divided factory work, bolt by bolt, into simple, repetitive steps.

Alfred Sloan, the creator of General Motors, devised a "functional" organisation of management which similarly separated white-collar workers into various classes of salesmen, accountants and so forth.

Such techniques made the growth of the 20th century's industrial giants possible, but they are now reaching the point of diminishing returns. Sheer economies of scale in production provide less competitive advantage than they did when Henry Ford made the Model T. Similarly, the disadvantages of classical management are becoming more burdensome now that change comes more often and more quickly. The disadvantages of dividing work to make it more manageable are bureaucracy, rigidity and inertia. Bureaucratic organisations are slow to notice the need to change, because no single person sees enough of the overall picture. And once organisations do realise the need, they are also slow to act: the division of labour means that even smallish changes to one job ripple through to a host of others, so even small changes require lots of reorganisation.

Some companies have resolved this conundrum by giving workers more and broader responsibilities. Instead of being asked, say, to "expedite customer-complaint form 2-112/B", workers are charged simply with "solving the customers' technical problems". One big (and as yet largely unresolved) difficulty is keeping these newly liberated problem-solvers working in harmony. Another related burden is making sure that they have all the information they need. On both counts, the technology of AI has already shown it can help.

Power to the people

At US West, a big American telecoms company, executives reorganised the customer-service department. So far, so boring. But instead of putting workers in charge of fixing a particular sort of fault, they made them responsible for satisfying a certain number of customers – whatever the fault may be. To help these newly solicitous employees do their jobs, US West, together with consultants from the Carnegie Group, gave each worker a computer that contained a small expert system to advise him on whom he should talk to about getting various faults fixed.

Like any useful technology, AI is no panacea. Sometimes the technology just does not work. Sometimes the technology is badly managed. An American airline (which prefers to remain nameless) proved the fact that people do not like taking orders from a machine when it installed an expert system to schedule the work of maintenance engineers. The engineers simply rejected the system's plans and it had to be withdrawn. But when, after a suitable delay, the airline reintroduced more or less the same system for engineers to use when and if they wanted, it was much better received.

In all branches of industry there are experiments going on to see how fast-changing technology can improve fast-changing work practices. Amid all the chaos, finding the right match of technology and business is not easy. One sort of AI system that seems to be popping up in all sorts of places, however, is the expert system. The next article explains why.

Bureaucrats of the mind

THEY are the bureaucrats of AI: expert systems see life as a book of rules. They apply these rules rigorously, fairly and predictably. But they are utterly lost when they meet something that is not in the book. It is perhaps not surprising that mechanical bureaucrats have become the favourite creation of AI – and it is somewhat ironic that they have often been cast in the role of human-bureaucracy busters.

Rules are the very stuff of expert systems. The business of making such a system involves sitting down with an expert in the relevant field and trying to codify his knowledge. This knowledge is typically fed into the computer in the form of "if... then..." rules. Thus an expert system for the identification of trees might contain rules like:

> If the season is winter and the tree has foliage, then the tree is evergreen. If the tree is evergreen and the foliage is needle-shaped, then the tree is a pine. If the tree is evergreen and the foliage is leaf-shaped and spiky, then the tree is a holly.

The expert system also contains a piece of software, called an inference engine, to apply these rules to whatever facts are fed in. Thus if a system with those rules were to be told that the season is winter and the tree has leaves, it would conclude that the tree is evergreen. It would then try to apply the rules about evergreen trees by finding out about the shape of the foliage. And so on, until it either reached a conclusion or ran out of rules to apply.

By the numbers

Such simple, mechanical reasoning can go a surprisingly long way, provided there is a well-constructed collection of rules. One perennial problem, however, is the literal-mindedness of computers. Unless it is explicitly told how to do so, the machine has no way of translating the knowledge that, say, a tree is green in January into the more relevant fact that it has foliage in winter.

Given the amount of detail in which propositions have to be laid out for a computer to make use of them, another problem for expert systems is managing a profusion of rules. A typical system will have hundreds of them. Often more than one rule seems to be applicable. Finding a way to choose between them is one of the hardest challenges for expert-system designers. Because most expert systems have no way to retract a conclusion that has been drawn by applying the wrong rule, getting it right first time is crucial.

One technique for dealing with a confusion of rules, pioneered by MYCIN, the grandfather of expert systems, is to associate a number, called a certainty factor, with each assertion. This indicates how sure the system is about its truth. A certainty factor of one typically indicates that the system believes this "fact" absolutely; a factor of minus one indicates absolute disbelief; anything between the two indicates some measure of ignorance or doubt. As it applies rules, the system's inference engine also combines certainty factors. With this system, all applicable rules are typically applied at each opportunity. At the end the system adopts the conclusion with the highest certainty factor.

Another technique for managing the complexity of knowledge, originally proposed by Marvin Minsky of MIT, is to link intuitively related ideas together in "frames". In the human mind most ideas carry with them a fairly predictable set of associations. The idea of "car", for example, carries with it wheels, tyres, driving, roads and so on. Through clever programming, ideas can similarly be linked within the computer.

A third approach is to remove the limitation that an expert system cannot retract any inference drawn from its rules. Some inference engines do allow the system to back up and start again if a line of reasoning runs into a dead end. In this way it tries all possible combinations of rules, so the choice of which one to apply affects only how quickly a conclusion is reached.

Each of these techniques has its drawbacks. People turn out to be remarkably bad at estimating certainty factors. Getting the right combination of ideas in a frame can be frustratingly less intuitive than it first appears. And although backtracking over inferences that had led to a dead end allows the system to consider a broader range of possibilities, the time needed to do so can make it unusably slow.

Caution: machine at work

With time and experience, computer scientists have nevertheless built these technologies into ready-to-use packages. So-called expert-system shells, which a buyer can customise in order to apply to many fields of expertise, are available from several companies – including young firms like Inference in Los Angeles, Aion and Neuron Data, both of Palo Alto, California, alongside computer giants like IBM and DEC.

Even with the benefit of all these techniques, the range of expertise that can be captured by an expert system is limited to simple, self-contained jobs which require no commonsense reasoning. But in part because the trend in management over the past century has been to break jobs into smaller, and supposedly more manageable, pieces, there turn out to be many things that expert systems can do without stretching.

Because business procedures can often be expressed more easily as expert-system rules than as programs written in conventional computer languages, companies have discovered that they can be particularly useful to meet fast-changing competition. American Airlines used an expert-system shell from Inference to update the rules of its frequent-flyer benefits in order to keep up with rival airlines. California's state government uses an expert system to process employee travel claims – more reliably, it reckons, than people used to do.

Much of the innovation needed to make better use of a machine's skills is managerial rather than technical; what it takes is the creation of organisations that can use the machine's bureaucratic skills to reduce human bureaucracy. The rudiments of the task are straight-forward. Get the expert systems working in close harness with people. The machine does the routine work by the rules; the person then has more scope to do the rest of the job, which is typically the parts requiring real human intelligence, commonsense and creativity.

For several years American Express has approved credit-card trans-actions this way. To cope with millions of transactions each day, it built an expert system, called the Authoriser's Assistant. About two-thirds of the transactions are so routine that the system can handle them itself. If it finds anything out of the ordinary, it hands the facts of the case over to a person for a final decision.

The bad news for managers trying to recreate such success stories is that changing the way people work together is one of the hardest things to do. The process is messy, and bright-sounding theories can founder on any number of apparently trivial details. The good news is that the technology itself is becoming more capable, which at least provides more room to manoeuvre in tackling the problems posed by people. To see how the machines are improving, start with the prob-lem of knowledge.

The burden of knowledge

ONE reason why today's expert systems are so narrow-minded is that they are ignorant. Although computers can calculate *pi* to a thousand decimal places in the twinkling of an eye, they do not know any of the things that people learn in the playpen: such as that apples are to eat, that shoes are not, and that heads are more or less permanently attached to bodies.

In retrospect, one of the surprises of AI has been how far computers have got without such knowledge. Chess-playing programs have no more knowledge of the game than the rankest human amateur. They know the legal moves, and they have a simplistic idea of what constitutes a good position: eg, having more pieces than the opponent. But they are completely ignorant of strategy. They make up for this ignorance by their ability to search through billions of possible sequences of moves in order to find the best one.

In the 1960s and 1970s, AI researchers found a number of elegant ways of organising such exhaustive, "brute-force" searches for solutions. American Airlines today uses one such technique to find routes for jetliners that will put them in the same cities as the maintenance facilities they need when they need them and not before.

In practice such techniques work only for problems in which the range of possible solutions is relatively limited; otherwise they are overwhelmed. In chess, for example, there are about 35 legal moves that can follow from each board position. Today's most powerful chess-playing computers can examine all those possibilities for 10–12 moves into the future, which is more than enough to play a good game. But in the Japanese game of Go there are 100 or so possible moves at each board position, and computers are just about useless.

Just the facts, ma'am

Having bumped up against the limits of ignorance, AI researchers have become increasingly enthusiastic about knowledge. They hope it will make their machines more efficient at reasoning, by enabling them to concentrate on relevant possibilities. They also hope it will make them less prone to moronic mistakes. More ambitiously, Mark Stefik of Xerox's Palo Alto Research Centre, and others, predict a new sort of publishing industry. Alongside "do-it-yourself" books will pop up "do-it-itself" software which, in addition to teaching a person, say, how to do his taxes in theory, can actually work through the forms with him.

This attractive vision raises several unanswered questions. First, how much knowledge would a "do-it-itself book" need? In the case of people, the magpie-like collection of facts that makes up commonsense knowledge comes as a complete package. Although it would be nice to give, say, a tax-accountancy expert system a basic idea of what money is, nobody really knows how to disentangle this idea from the mess of other facts in the human brain – or indeed if it can be disentangled at all. Must the idea of money include "retirement", for example? And if so, must it also include "time"?

The most ambitious effort to answer these question is being undertaken by Doug Lenat and his colleagues at the Microelectronics and Computer Consortium, an industry-financed research group in Austin, Texas. Since 1986 Dr Lenat and his colleagues have been painstakingly typing knowledge into a computer called Cyc. By the mid-1990s they hope to equip Cyc with about 10m pieces of information. The hope is that it will then know about as much as a five-year-old – including a rough grasp of gravity, bodies, money, shopping, time, and fairy tales. With that much knowledge, Dr Lenat hopes that Cyc will be able to do a number of things that existing AI systems cannot do, including translate new ideas into concepts with which it is already familiar, and thus help to teach itself.

Meanwhile, Edward Feigenbaum and his colleagues at Stanford's Knowledge Systems Laboratory are taking a different approach to making more knowledgeable machines. Instead of typing in all the knowledge that a person might have, they want to enable a machine simply to share the knowledge that other computers already possess. The knowledge in today's expert systems is so tangled up with the structure of the programs themselves that it cannot be shared with any other system. So expert systems cannot co-operate in solving problems. Nor can the knowledge of one easily serve as the building-blocks for another.

Up in the morning and off to school

The heart of the expert-system challenge is providing computers with a common core of concepts with which to describe the knowledge they would share. The more general descriptions need to be, the harder this becomes. For two computer-aided design (CAD) programs, say, to share knowledge about an engine part is relatively straightforward, because both think of parts in terms of geometry: ie, lines and dimensions. But for a CAD program to describe the same part to, say, a design expert system searching for a component, it would have to use a broader vocabulary of ideas to describe what the part might be used for. Tom Gruber at Stanford is leading a group trying to provide machines with just such concepts. Although the ability to reuse knowledge that has already been mastered by one system will provide huge practical benefits (and probably create a medium-sized industry or two of knowledge-providers) it will solve only part of the problem of creating more knowledgeable computers. For that, machines must be taught to learn.

Artificial-intelligence researchers do not, by and large, share the views of that great 17th-century philosopher, John Locke. They do not believe that the human mind begins as a blank slate, to be filled by experience. Most would argue that you need some knowledge first in order to learn. One prerequisite is a basic vocabulary of concepts, such as the one Dr Gruber is trying to create. Another, implicit, form of knowledge lies in the rules which govern the combining of these concepts to form new ideas.

Over the years the hope of letting machines learn from their own experiences has inspired the creation of a number of machine-learning techniques. One popular one, called inductive learning, picks up new ideas by sifting through a stream of concepts to find the common ground. For example, Patrick Winston of MIT wrote a program that could learn the concept of an arch by examining descriptions of simple structures made of blocks, and distilling common qualities of those which it was told were arches – thus learning that the colour of blocks was not relevant to "archness" but that their position was.

Another way of learning from experience is to generalise from past successes and failures. As it tries to solve problems, SOAR, a program created by Allen Newell of Carnegie Mellon University and John Laird of the University of Michigan, keeps track of which lines of reasoning have turned out to be useful. When it comes up with a helpful line of reasoning, it stores it away, indexed by a description of the situation in which it helped.

Although several learning techniques are creeping into working systems, trying to get good results out of them can be frustrating. One problem is that the knowledge needed to learn inevitably introduces bias. And bias subtly affects what can be learnt. An inductive learner, trying to grasp the concept "dog", would classify the qualities of the examples it was shown into three categories: must-have (for those qualities that only dogs have); can't-have (for those that no dogs have); and don't-care (for qualities that only some dogs have). With this scheme it could learn that having a head can help distinguish a dog from a carrot, because all dogs have one head and no carrots do. But it could not learn that colour can help to distinguish a dog from a carrot, because dogs can be black, brown, white and so on, but not garish, bright orange.

A related problem is that the lessons man or machine can most profitably learn depend on what he wants to do with the knowledge – ie, what sort of reasoning he wants to use. And techniques for computer reasoning are changing fast.

An answer to everything

FOR centuries people have dreamed of a reasoning machine so powerful that it could eliminate human argument. A 17th-century mathematician and philosopher, Gottfried Leibniz, fantasised about devising logical techniques that would let any two philosophers settle any debate once and for all just by sitting down and "calculating". The more time people spend searching for the ultimate reasoning mechanism, the more evidence piles up that such things cannot exist.

Some things are just not decidable by logic – even if they are logical problems. Although computer reasoners can be guaranteed to answer some (but only some) sorts of questions, they cannot be guaranteed to answer all questions of that sort. And even for the sort of work that automated reasoners can do, there is no guarantee that they will grind to a halt and reach a conclusion before the universe itself does.

Such realisations are humbling for researchers looking into computer reasoning. They would love to come up with ways of improving on human reasoning; but many would be happy just to devise ways of muddling along as well as people do. Even that is proving to be quite a challenge. The research is proceeding on two levels. Theoretically, the task is to come up with better theories for understanding reasoning. Practically, the task is building these new theories into working computer programs. Muddled progress is being made on both fronts.

Wrong again

Some of the most interesting results come from trying to extend the deductive procedures of formal logic to the real world. Historically, systems of logic were designed to study problems in which all the relevant facts are known and any new information is guaranteed not to contradict the old. Such assumptions turn out to be completely unrealistic for solving practical problems.

For example, conventional theories of logic are flummoxed by the introduction of anomalous terms such as "penguin". A useful assumption for anyone or anything that wants to reason about the world is that birds fly. Yet penguins are defined as birds, and penguins do not fly. Faced with such a contradiction, conventional logics must either give up the convenient assumption that birds can fly, or foreswear thinking about penguins. So-called non-monotonic logics can do better.

At the theoretical level, John McCarthy of Stanford University has proposed a theory called circumscription. This shows that most of the useful deductive tools of logic still apply if generalisations such as "birds can fly" are qualified by a phrase like "assuming there is nothing abnormal about them". And there are other variants on this approach.

At a practical level, the real work of non-monotonic reasoning is done by the wonderfully named "truth-maintenance system" (TMS), originally developed by Jon Doyle of MIT (and since improved upon by others, notably Johan de Kleer of Xerox's Palo Alto Research Centre). At heart, a truth-maintenance system is a sort of book-keeping device that keeps track of which conclusions depend on which premises. When a contradiction (eg, a flightless bird) is found, the TMS can work through the chain of reasoning to see which assumptions will have to be withdrawn to restore consistency.

Dr de Kleer reckons that a TMS could be used to help machines diagnose themselves – predictably, the Xerox researcher has photocopiers in mind. The idea is to build into the machine a logical model of how it should work: eg, "if the roller turns, the paper will be drawn into the slot". When something does not work, the symptoms would contradict the predictions of the logical model. The TMS could then see which of the model's assumptions led to those false predictions, and so diagnose the problem.

Jumping to conclusions

But in machines, as in people, logic is not the only way to reach a conclusion. One alternative is statistics. Instead of making assumptions that later have to be retracted, statistical reasoning uses probabilities to express the idea of "maybe". For example, one popular technique for statistical reasoning, called fuzzy logic, expresses the idea that someone is tall in terms of the probabilities that someone of a given height would be considered tall. So a five-foot man might have a 10% chance of being regarded as tall, while a six-footer would have a 60% chance, and so on. A machine can then reason by combining probabilities. For example, it could use the chance that someone is tall, together with the chance that he is fat, to calculate the chance that he can fit into a small car.

The attractive thing about all the techniques for combining probabilities is that they work with a continuous range of values, not just the narrow-minded pair, "true" and "false". This makes them wonderful for controlling machinery. If the clothes are very dirty, the machine washes them very hard; not-so-dirty clothes get a not-so-hard wash; and so flexibly on through the scale of dirtiness. Japanese companies are taking advantage of these abilities by building fuzzy logic into machines ranging from vacuum cleaners to passenger trains.

Statistical reasoners, however, are not much good for repairing, say, photocopiers: one cannot replace 60% of a roller. Another snag with most forms of statistical reasoning is that they only approximate the real rules of statistics, so their conclusions are only approximately right. Although exactly the sort of statistical theories that computer-reasoners would like to use were thoughtfully created in the 18th century by Thomas Bayes, a British philosopher, their accuracy depends on keeping track of the interdependence of various sorts of evidence. If A serves as evidence for B while B serves as evidence for A, a naive statistical reasoner can create certainty from a mere fragment of evidence for either. In recent years, however, Judea Pearl of the University of California at Los Angeles and others have found ways to cope with such tricky interdependence, and more accurate Bayesian reasoners are being tested in several laboratories.

When neither statistics nor logic will do, yet another alternative is to proceed by analogy and example. Janet Kolodner of the Georgia Institute of Technology has created methods of "case-based reasoning" to let computers solve problems by finding a precedent. One ambitious use of this is evolving at Compaq Computer, which is using a case-based reasoning tool created by Inference. This lets technicians at Compaq's support centre type in the symptoms of a sick computer and retrieve the cure that has been recommended for similar symptoms in the past. If the symptoms are unfamiliar, or a previous cure does not work, Inference's tool makes a new entry for whatever cure the technician comes up with, so that others will gain the benefit of his experience.

One snag with case-based reasoning, as Katia Sycara of Carnegie Mellon points out, is giving the computer a reasonable idea of similarity so that it can find relevant precedents. This restricts its use to problems that can be described clearly and simply. And even in the technical languages of computer faults, according to Brad Allen of Inference, everybody involved in the systems needs to get together regularly to make sure they are speaking the same language.

Only connect

FOR most of the history of AI, it has been assumed that the mind is best understood in its own terms: as a collection of ideas and arguments. Over the past decade, however, more researchers have begun to wonder if it might not be better to look at the circuitry of the brain. Efforts to recreate similar circuitry on silicon have shed new light on some areas, including speech and vision.

At first glance, the brain is not a particularly impressive piece of engineering. Its basic circuitry, the neuron, works at a pace measured in thousandths of seconds. The pace of a digital computer, by contrast, is measured in billionths of seconds. But in about a tenth of a second the brain can recognise a friend's face or do any number of other things which a computer cannot. How come?

A big part of the answer lies in teamwork. Although neurons may individually be weaklings, there are a lot of them. They work on problems together, each sharing a bit of the job. A variety of different researchers are now trying to replicate this style of "parallel distributed processing" – sometimes called connectionism – on computers.

Some of these creations are impressive. Tommy Poggio at MIT has created parallel programs that can recognise faces, which no conventional AI program can do. Terence Sejnowski of the Salk Institute has created a connectionist net that can pronounce English. But nets also have big drawbacks.

Try, try again

One fundamental problem is that the inner workings of most nets defy exact comprehension. Each net is composed of a few hundred or a few thousand simple processors, called nodes. The nodes are wired so that each one can send signals to several others, and the signals that each node sends out depend on the ones it receives. So sending a signal into a connectionist net results in a ricocheting flurry of signals, counter-signals and counter-counter signals. The trick to making a net do useful computations lies in ensuring that this flurry will eventually settle down into a stable pattern of signals, which can be thought of as the "answer" to the "question" represented by the input.

Guaranteeing that there will be such an answer has been one of the bugbears of connectionism. There is too much going on in a net at once for it to be possible to program it by specifying exactly how each node should respond to each combination of signals. In the early 1960s

Frank Rosenblatt showed that by connecting nodes in a particular way he could create devices, called perceptrons, that can be "programmed" by example.

Each node of a perceptron can do simple calculations like adding and subtracting as well as sending and receiving signals. To decide which signal to send, a node adds up its inputs. Before adding, however, it multiplies each input by an arbitrary "weight". Positive weights make the node more likely to fire if it receives that signal; negative weights make it less likely. Perceptrons are "programmed" by giving them an input, then adjusting the weights to make the output more like the "right" answer. Dr Rosenblatt found a straightforward technique for adjusting the weights that enabled perceptrons to be trained to compute by repeated cycles of showing them examples and fiddling with weights.

Unfortunately, a few years after he did this, Marvin Minsky and Seymour Papert at MIT wrote a book in which they pointed out that, although it was wonderful that perceptrons could be trained to compute, they could not in fact compute anything very interesting. Though more intricate networks can compute anything a computer can, there is no guarantee that they can be trained. The book killed connectionist research for about a decade. Then a new generation of researchers began experimenting with more powerful nets to see what they would do. They found that in practice the nets could be trained by more or less the same techniques that work for perceptrons. And they displayed some advantages over conventional computing, including:

❖ **Speed**   Nets and other parallel programs can take account of a lot of information at once. Instead of working through a picture one bit at a time, as conventional computers painstakingly do, a picture can be fed into a net so that each bit is the input to a separate node. All the information contained in the picture is then considered simultaneously in a flurry of computation.

❖ **Reliability**   Because computing is distributed all over a parallel system, the system can usually soldier on if a few nodes break down, or if part of the input is not exactly what is expected.

❖ **Generalisation**   The real wonder of connectionist nets is that training teaches them to recognise more than just the specific set of examples that they have already seen. They can also recognise things that resemble the training examples. David Rumelhart of Stanford University, one of those responsible for the rebirth of connectionist research, points out that the nets' ability to recognise things that are somehow "in-between" the examples they have seen allows them to capture the variety inherent in everyday ideas. It is hard to come up with words to encompass the many forms of "cup". Yet some nets seem to grasp it automatically after being trained on a few examples.

Just digging the vibes

Getting a grip on this remarkable ability to generalise has provided much of the excitement in connectionist research. At Carnegie Mellon, researchers in the NavLab project use a connectionist net to enable their self-driving vehicle to recognise where the road is by looking at the picture from a videocamera mounted on the front of the van. Conventional programs could not cope with the many subtle signs that can indicate the twists and turns of asphalt. Nets can do better, but they are not perfect. The NavLab's nets, according to one of their developers, can be trained to recognise country roads, or suburban streets, or highways. But they cannot, for example, turn off a highway onto a country road.

Dr Poggio explains the generalising skills of nets as a complex form of interpolation. In effect, he argues, training a net to recognise a series of faces builds up a composite idea of a face in much the same way that a police artist might draw up a composite picture of a suspect by combining several sketches drawn from witnesses' descriptions. Armed with a mathematical theory of how this interpolation works, he has shown that the nets' abilities can be manipulated in novel ways.

One trick that can be worked with Dr Poggio's nets is to get them to display an "archetype" of, say, a woman's face by displaying a face which is least unlike all of the features of all the women's faces it has seen. Not surprisingly, the archetypal woman's face looks different from the archetypal man's face. More intriguing, however, is the ability of nets to do simple animation by interpolating between specific examples. Dr Poggio has made a net rotate a cartoon head, for example, by training the net with a full-face picture, a profile and a three-quarter profile, and then asking it to interpolate the in-between images.

The pattern-recognising and pattern-manipulating skills of connectionist nets are now being tried out on jobs ranging from recognising parts on a factory assembly line to winnowing out patterns in the price movements of securities. There have been some successes, but nets are by no means the answer to everything that enthusiasts sometimes claim. One practical problem is that it takes a long time to train them. A more fundamental one is that nets can neither explain why they have reached a conclusion nor follow what people would call a logical argument. If a net tells a stockbroker to sell 1m IBM shares, he has no alternative but to trust it, which is asking a lot of both man and machine.

Sound and fury

FEW skills seem more quintessentially intelligent than vision or speech. Both have ranked high on AI's agenda since its inception. But progress has been frustrating. Vision and language turn out to be too quintessentially intelligent. Complete solutions to the problems they pose depend on solutions to almost every other problem in AI.

To see what is so troublesome about language, consider the question "Do you have the time?". To understand why the appropriate answer is not simply "yes" or "no" requires a wealth of knowledge about human intentions, the practicalities of telling time and so on. Machines do not have either that knowledge or the reasoning skills that would let them use it. Similarly, even if a computer-vision system could manage to see objects in a factory, it would not appreciate that the yellow blur of a fork-lift truck might be more important than the parts on the assembly line – if the truck was coming straight towards it.

That said, some of the techniques that have proved inadequate for solving all the problems of language or vision can be honed to work on parts of them. And while theoreticians ponder what light computer models might help to shed on how people really see and talk, more practical researchers are looking for problems to fit the tools that the theoreticians have already created.

See the light

From the start, vision researchers have known how to transform a picture into rows and columns of numbers, with each number representing the brightness of a point in the picture. What they have spent decades working out are ways of transforming that mind-numbing field of numbers into the beginnings of useful information.

Over the years they have built up an impressive array of techniques. Traditional ones have drawn heavily on the mathematics of signal processing, originally created for radio and television. More recently, these have been joined by methods relying on the power of connectionist nets. At MIT, Tommy Poggio and his graduate students and colleagues have been building an ambitious "Vision Machine" to experiment with ways of combining various sorts of visual information – depth, colour, texture and so on – in order to recognise objects.

In practice, the way to get computer-vision systems to work is simply to give them something very precise to look for. British Petroleum, for example, uses computer vision to help scan micro-photographs of earth taken from drilling samples to find the tiny fossil shells that can provide clues to help find oil. It has also adapted vision techniques to help analyse the results of a type of oil exploration that uses an airborne laser to scan large areas of ground, looking for a particular wavelength of light that indicates hydrocarbons seeping from the soil.

One big commercial prize in computer vision, however, is text and handwriting. To make computers easier to use, any number of companies are trying to make machines that can recognise the scrawl of handwriting. They are trying several tacks. Some use neural nets. Another approach is to have teams of automated specialists, each of which looks for a particular feature of a letter – say the descending stroke of a "g" or a "j" – and which then pool their results. So far, research has created systems that can usually recognise printed text, in which the characters are well separated from one another. But they all have problems with joined-up writing.

Hear the word

Research aimed at teaching computers to cope with human language shows a similar contrast between research into general tools and applications to specific problems. Here the most generally applied tool is called a parser, and its job is to break a sentence down into nouns, verbs and other parts of speech. Having this information makes language much easier to deal with; plenty of hard work has gone into creating parsers that can recognise the various tenses of verbs, decide when a verb needs an object, capture the essential similarity of, say, the active and passive forms of a sentence, and so on. But all of this is far from enough to understand language.

One problem with parsers is that most are flummoxed by ungrammatical sentences, whereas people can usually salvage some meaning out of them. A more fundamental problem with parsing is that it looks only at the structure of language. And structure is not enough to determine why "the children are ready to eat the porridge" makes sense, while "the porridge is ready to eat the children" does not.

Finding a complete solution to such problems will require huge improvements to computers' knowledge and reasoning abilities. But, as with vision, ingenious researchers are finding useful incomplete solutions.

One growing application of language-processing is the classification of messages. For example, Chase Manhattan and other American banks automatically forward incoming telexes to the right department using a program called PRISM, developed by Cognitive Systems, a small company in Cambridge, Massachusetts. In this narrow realm, it can be confident of not meeting any carnivorous breakfast cereals. PRISM tackles telexes with a combination of parsing, inductive learning and case-based reasoning. Although it classifies only about three-quarters of its telexes correctly, that is not much worse than people manage to do.

Another growing application of computers' linguistic skills lies in providing an easy-to-use way of interrogating big databases. Here the trick is to enable the computer to use the structure inherent in the database to help it resolve the ambiguities of languages. And though for simple databases it is still easier to get people to learn computer languages rather than vice versa, for complex databases there is a variety of products which promise to let a person type in more-or-less English and get an answer that usually more or less makes sense. One such is Intellect from AICorp, which is now being used by over 300 companies around the world.

Researchers also have high hopes for machine translation. Although computers are nowhere near good enough to produce finished copy, organisations ranging from IBM to the European Commission are trying them out at producing rough drafts of translations for a person to polish. Canadians, meanwhile, have been listening to machine-translated weather reports for several years.

A further challenge is for computers to cope with spoken as well as written messages. The obvious complication is to translate sounds into words. So far researchers have managed to work that trick reliably only when the words are all separated by a bit of silence, and when there are only a limited number of words to consider. But within those limitations, real progress is being made. IBM has teamed up with a small company called Dragon Systems to produce an "automated typist" that can recognise 7,000 different words and runs on a personal computer. Raymond Kurzweil of Kurzweil Intelligent Systems in Waltham, Massachusetts, sells a system that enables doctors to dictate reports to a computer while their hands are busy doing something messy.

More capable machines are wending their way out of the laboratories. At MIT, Victor Zue and his team are working on a system called Voyager, which – haltingly, but astonishingly – can answer spoken questions about how to find one's way around the city of Cambridge. Like PRISM, Voyager works because it knows what sort of questions to expect, and it can use this knowledge together with information from sound and parsing.

Doing the right thing

IF, AS Jean-Paul Sartre might have said, to do is to be, then today's artificial intelligences are not. The progress of computers as doers has lagged behind even their fitful progress as thinkers. Like all machines, they can mindlessly repeat actions. But they have severe difficulty in planning them, and even more in recovering when, as inevitably happens, a plan goes awry. Unless they get better at planning, even the brainiest of machines will remain armchair generals.

The challenges of planning are threefold. One is the perennial problem of knowledge: machines still have a long way to go before they know what is do-able. Another is the lack of a reliable ability to look far enough ahead before acting. Computers are still frequently confounded when one step in their carefully laid plans undoes some work that has been done before. Last, and perhaps trickiest, is the necessity for speed. Even when computers can work out the right thing to do, their thought processes are often so cumbersome that they come to the answer long after the chance to apply it has passed.

Facing up to such problems has sparked one of AI's hottest debates. Traditionally, researchers have tackled the problems of planning and doing with the same reasoning tools with which they have tackled every other AI problem. Now a small but vocal minority, led by Rodney Brooks of MIT, argues that machines would often be more intelligent if they discarded rationality. Dr Brooks argues that AI researchers should model their efforts on insects, not on people. He reckons that insect behaviour is a complex set of automatic reactions to the stimuli of the world, and he is trying to replicate that behaviour in silicon circuitry. But he has yet to bring a robot even to bug-like levels of skill.

Look before you leap

The grandfather of the "traditional" approach to planning is SHAKEY, a robot mentioned earlier which was built in the early 1970s by Nils Nilsson, Richard Fikes and others at the Stanford Research Institute. SHAKEY could do simple things with blocks, such as pushing them about the floor. At the time this was quite an achievement.

The planning part of SHAKEY was a program called STRIPS that was equipped with knowledge of a repertoire of things that SHAKEY could do: eg, push a block up a ramp to place it on top of another block, push it back down, and so on. To plan its way towards some goal, STRIPS looked to see which of SHAKEY's skills could help to achieve it. If that skill could be applied, it was added to the plan; if it could not, STRIPS postponed its original goal and began trying to plan a way to let SHAKEY do the next envisioned step in the plan – returning to the original goal only after that is achieved.

Where STRIPS gets muddled, however, is if one step undoes the work of a previous step. Then it can find itself repeatedly doing and undoing the same work. One way of getting round this, called plan repair, is to try to detect such cycles of futility and purge them. A better way, most researchers now reckon, is to try to stop them arising.

"Non-linear" planning techniques, developed in the late 1970s and 1980s by, among others, Austin Tate of Edinburgh University, consider the possible interaction of steps in a plan from the very beginning. To make this work, however, such planners must think of their world in a much more complicated way than STRIPS does. Instead of proceeding step-by-step, non-linear planners build up a collection of partially finished plans, specified at various levels of detail, and proceed by interleaving one partially finished plan into another.

Just do it

Apart from the sheer cumbersomeness of planning, would-be rational robots suffer from a minimal grasp of cause and effect. If you move one block, which others will move too?

Rather than have machines spend hours pondering such mysteries, Dr Brooks, and Jean-Luc Steels at the Free University of Brussels, want to endow each machine with a repertoire of "instinctive" skills, each triggered automatically in response to some stimulus. By cleverly organising the interplay of these instincts, they believe they can create machines that are in many ways more capable than those that have to ponder every action.

The favourite testing grounds for Dr Brooks's ideas are terrier-sized, six-legged robots called GHENGIS and ATILLA. The skills of such robots are organised in a hierarchy. At the bottom levels are basic skills like "walking" and "avoiding obstacles". When all is going well, these can be overridden by more advanced skills, such as "looking around" or "approaching an interesting object". But if the robot falls over or bumps into something, the lower instincts reassert control. Eventually, Dr Brooks hopes to build cheap, simple robots that can do tasks like cleaning dust off a floor or barnacles off a ship. But there is still a long way to go.

Meanwhile, the debate sparked by Dr Brooks's ideas has prompted all sorts of experiments. Although few researchers go along with him in abandoning contemplation, more question whether it is really necessary to ponder everything.

At the University of Edinburgh, Chris Malcolm is trying to improve robots' assembly skills by combining planning and instinct – with promising results. His idea is to endow the robot with a set of basic, instinctive patterns of behaviour that are flexible enough to overcome small mistakes in planning. The robot can then make its plans without getting bogged down in the details of everything that might go wrong.

Brother robot

HOW intelligent can machines become? Philosophers and scientists have inconclusively debated this question since before the computer age. Intriguingly, some of the issues that have shaped the philosophical debate are now beginning to crop up in practical decisions over where and how to apply AI. They concern words and will – and, whether or not answering them creates true artificial intelligences, it seems likely to change the experience of being human.

One of the reasons put forward for believing in the impossibility of truly intelligent machines is simply that machines are created by people. This, it is argued, makes them man's slaves rather than his equals. They do whatever he wants them to – or, in the jargon of the debate, machines have "derived intent" while only humans have "original intent".

Computers themselves are now presenting a more practical side to this debate. From the most human of motives, namely laziness, people are giving machines more and more responsibility. It is simply easier if the machine flies the aircraft, or re-orders the inventory, or works out today's manufacturing plan. The more complex the tasks that machines take on, the more they are being asked to behave as if they had will and purpose of their own.

The programmer of an auto-pilot cannot anticipate every movement of the flaps and every twist of the rudder on a long voyage – nor would he want to. He gives the auto-pilot a goal, and trusts that the machine has the skills to get on with it (though, just to make sure, a human pilot periodically peeks over the machine's shoulder). In this way the use of machines begins to shade over the indistinct border between the design and manipulation of inanimate objects (engineering) to the negotiation and alignment of goals (management).

The trend looks set to continue. Computer-makers everywhere are trying to make their machines more "user-friendly". But, as Candy Sidner of DEC's Cambridge Research Laboratory points out, the sentence "Can I help?" is loaded with intention. To utter it with any real meaning, a machine must have some idea of what it can do, what the person is trying to do – and some way of appreciating how a person's goals and skills and its own can be aligned to a common purpose.

Where there's a will

Such alignment implies that there is some common ground where each

329

can understand the other. And to do that, both must at least roughly agree on the meanings of words. Some sceptics doubt that computers will in fact ever be able to do that.

One exponent of this view is Terry Winograd of Stanford University. In 1971 Dr Winograd created a program called SHRDLU which was the first to demonstrate that a machine could have any real grasp of language. But Dr Winograd soon became convinced that, although a machine could have some grasp of language, a complete grasp would always elude it. Inspired by a German philosopher, Martin Heidegger, Dr Winograd argues that the meaning of human words is inextricably bound up with human activity. And human activity, in turn, is inextricably bound up with being in a particular body, living a particular life, in a particular culture at a particular place and time.

An experiment conducted at London's Imperial College illustrates the point. Marek Sergot and Robert Kowalski wrote a program to interpret the British Nationalities Act. The logic of the law, they found, could relatively easily be mastered by the machine. But it proved largely impossible to explain the meaning of phrases like "of good character", "intent to reside" and so on to the machine. As a purely practical matter, such difficulties with words are not, argues Dr Sergot, a fundamental impediment. In law many words have precise, though somewhat artificial legal meanings that a machine can grasp. If legal verbiage still eludes the machine, it can simply phrase its advice in the form "if you think he is 'of good character' then this law applies, otherwise that law does".

In a sense, such practical solutions solve the problem by flipping it on its head. Instead of teaching machines the full meaning of words, people simply agree to work with meanings that the machines can understand. This alters the way in which words develop their meanings in the first place. In the Anglo-Saxon tradition of common law, at least, many words are left vague on purpose so that they can be redefined in the courtroom by a jury, thus helping the law to evolve in step with society.

New world

Had the quest for AI succeeded in creating artificial people, getting machines to do jobs that are now done by people would have had little impact on anything except the economics of employment. Instead, it is doing something more revolutionary. To the extent that AI, together with the rest of information technology, has created tools worth using, it is starting to cause a deeper social transformation, by affecting the flow of information and ideas by which people define their culture.

Such change is not without precedent. Books and television have transformed the flow of information. The industrial revolution transformed work by applying machinery. But just as the industrial revolution was marked by a long apprenticeship of learning how to share work with machines, so too will the decades ahead be marked by a long apprenticeship of learning how to share information and decision-making with machines.

In the law, for example, the convenience of quicker, more predictable decision-making by computer may be worth the price of fewer arguments in the court room. Continental European countries have for centuries lived with a system of administrative law, derived from Roman tradition, in which juries and case law have little role to play. But learning how to make decisions in harmony with other people is hard enough; learning how to share decision-making with a machine is harder still. To glimpse some of the pitfalls that lie ahead, look at hospitals.

In many parts of medicine, computers have been doing better than doctors on tests of diagnostic ability for nearly two decades. But no hospital relies on a computer in diagnosis. One problem, points out Peter Szolovits of MIT, is that good performance on average is not enough in medicine. It is no good being brilliant on 96% of your patients if you stupidly kill the other 4%. The narrow abilities of today's artificial intelligences provide no firm guarantees that they will not do that.

One practical solution might be to put computers to work advising doctors, so that the doctor can make sure that the computer does not do anything stupid and vice versa. Here a more fundamental problem arises: time. Dr Szolovits recalls demonstrating an expert system to a heart specialist. The doctor was impressed by the computer's capabilities, but pointed out that he had spent 25 minutes typing questions and data into the machine for each case – and he saw 30–40 patients a day. Although a doctor's assistant might have more time to do the typing, he lacks the knowledge to take advantage of the machine's capabilities. He cannot know when to ask questions, which questions to ask or when to challenge the machine's assumptions.

Despite these pitfalls, the allure of AI is strong enough for the technology to be making gradual headway in hospitals – particularly in the role of error-catcher, looking at orders for treatment filed electronically by doctors into a hospital database and warning of potential hazards. But the medical history of AI highlights an uncomfortable fact: that the greatest obstacle to more intelligent machines is unintelligent people.

Much though computer companies would like to promote the illusion that owning a clever, powerful computer will somehow make you a cleverer, more powerful person, it will not. However full of answers an artificial intelligence may be, it is of limited use to someone who does not understand the questions in the first place.

The history of science is filled with illustrations of the principle that intelligence is in large part in the eye of the beholder. Just as scientists have rejected theories whose importance or workings they could not understand, so too will people reject machines that do not speak their language. AI has a bright future in promoting human intelligence – helping with deductions, providing memory aids, detail-handlers, tutors and so on. But neither people nor machines can provide answers better than the questions they are asked. It is up to people to make sure that the questions are good ones.

THIS SURVEY ON ARTIFICIAL INTELLIGENCE WAS FIRST PUBLISHED IN
THE ECONOMIST ON MARCH 14TH 1992

11

THE DEATH OF TELEPHONY

*Why the telephone and TV will not be the stars
of a communications revolution*

GEORGE GILDER

PROCLAIMING "multimedia convergence," "interactivity," "intelligent networks," "electronic yellow pages," "caller ID," "500 channels of pay-per-view" and invoking vistas of "high-definition television", seers in telephone and television companies give stirring speeches about the future. Contemplating their revenues of tens of billions of dollars, their laboratories full of new technology, their millions of mostly satisfied shareholders and customers, their multiplying masses of trade publications and cover-stories in national magazines, telephone and television executives all too often seem unaware that their basic technologies are dead.

Such concepts as "high definition", "interactivity", "intelligent networks" or "electronic yellow pages" are merely cosmetics for the corpse. In order to see the future of telecommunications, it is necessary to lug the dead body out of the way first.

Life and death in technology is a matter not of revenues but of prospects. Vacuum tubes reached a pinnacle of sales in the 1970s. Revenues from telephones and televisions are currently at an all-time peak. But the industries organised around these two machines will not survive the century. Still, telecoms executives want to believe that televisions and telephones can evolve bit by bit into the new digital world, with the same companies supplying essentially the same products and offering essentially the same jobs.

This dream cannot come true. Even to talk of "telephones" and "televisions" reflects a lexicographic lag that prevents many business leaders from detecting the onset of *rigor mortis* in their still-profitable products. In coming years, the very words will ring as quaintly as "horseless carriage," "icebox" or "picture radio" today.

Dying industries exude an increasingly fetid air. It is not just that some 100,000 acts of television violence are seen by the average American child before the age of 13, or the obtuse denial that such a diet could affect behaviour. Or the perverse drive by television magnates to ensure that the new American HDTV standards preserve the interlaced TV screen (alternately filling every other line) that is wholly unsuited to computer text or multimedia. It is not just the increasing amounts of broadcast advertising needed to support diminishing amounts of substantive programming. Nor yet the continued lobbying by American telephone companies against any encroachment by cable television in their domains, accompanied with constant trysts and cohabitations with the same cable firms on foreign shores, or even in distant states.

Closer to the heart of the matter is the constant celebration of fibre optics by telephone executives in public forums, accompanied by the continued installation of millions of miles of the old twisted-pair copper wire every year. The very same trumpets that blared ineffectually for ten years for ISDN (integrated services digital networks) now toot for an amazing new redeemer of twisted copper called asymmetrical digital subscriber loop (ADSL). As developed by a tiny California company called Amati and adopted by Northern Telecom, ADSL sends a stunning 6m bits per second of full-motion video down a conventional telephone line.

As a technological breakthrough, ADSL is stupendous. But it resembles the varistor, a brilliantly crafted device excogitated in the late 1960s by the vacuum-tube people at RCA in the face of the new threat of silicon transistors. Even in strategic terms, it is a distraction. ADSL provides a new weapon for a losing fight with cable and satellite firms sending hundreds of channels of pay-per-view films and games to the household. A dying telephone technology clutches at a shiny new broadcast-industry death rattle.

As the voices die away

Telecommunications is in a transition that is too fundamental for any such quick fixes. It is moving towards an era in which person-to-person communications will give way to links between computers. And although imaginative writers persist in using anthromorphic language to describe computers, in fact they have virtually nothing in common with people. People have associative memories that are millions of times larger than computer "memories"; two eyes can do more image processing than all the supercomputers in the world put together. But in terms of communications bandwidth, people lag hopelessly behind computers, with nearly a billion times less communications power than the best machines.

Almost every feature of the telephone network, from its 4kHz wires to its circuit-switched lines, is designed for the sluggish human voice (which communicates at about 55 bits per second). Telephones give us dysphasics what we need: a very small bandwidth connection for a relatively long time. Computers, by contrast, need huge bandwidth for microsecond bursts. Their networks transmit digital data at a minimum rate of some 10m bits per second, going up soon to 155m bits a second. On such a digital flood, 64 kilobits per second of voice can ride as an imperceptible trickle.

Data already comprise half of the bits in a telephone network and account for 20% of the profits. Data income is growing six times as fast as voice income. As the telephone network becomes a computer network, it will have to change root and branch. All the assumptions of telephony will have to give way. Thus telephony will die.

Television faces a similar problem. It is a broadcast analogue system which assumes that all people are essentially alike and at any one time can be satisfied with a set of 40–50 channels. In Europe and Asia, 40 or 50 channels may seem wretched excess. But compare this array to some 14,000 magazines and a yearly output of some 55,000 trade books published in America alone. Television defies the most obvious fact about its customers: their prodigal and efflorescent diversity. It ignores the fact that people are not inherently couch potatoes; given a chance, they talk back and interact. People have little in common with one another except their prurient interests and morbid fears and anxieties. Aiming its fare at this lowest-common-denominator target, television gets worse and worse year after year.

Computer networks respond to all the human characteristics that television networks defy. Computer nets permit peer-to-peer interactivity rather than top-down broadcasts. Rather than a few "channels", computer networks offer as many potential connections as there are machines linked to the web. Rather than a system in which a few "stations" spray images at millions of dumb terminals in real time, computer networks put the customer in control. Television will die because it affronts human nature: the drive to self-improvement and autonomy that lifted the race from the muck and offers the only promise for triumph in our current adversities.

Confidence in the new paradigm, however, does not spring only from the desire for a better culture, and it cannot be stemmed by some new global plague of passivity and tube addiction. Propelling the new order is the most powerful juggernaut in the history of technology: an impending millionfold rise in the cost-effectiveness of computers and their networks.

Early in the next decade, the central processing units of 16 Cray YMP supercomputers, now costing collectively some $320m, will be manufacturable for under $100 on a single microchip. Such a silicon sliver will contain approximately 1 billion transistors, compared with some 20m in currently leading-edge devices. Meanwhile, the 4kHz telephone lines to America's homes and offices will explode into some 25 trillion possible hertz of fibre optics.

At the same time, the supposedly scarce realms of the radio-frequency spectrum will open up to a series of innovations that make communications power (bandwidth) as cheap and abundant in the air as it is in wire today. Microcells using a protocol called Code Division Multiple Access can use the entire radio-frequency spectrum every few miles or even hundreds of yards. Billions of hertz of little-used spectrum are available in the microwave domain and can be used for television broadcasts or computer networks.

All these developments converge in one key fact of life, and death, for telecommunications in the 1990s. Television and telephone systems – designed for a world in which spectrum or bandwidth was scarce – are utterly unsuited for a world in which bandwidth is abundant. The key strategy of both systems has been to centralise intelligence in local central offices, cellular base stations, cable-television nodes, and broadcast centres, and give the user a stripped-down commodity terminal, whether a telephone or television set. For telephony, this meant making up for scarce bandwidth with powerful centralised switches. For cellular phones, it meant making up for scarce spectrum with high-powered narrow-band radio phones and smart cell sites. For television, it meant making up for scarce bandwidth with powerful centralised transmitters.

In all these cases, intelligence at the centre made up for a lack of bandwidth and computer power on the fringes of the network. But with new bandwidth galore in fibre and air, and video supercomputers on the way for under $1,000, all these structures are obsolete. Over the next decade, engineers will use bandwidth and computer power on the edges of networks as a substitute for switching and intelligence at the centre.

The computer paradigm will prevail. Just as the 1980s brought the collapse of the centralised scheme of a few thousand mainframes and millions of dumb terminals, the 1990s will see the collapse of similar structures in television and telephony. First to fall will be the broadcast system of a few thousand stations and a few networks serving millions of idiot boxes. Next to fall will be the telephone scheme of a few thousand local central offices serving millions of dumb telephones.

Telecosmonauts and their laws

Governing this transition will be the two key laws of modern digital electronics. One, the law of the microcosm, holds that the more transistors are linked together on single chips the more coolly, swiftly and cheaply they function. Measured in power-delay product (roughly, transistor speeds times their heat dissipation), the efficiency of transistors has risen exponentially for two decades as their size dropped and chip densities rose. Judging by recent news from the laboratories – describing such exotic stuff as single-electron electronics and electron-spin transistors and such practical advances as three-dimensional and holographic memory devices – the trend is likely to continue through the next two decades. This will ensure a continued onrush of low-cost computer intelligence on the edges of all networks.

Now the law of the microcosm merges with the law of the telecosm. Just as the law of the microcosm essentially showed that linking any number n of transistors on a single chip leads to n^2 gains in computer efficiency, the law of the telecosm finds the same kind of exponential gains in linking computers: connect any number n of computers and their total value rises in proportion to n^2.

The result is twofold: the cost-effectiveness of individual computers measured in MIPS (millions of instructions per second) per dollar approximately doubles every 18 months and the value of computers in networks rises as the square of the rise in the number of networked machines. In a top-down network, such as a conventional telephone or cable system, attaching a new device may burden the central switch or head-end; in broadcasting over the air, each additional receiver has no effect on the technical power of the system. But in a peer-to-peer computer arrangement, each new device is a resource for the system, expanding its capabilities and potential bandwidth. The larger the network grows, the more efficient and powerful are all its parts.

Gathering irresistable momentum over the next decade, these forces will blow away the old analogue establishments of television and telephony. Both can survive only to the extent that they transform themselves into digital computer networks.

There will be little time to spare. Judging from the sales of microprocessor central processing units so far this year, some 50m computers will be sold worldwide in 1993 at an average price close to $1,500. That price will continue to fall, sustaining a continued pellmell pace of sales far exceeding the sales of analogue televisions or telephones. Meanwhile, American experience offers a portent of the future of networks. Between 1989 and 1993, the proportion of computers in America connected in networks rose from under 10% to over 60%.

In sum, both television and telephony suffer from information hierarchies that are totally unsuited to the coming era of billion-transistor chips and terahertz nets. These digital computer networks will function both over wires and in the air. Indeed, the most common personal computer of the next decade will be based on the digital cellular telephone. Called personal digital assistants, among many other coinages, they will be as portable as a watch and as personal as a wallet. They will recognise speech and navigate streets, open the door and start the car, collect the mail and the news and the pay-cheque, connecting to thousands of databases of all kinds.

As for the descendant of television, the dominant traffic of the future will be store-and-forward transmission of digital data among millions of telecomputers. These machines will be capable of summoning or sending films or files, news stories and clips, courses and catalogues anywhere in the world. Whether offering 500 channels or thousands, television will be irrelevant in a world without channels, where you can always order exactly what you want when you want it, and where every terminal commands the communications power of a broadcast station today.

The same couch potatoes who, in the absence of a better choice, now settle for a Donahue show on lesbian nuns or for a sanguinary stew of cops and prostitutes, will turn to favourite films or local sports or career education. Many of the same people who now sink into a passive stupor before the tube will find themselves using teleputers to travel around the world, taking courses, conducting transactions, and shaping their own programs and software.

The new computer networks will have virtually nothing in common with existing hybrid networks that combine analogue and digital functions. Telephone companies currently use their digital switches to relieve the pressures on their current copper wires. Most television companies plan to use digital electronics to increase the choices of couch potatoes, allowing them to choose a pay-per-view film or play a video game without going out of the house. But end-to-end digital systems will bring something quite different, and a true paradigm shift.

As Richard Solomon of MIT's Media Lab pointed out some years ago, the new broadband networks will reverse the current relationship between computer speeds and network speeds. At present, telephone networks work far more slowly than the internal communications "buses" of individual computers (the electronic pathways linking processors to memory and screen). Transferring data far faster internally than externally, computers are decoupled from the telephone network; they can legitimately be seen as outside the system, interconnecting to it only through complex modems. The new broadband networks, however, will dissolve this boundary between the computer and the network. As Professor Solomon puts it, "With end to end digitisation, the public switched network will be transformed into one large processor." In it, computers may be able to tap remote databases more readily than they can reach their own hard disks or CD-ROM drives.

This vision of the network as one colossal processor goes well beyond mere metaphor. With the new generation of microprocessors, such as the DEC Alpha and the Silicon Graphics Cray-on-a-chip, computers are shifting from processing data in 32-bit clumps ("words") to 64-bit words. This change means a 4-billion-fold rise in the ability of computers to address memory directly. Since few computers command storage above the current 4-gigabyte limit, this new increment of capacity may be irrelevant locally for some time. But it will let teleputers enter and interact with huge databases of digital video – tens of thousands of films, art exhibits, courseware, three-dimensional experiences and other possibilities bounded only by the reach of the mind and the span of the global ganglion of computers and cables, the new worldwide web of glass and light. Within these miraculous mansions of imagination, however, one thing is clear. There will be no room for televisions or telephones, or for the companies that make them.

THIS ARTICLE WAS FIRST PUBLISHED IN *THE ECONOMIST* ON SEPTEMBER 11TH 1993
IN A SURVEY OF THE FUTURE THAT MARKED THE PAPER'S 150TH ANNIVERSARY